The *PowerPC*™ Architecture:

A SPECIFICATION FOR A NEW FAMILY OF RISC PROCESSORS

IBM INTERNATIONAL BUSINESS MACHINES, INC.

The *PowerPC*™ Architecture:

A SPECIFICATION FOR A NEW FAMILY OF RISC PROCESSORS

Edited by Cathy May, Ed Silha,
Rick Simpson, Hank Warren

MORGAN KAUFMANN PUBLISHERS, INC.   SAN FRANCISCO, CALIFORNIA

To order copies of this book, please contact the publisher at (800)745-7323 or your IBM Marketing Representative.

Morgan Kaufmann Publishers, Inc.
Editorial Office:
340 Pine Street, Sixth Floor
San Francisco, CA 94104

Executive Editor: Bruce M. Spatz
Production Manager: Yonie Overton
Assistant Editor: Douglas Sery
Assistant Production Editor: Vicki Van Ausdall
Production Coordinator: Julie Pabst
Composition: Ed Sznyter, Babel Press
Cover and Text Design: Carron Design
Copyediting: Fran Taylor
Proofreading: Gary Morris
Printer: Courier Corporation

QA
76.8
P67
P68
1994

Printed in the United States of America

98 97 96 95 94   5 4 3 2 1

Library of Congress Cataloging-in-Publication Data is available for this book.

ISBN 1-55860-316-6

Foreword

By
Phil Hester
Vice President
IBM RISC System/6000 Division—Systems and Technology

IBM first introduced the POWER architecture with the RISC System/6000 in early 1990. POWER, an acronym for "Performance Optimization With Enhanced RISC," was one of the first superscalar RISC microprocessors. The original microprocessor for these products consisted of a multi-chip implementation which set new performance and price/performance standards at the time of announcement. However, it soon became apparent that a single-chip version would be needed in order to include future lower cost members in the RISC System/6000 family. Systems would be needed that could span the range from personal computers through high end computers. As a result, work was started on a single-chip version of the POWER architecture. In early 1991 it became evident that this single-chip design could potentially become a high volume standard in the industry. Accomplishing this objective would clearly require the development of a superior family of single-chip microprocessors, and the ability to supply these at competitive prices. IBM then began discussions with Motorola concerning potential collaboration to develop this family of microprocessors. As these discussions progressed, it became clear that both our general microprocessor requirements and our belief that the high performance and low cost of these microprocessors could be exploited in systems was shared by another of Motorola's large customers, Apple. This lead to discussions among Apple, IBM, and Motorola, in which it became clear that we did share common objectives for the microprocessors. Based on this, we could define complementary roles for each of the companies in the development of these microprocessors as well as the object-oriented and multi-media software technology needed to exploit them.

Through both a commitment by all three companies to make this alliance a success and the dedication of extremely talented people from each company, negotiations were completed and PowerPC ("PC" stands for "Performance Computing") was born in October of 1991. With Apple's personal computer systems experience, Motorola's high volume micro-processor and silicon knowledge, and IBM's RISC expertise and silicon technology capability, the components were in place to begin develop-ment of an entire family of RISC microprocessors which support a com-mon architecture and can span a wide range of computing requirements. Within six months a new development site, now known as the Somerset Design Center, was dedicated, and staffing was well underway for the design teams.

Time to market for the first PowerPC microprocessor was viewed as a critical factor in the future success of PowerPC. As a result, an aggressive plan was put together to allow development of the first PowerPC micro-processor (PowerPC 601) as quickly as possible. It was also important that this microprocessor not sacrifice competitiveness as a result of its aggressive schedule. To achieve these goals, we combined the work already going on in IBM developing a single-chip version of the POWER architecture with the 88110 work going on in Motorola. This allowed us to develop a microprocessor very quickly that was compliant with the PowerPC architecture and utilized the expertise of both IBM and Motorola.

Additional microprocessors were planned as part of the initial effort to be tailored to the various segments of the computing marketplace. The 603 microprocessor is intended for very low end and battery powered products. Satisfying mid-range system needs, primarily optimizing price/ performance and permitting symmetric multiprocessor (SMP) scalability, is the major goal for the 604. The 620 is optimized for high end scientific and commercial environments, in which raw performance is critical. This microprocessor, with a goal of achieving the best possible performance from a single-chip technology, supports SMP and implements the 64-bit PowerPC architecture. In 32-bit mode, the 620 is fully compatible with all the 32-bit members of the PowerPC family (601, 603, and 604).

As of November 1993 we are well on our way to delivering this family of PowerPC microprocessors. In September 1993 IBM announced the first product using the PowerPC 601—the RISC System/6000 Model 25. In October 1993 IBM and Motorola announced functional first silicon for the 603. It is important to note that the 601 and 603 were both com-pleted on schedule while also achieving their performance, functionality, and die size objectives. This success gives us high confidence that we will achieve similar results for the 604 and 620. In addition, by having fabri-cated the 603 separately in both IBM and Motorola manufacturing facilities, we have validated the compatibility of our manufacturing processes. Since these same processes will be used for the 604 and 620, we feel confident of our ability to produce these microprocessors.

Over time, the Somerset Design Center will continue to broaden and improve the product line to exploit both the PowerPC architecture and advances in silicon technology as they become available. Our vision of providing one architecture, implemented in a family of microprocessors each of which is optimized for a particular environment ranging from "palmtops to teraFLOPS," is well on the way to becoming a reality.

Contents in Brief

Book II   PowerPC Virtual Environment Architecture

Book III PowerPC Operating Environment Architecture

Contents

Book II   PowerPC Virtual Environment Architecture

Book III PowerPC Operating Environment Architecture

Figures

Tables

Preface

Preamble

Some of us wanted to send this book to every household in America, or even in the world, so that everyone who might potentially be interested in PowerPC would easily be able to learn about it. But saner heads prevailed, realizing that some few households might not welcome such a gift, so the book is offered in the normal manner.

About This Book

The PowerPC Architecture supports a family of processors that spans a wide range of system and application environments. It also provides a stable base for software, allowing applications that run on one PowerPC processor to run consistently on any other PowerPC processor and well-designed operating systems to be moved from one processor implementation to another by making a few minor changes. These desirable yet seemingly conflicting attributes are achieved by structuring the architecture specification into three *Books*, and relegating all implementation-specific aspects of the architecture to a fourth Book that is unique for each implementation. The first three Books correspond to three levels of the architecture, as follows.

- Book I, User Instruction Set Architecture
  This Book describes the registers, instructions, storage model, and execution model that are available to all application programs.

- Book II, Virtual Environment Architecture
  This Book describes features of the architecture that permit application programs to create or modify code, to share data among pro-

grams in a multiprocessing system, and to optimize the performance of storage accesses.

■ **Book III, Operating Environment Architecture**
This Book describes features of the architecture that permit operating systems to allocate and manage storage, to handle errors encountered by application programs, to support I/O devices, and to provide the other services expected of secure, modern, multiprocessor operating systems.

This volume consists of Books I, II, and III. The fourth Book, called Book IV, *PowerPC Implementation Features*, differs for each implementation and is not included herein.

An important attribute of Books I, II, and III is that they do not constrain implementations on matters that would not affect software compatibility. For example, the effects of executing an invalidly coded instruction are not defined and can differ between implementations. Compilers and assemblers are responsible for generating only correctly coded instructions.

An even more important attribute of these three Books is that they specify the architecture in a manner that is independent of implementation. For example, Book III specifies the rules by which storage addresses are translated from the "effective addresses" generated by a program to the "real addresses" that are used to access storage, including the format of related tables and registers that are needed by the operating system. However, it does not specify *how* a processor should accomplish the translation. Thus, it permits translation lookaside buffers (TLBs) to be used, but does not require that they be used and does not specify their organization or contents. Book IV for each processor specifies all such implementation details, and use of the related facilities can be isolated to small portions of the operating system.

All PowerPC processors conform to Book I. The PowerPC processors being developed jointly by Motorola and IBM for the general computer market conform to Books II and III as well. Other implementations may support only a subset of the features described in these two Books. (In effect, such an implementation would have its own private Book II or III.) For example, a processor used as an embedded controller might conform to Books I and II but implement a simpler storage model than the one described in Book III.

Because the features described in Book III are available only to "privileged" programs such as operating systems, application binary compatibility is assured even for processors that implement a different Book III. The ability to change portions of Book III in the future may prove very useful, to support new developments in operating system and hardware technology and unforeseen processor requirements.

As used in this volume, the term "PowerPC Architecture" refers generically to the instructions and facilities described in Books I, II, and III. However, it is important to remember that these Books define three distinct levels of the architecture, and thus three different levels of compatibility.

Acknowledgements

We would like to acknowledge Keith Diefendorff, Ron Hochsprung, Rich Oehler, and John Sell for providing the technical leadership that made it possible for the group of architects, programmers, and designers from Apple, Motorola, and IBM to produce an architecture that met the goals established by the alliance these companies formed.

Many people contributed to the definition of the architecture, and it is not practical to name each of them here. However, a core group worked long hours over an extended period contributing ideas, evaluating options, debating costs and benefits of each proposal, and working together toward the goal of establishing a competitive architecture for the member companies of the alliance. This group of dedicated professionals included Richard Arndt, Roger Bailey, Al Chang, Barry Dorfman, Greg Grohoski, Randy Groves, Bill Hay, Marty Hopkins, Jim Kahle, Chin-Cheng Kau, Cathy May, Chuck Moore, Bill Moyer, John Muhich, Brett Olsson, John O'Quin, Mark Rogers, Tom Sartorius, Mike Shebanow, Ed Silha, Rick Simpson, Hank Warren, Lynn West, Andy Wottreng, and Mike Yamamura.

Book I

This book describes the base instruction set and related facilities available to the application programmer. It covers data and instruction formats, instruction classes and descriptions, registers accessible to the application programmer, and compatibility with the POWER architecture.

PowerPC User Instruction Set Architecture

Introduction

1.1 Overview

This chapter describes computation modes, compatibility with the POWER Architecture, document conventions, a processor overview, instruction formats, storage addressing, and instruction fetching.

1.2 Computation Modes

The PowerPC Architecture allows for the following types of implementation:

■ 64-bit implementations, in which all registers except some Special Purpose Registers are 64 bits long and effective addresses are 64 bits long. All 64-bit implementations have two modes of operation: 64-bit mode and 32-bit mode. The mode controls how the effective address is interpreted, how status bits are set, and how the Count Register is tested by *Branch Conditional* instructions. All instructions provided for 64-bit implementations are available in both modes.

■ 32-bit implementations, in which all registers except Floating-Point Registers are 32 bits long and effective addresses are 32 bits long.

Instructions defined in this document are provided in both 64-bit implementations and 32-bit implementations unless otherwise stated. Instructions that are provided only for 64-bit implementations are illegal in 32-bit implementations, and vice versa.

1.2.1 64-bit Implementations

In both 64-bit mode and 32-bit mode of a 64-bit implementation, instructions that set a 64-bit register affect all 64 bits, and the value placed into the register is independent of mode. In both modes, effective address computations use all 64 bits of the relevant registers (General Purpose Registers, Link Register, Count Register, etc.) and produce a 64-bit result. However, in 32-bit mode, the high-order 32 bits of the computed effective address are ignored when accessing data and are set to 0 when fetching instructions.

1.2.2 32-bit Implementations

For a 32-bit implementation, all references to 64-bit mode in this document should be disregarded. The semantics of instructions are as shown in this document for 32-bit mode in a 64-bit implementation, except that in a 32-bit implementation all registers except Floating-Point Registers are 32 bits long. Bit numbers for registers are shown in braces ({ }) when they differ from the corresponding numbers for a 64-bit implementation, as described in Section 1.5.1, "Definitions and Notation," on page 5.

1.3 Instruction Mnemonics and Operands

The description of each instruction includes the mnemonic and a formatted list of operands. Some examples are the following.

stw   RS,D(RA)
addis   RT,RA,SI

PowerPC-compliant assemblers will support the mnemonics and operand lists exactly as shown. They will also provide certain extended mnemonics, as described in Appendix C, "Assembler Extended Mnemonics," on page 215.

1.4 Compatibility with the POWER Architecture

The PowerPC Architecture provides binary compatibility for POWER application programs, except as described in Appendix G, "Incompatibilities with the POWER Architecture," on page 271.

Many of the PowerPC instructions are identical to POWER instructions. For some of these the PowerPC instruction name and/or mnemonic differs from that in POWER. To assist readers familiar with the POWER Architecture, POWER mnemonics are shown with the individual instruction descriptions when they differ from the PowerPC mnemonics. Also, Appendix F, "Cross-Reference for Changed POWER Mnemonics," on page 267, provides a cross-reference from POWER mnemonics to PowerPC mnemonics for the instructions in this document.

1.5 Document Conventions

1.5.1 Definitions and Notation

The following definitions and notation are used throughout the PowerPC Architecture documents.

■ A program is a sequence of related instructions.

■ Quadwords are 128 bits, doublewords are 64 bits, words are 32 bits, halfwords are 16 bits, and bytes are 8 bits.

■ All numbers are decimal unless specified in some special way.

— 0bnnnn means a number expressed in binary format.

— 0xnnnn means a number expressed in hexadecimal format.

Underscores may be used between digits.

■ RT, RA, R1, ... refer to General Purpose Registers.

■ FRT, FRA, FR1, ... refer to Floating-Point Registers.

■ (x) means the contents of register x, where x is the name of an instruction field. For example, (RA) means the contents of register RA, and (FRA) means the contents of register FRA, where RA and FRA are instruction fields. Names such as LR and CTR denote registers, not fields, so parentheses are not used with them. Parentheses are also omitted when register x is the register into which the result of an operation is placed.

■ (RA|0) means the contents of register RA if the RA field has the value 1–31, or the value 0 if the RA field is 0.

■ Bits in registers, instructions, and fields are specified as follows.

— Bits are numbered left to right, starting with bit 0.

— Ranges of bits are specified by two numbers separated by a colon (:). The range p:q consists of bits p through q.

— For registers that are 64 bits long in 64-bit implementations and 32 bits long in 32-bit implementations, bit numbers and ranges are specified with the values for 32-bit implementations enclosed in braces ({ }). {} means a bit that does not exist in 32-bit implementations. {:} means a range that does not exist in 32-bit implementations.

■ X_p means bit p of register/field X.
$X_{p\{r\}}$ means bit p of register/field X in a 64-bit implementation, and bit r of register/field X in a 32-bit implementation.

■ $X_{p:q}$ means bits p through q of register/field X.
$X_{p:q\{r:s\}}$ means bits p through q of register/field X in a 64-bit implementation, and bits r through s of register/field X in a 32-bit implementation.

■ $X_{p\ q\ ...}$ means bits p, q, ... of register/field X.
$X_{p\ q\ ...\ \{r\ s\ ...\}}$ means bits p, q, ... of register/field X in a 64-bit implementation, and bits r, s, ... of register/field X in a 32-bit implementation.

■ ¬(RA) means the one's complement of the contents of register RA.

■ Field i refers to bits $4 \times i$ through $4 \times i + 3$ of a register.

■ A period (.) as the last character of an instruction mnemonic means that the instruction records status information in certain fields of the Condition Register as a side effect of execution, as described in Chapter 2 through Chapter 4.

■ The symbol ‖ is used to describe the concatenation of two values. For example, 010 ‖ 111 is the same as 010111.

■ x^n means x raised to the nth power.

■ ^nx means the replication of x, n times (i.e., x concatenated to itself $n-1$ times). $^n0$ and $^n1$ are special cases:

— $^n0$ means a field of n bits with each bit equal to 0. Thus ^{50} is equivalent to 0b00000.

— $^n1$ means a field of n bits with each bit equal to 1. Thus ^{51} is equivalent to 0b11111.

■ Positive means greater than zero.

■ Negative means less than zero.

■ A system library program is a component of the system software that can be called by an application program using a *Branch* instruction.

■ A system service program is a component of the system software that can be called by an application program using a *System Call* instruction.

■ The system trap handler is a component of the system software that receives control when the conditions specified in a *Trap* instruction are satisfied.

■ The system error handler is a component of the system software that receives control when an error occurs. The system error handler includes a component for each of the various kinds of error. These error-specific components are referred to as the system alignment error handler, the system data storage error handler, etc.

■ Each bit and field in instructions, and in status and control registers (XER and FPSCR) and Special Purpose Registers, is either defined or reserved.

■ /, //, ///, ... denotes a reserved field in an instruction.

■ Latency refers to the interval from the time an instruction begins execution until it produces a result that is available for use by a subsequent instruction.

■ Unavailable refers to a resource that cannot be used by the program. Data or instruction storage is unavailable if an instruction is denied access to it. Floating-point instructions are unavailable if use of them is denied. See Book III, *PowerPC Operating Environment Architecture*.

■ The results of executing a given instruction are said to be boundedly undefined if they could have been achieved by executing an arbitrary sequence of instructions, starting in the state the machine was in before executing the given instruction. Boundedly undefined results for a given instruction may vary between implementations, and between different executions on the same implementation, and are not further defined in this document.

It is the responsibility of software to preserve bits that are now reserved in status and control registers and in Special Purpose Registers (and Segment Registers: see Book III, *PowerPC Operating Environment Architecture*), as they may be assigned a meaning in some future version of the architecture.

In order to accomplish this preservation in implementation-independent fashion, software should do the following.

■ Initialize each such register supplying zeros for all reserved bits.

■ Alter (defined) bit(s) in the register by reading the register, altering only the desired bit(s), and then writing the new value back to the register.

The XER and FPSCR are partial exceptions to this recommendation. Software can alter the status bits in these registers, preserving the reserved bits, by executing instructions that have the side effect of altering the status bits. Similarly, software can alter any defined bit in the FPSCR by executing a *Floating-Point Status and Control Register* instruction. Using such instructions is likely to

1.5.2 Reserved Fields

All reserved fields in instructions should be zero. If they are not, the instruction form is invalid: see Section 1.9.2, "Invalid Instruction Forms," on page 25.

The handling of reserved bits in status and control registers (XER and FPSCR) and in Special Purpose Registers (and Segment Registers: see Book III, Section 4.5, "Segmented Address Translation, 32-Bit Implementations," on page 412) is implementation dependent. For each such reserved bit, an implementation shall either:

■ ignore the source value for the bit on write, and return zero for it on read; or

■ set the bit from the source value on write, and return the value last set for it on read.

1.5.3 Description of Instruction Operation

A formal description is given of the operation of each instruction. In addition, the operation of most instructions is described by a semiformal language at the register transfer level (RTL). This RTL uses the notation given below, in addition to the definitions and notation described in Section 1.5.1, "Definitions and Notation," on page 5. Some of this notation is also used in the formal descriptions of instructions. RTL notation not summarized here should be self-explanatory.

The RTL descriptions cover the normal execution of the instruction, except that "standard" setting of the Condition Register, Fixed-Point Exception Register, and Floating-Point Status and Control Register are not shown. ("Non-standard" setting of these registers, such as the setting of Condition Register Field 0 by the *stwcx.* instruction, is shown.) The RTL descriptions do not cover cases in which the system error handler is invoked, or for which the results are boundedly undefined.

The RTL descriptions specify the architectural transformation performed by the execution of an instruction. They do not imply any particular implementation.

Notation	Meaning
←	Assignment
←$_{iea}$	Assignment of an instruction effective address. In 32-bit mode of a 64-bit implementation, the high-order 32 bits of the 64-bit target are set to 0.

$\neg$	NOT logical operator
+	Two's complement addition
−	Two's complement subtraction, unary minus
×	Multiplication
÷	Division (yielding quotient)
√	Square root
=, ≠	Equals, Not Equals relations
<, ≤, >, ≥	Signed comparison relations
≮, ≯	Unsigned comparison relations
?	Unordered comparison relation
& , |	AND, OR logical operators
⊕, ≡	Exclusive OR, Equivalence logical operators $((a\equiv b) = (a\oplus\neg b))$
ABS(x)	Absolute value of x
CEIL(x)	Least integer ≥ x
DOUBLE(x)	Result of converting x from floating-point single format to floating-point double format, using the model shown on page 168
EXTS(x)	Result of extending x on the left with sign bits
GPR(x)	General Purpose Register x
MASK(x, y)	Mask having 1s in positions x through y (wrapping if x > y) and 0s elsewhere
MEM(x, y)	Contents of y bytes of memory starting at address x. In 32-bit mode of a 64-bit implementation, the high-order 32 bits of the 64-bit value x are ignored.
ROTL$_{64}$(x, y)	Result of rotating the 64-bit value x left y positions
ROTL$_{32}$(x, y)	Result of rotating the 64-bit value x||x left y positions, where x is 32 bits long
SINGLE(x)	Result of converting x from floating-point double format to floating-point single format, using the model shown on page 173
SPREG(x)	Special Purpose Register x

yield better performance than using the method described in the second item above.

When a currently reserved bit is subsequently assigned a meaning, every effort will be made to have the value to which the system initializes the bit correspond to the "old behavior."

TRAP   Invoke the system trap handler

characterization   Reference to the setting of status bits, in a standard way that is explained in the text

undefined   An undefined value. The value may vary between implementations, and between different executions on the same implementation.

CIA   Current Instruction Address, which is the 64{32}-bit address of the instruction being described by a sequence of RTL. Used by relative branches to set the Next Instruction Address (NIA) and by *Branch* instructions with LK=1 to set the Link Register. In 32-bit mode of 64-bit implementations, the high-order 32 bits of CIA are always set to 0. Does not correspond to any architected register.

NIA   Next Instruction Address, which is the 64{32}-bit address of the next instruction to be executed. For a successful branch, the next instruction address is the branch target address: in RTL, this is indicated by assigning a value to NIA. For other instructions that cause nonsequential instruction fetching (see Book III, Section 2.3.1, "System Linkage Instructions," on page 378), the RTL is similar. For instructions that do not branch, and do not otherwise cause instruction fetching to be nonsequential, the next instruction address is CIA+4. In 32-bit mode of 64-bit implementations, the high-order 32 bits of NIA are always set to 0. Does not correspond to any architected register.

if ... then ... else ...   Conditional execution, indenting shows range; else is optional

do   Do loop, indenting shows range. "To" and/or "by" clauses specify incrementing an iteration variable, and a "while" clause gives termination conditions.

leave   Leave innermost do loop, or do loop described in leave statement

The precedence rules for RTL operators are summarized in Table 1 on page 11. Operators higher in the table are applied before those lower in the table. Operators at the same level in the table associate from left to right, from right to left, or not at all, as shown. (For example, − associates from left to right, so a−b−c = (a−b)−c.) Parentheses are used to override the evaluation order implied by the table or to increase clarity: parenthesized expressions are evaluated before serving as operands.

Operators	Associativity
subscript, function evaluation	left to right
pre-superscript (replication), post-superscript (exponentiation)	*right to left*
unary −, ¬	*right to left*
×, ÷	left to right
+, −	left to right
‖	left to right
$=, \neq, <, \leq, >, \geq, \overset{u}{<}, \overset{u}{>}, ?$	left to right
& , ⊕, ≡	left to right
		left to right
: (range)	none
←	none

Table 1. **Operator precedence**

1.6 Processor Overview

The processor implements the instruction set, the storage model, and other facilities defined in Book I. Instructions that the processor can execute fall into three classes:

■ branch instructions,

■ fixed-point instructions, and

■ floating-point instructions.

Branch instructions are described in Section 2.4, "Branch Processor Instructions," on page 35. Fixed-point instructions are described in Section 3.3, "Fixed-Point Processor Instructions," on page 49. Floating-point instructions are described in Section 4.6, "Floating-Point Processor Instructions," on page 167.

Fixed-point instructions operate on byte, halfword, word, and, in 64-bit implementations, doubleword operands. Floating-point instructions operate on single-precision and double-precision floating-point operands. The PowerPC Architecture uses instructions that are four bytes long and word-aligned. It provides for byte, halfword, word, and, in 64-bit implementations, doubleword operand fetches and stores between storage and

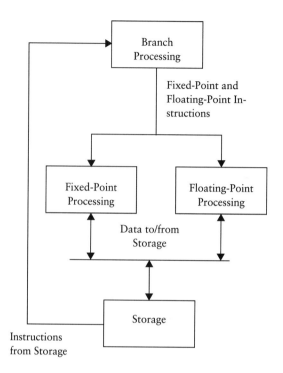

Figure 1.   **Logical processing model**

a set of 32 General Purpose Registers (GPRs). It also provides for word and doubleword operand fetches and stores between storage and a set of 32 Floating-Point Registers (FPRs).

Signed integers are represented in two's complement form.

There are no computational instructions that modify storage. To use a storage operand in a computation and then modify the same or another storage location, the content of storage must be loaded into a register, modified, and then stored back to the target location. Figure 1 is a logical representation of instruction processing. Figure 2 on page 13 shows the registers of the PowerPC User Instruction Set Architecture.

1.7 Instruction Formats

All instructions are four bytes long and word-aligned. Thus, whenever instruction addresses are presented to the processor (as in *Branch* instructions) the two low-order bits are ignored. Similarly, whenever the

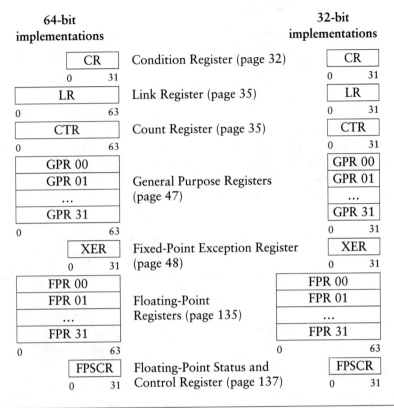

64-bit implementations		32-bit implementations

Figure 2.   **PowerPC user register set**

processor develops an instruction address, its two low-order bits are zero.

Bits 0:5 always specify the opcode (OPCD, below). Many instructions also have an extended opcode (XO, below). The remaining bits of the instruction contain one or more fields as shown below for the different instruction formats.

The format diagrams given below show horizontally all valid combinations of instruction fields. The diagrams include instruction fields that are used only by instructions defined in Book II, *PowerPC Virtual Environment Architecture,* or in Book III, *PowerPC Operating Environment Architecture.* See those Books for the definitions of such fields.

In some cases an instruction field is reserved, or must contain a particular value. If a reserved field does not have all bits set to 0, or if a field that must contain a particular value does not contain that value, the instruction form is invalid and the results are as described in Section 1.9.2, "Invalid Instruction Forms," on page 25.

Split Field Notation

In some cases an instruction field occupies more than one contiguous sequence of bits, or occupies one contiguous sequence of bits that are used in permuted order. Such a field is called a "split field." In the format diagrams given below and in the individual instruction layouts, the name of a split field is shown in small letters, once for each of the contiguous sequences. In the RTL description of an instruction having a split field, and in certain other places where individual bits of a split field are identified, the name of the field in small letters represents the concatenation of the sequences from left to right. In all other places, the name of the field is capitalized and represents the concatenation of the sequences in some order, which need not be left to right, as described for each affected instruction.

I-Form

Figure 3.   **I instruction format**

B-Form

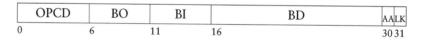

Figure 4.   **B instruction format**

SC-Form

Figure 5.   **SC instruction format**

D-Form

OPCD	RT		RA	D
OPCD	RT		RA	SI
OPCD	RS		RA	D
OPCD	RS		RA	UI
OPCD	BF	/ L	RA	SI
OPCD	BF	/ L	RA	UI
OPCD	TO		RA	SI
OPCD	FRT		RA	D
OPCD	FRS		RA	D

0   6   11   16   31

Figure 6. **D instruction format**

DS-Form

OPCD	RT	RA	DS	XO
OPCD	RS	RA	DS	XO

0   6   11   16   30 31

Figure 7. **DS instruction format (64-bit implementations only)**

X-Form

OPCD	RT		RA	RB	XO	/
OPCD	RT		RA	NB	XO	/
OPCD	RT	/	SR	///	XO	/
OPCD	RT		///	RB	XO	/
OPCD	RT		///	///	XO	/
OPCD	RS		RA	RB	XO	Rc
OPCD	RS		RA	RB	XO	1
OPCD	RS		RA	RB	XO	/
OPCD	RS		RA	NB	XO	/
OPCD	RS		RA	SH	XO	Rc
OPCD	RS		RA	///	XO	Rc
OPCD	RS	/	SR	///	XO	/
OPCD	RS		///	RB	XO	/
OPCD	RS		///	///	XO	/
OPCD	BF	/ L	RA	RB	XO	/
OPCD	BF	//	FRA	FRB	XO	/
OPCD	BF	//	BFA //	///	XO	/
OPCD	BF	//	///	U /	XO	Rc
OPCD	BF	//	///	///	XO	/
OPCD	TO		RA	RB	XO	/
OPCD	FRT		RA	RB	XO	/
OPCD	FRT		///	FRB	XO	Rc
OPCD	FRT		///	///	XO	Rc
OPCD	FRS		RA	RB	XO	/
OPCD	BT		///	///	XO	Rc
OPCD	///		RA	RB	XO	/
OPCD	///		///	RB	XO	/
OPCD	///		///	///	XO	/

0   6   11   16   21   31

Figure 8. **X instruction format**

XL-Form

OPCD	BT		BA		BB	XO	/
OPCD	BO		BI		///	XO	LK
OPCD	BF	//	BFA	//	///	XO	/
OPCD	///		///		///	XO	/

0   6   11   16   21   31

Figure 9.   **XL instruction format**

XFX-Form

OPCD	RT		spr		XO	/
OPCD	RT		tbr		XO	/
OPCD	RT	/	FXM	/	XO	/
OPCD	RS		spr		XO	/

0   6   11   21   31

Figure 10.   **XFX instruction format**

XFL-Form

OPCD	/	FLM	/	FRB	XO	Rc

0   6 7   15 16   21   31

Figure 11.   **XFL instruction format**

XS-Form

OPCD	RS	RA	sh	XO	sh	Rc

0   6   11   16   21   30 31

Figure 12.   **XS instruction format (64-bit implementations only)**

XO-Form

OPCD	RT	RA	RB	OE	XO	Rc
OPCD	RT	RA	RB	/	XO	Rc
OPCD	RT	RA	///	OE	XO	Rc

0   6   11   16   21 22   31

Figure 13.   **XO instruction format**

A-Form

OPCD	FRT	FRA	FRB	FRC	XO	Rc
OPCD	FRT	FRA	FRB	///	XO	Rc
OPCD	FRT	FRA	///	FRC	XO	Rc
OPCD	FRT	///	FRB	///	XO	Rc

0   6   11   16   21   26   31

Figure 14.   **A instruction format**

M-Form

OPCD	RS	RA	RB	MB	ME	Rc
OPCD	RS	RA	SH	MB	ME	Rc

0   6   11   16   21   26   31

Figure 15.   **M instruction format**

MD-Form

OPCD	RS	RA	sh	mb	XO	sh	Rc
OPCD	RS	RA	sh	me	XO	sh	Rc

0   6   11   16   21   27   30 31

Figure 16.   **MD instruction format (64-bit implementations only)**

MDS-Form

OPCD	RS	RA	RB	mb	XO	Rc
OPCD	RS	RA	RB	me	XO	Rc

0   6   11   16   21   27   31

Figure 17. **MDS instruction format (64-bit implementations only)**

1.7.1 Instruction Fields

AA (30)

Absolute Address bit

0   The immediate field represents an address relative to the current instruction address. For I-form branches the effective address of the
branch target is the sum of the LI field sign-extended to 64 bits and
the address of the branch instruction. For B-form branches the effective address of the branch target is the sum of the BD field sign-extended to 64 bits and the address of the branch instruction.

1   The immediate field represents an absolute address. For I-form
branches the effective address of the branch target is the LI field
sign-extended to 64 bits. For B-form branches the effective address
of the branch target is the BD field sign-extended to 64 bits.

BA (11:15)

Field used to specify a bit in the CR to be used as a source.

BB (16:20)

Field used to specify a bit in the CR to be used as a source.

BD (16:29)

Immediate field specifying a 14-bit signed two's complement branch
displacement, which is concatenated on the right with 0b00 and sign-
extended to 64 bits.

BF (6:8)

Field used to specify one of the CR fields or one of the FPSCR fields to
be used as a target.

BFA (11:13)

Field used to specify one of the CR fields or one of the FPSCR fields to
be used as a source.

BI (11:15)

Field used to specify a bit in the CR to be used as the condition of a *Branch Conditional* instruction.

BO (6:10)

Field used to specify options for the *Branch Conditional* instructions. The encoding is described in Section 2.4, "Branch Processor Instructions," on page 35.

BT (6:10)

Field used to specify a bit in the CR or in the FPSCR to be used as a target.

D (16:31)

Immediate field specifying a 16-bit signed two's complement integer which is sign-extended to 64 bits.

DS (16:29)

Immediate field specifying a 14-bit signed two's complement integer that is concatenated on the right with 0b00 and sign-extended to 64 bits. This field is defined in 64-bit implementations only.

FLM (7:14)

Field mask used to identify the FPSCR fields that are to be updated by the *mtfsf* instruction.

FRA (11:15)

Field used to specify an FPR to be used as a source.

FRB (16:20)

Field used to specify an FPR to be used as a source.

FRC (21:25)

Field used to specify an FPR to be used as a source.

FRS (6:10)

Field used to specify an FPR to be used as a source.

FRT (6:10)

Field used to specify an FPR to be used as a target.

FXM (12:19)

Field mask used to identify the CR fields that are to be updated by the *mtcrf* instruction.

L (10)

Field used to specify whether a Fixed-Point *Compare* instruction is to compare 64-bit numbers or 32-bit numbers. This field is defined in 64-bit implementations only.

LI (6:29)

Immediate field specifying a 24-bit signed two's complement integer which is concatenated on the right with 0b00 and sign-extended to 64 bits.

LK (31)

LINK bit.

0 Do not set the Link Register.

1 Set the Link Register. If the instruction is a *Branch* instruction, the address of the instruction following the *Branch* instruction is placed into the Link Register.

MB (21:25) and ME (26:30)

Fields used in M-form instructions to specify a 64-bit mask consisting of 1-bits from bit MB+32 through bit ME+32 inclusive and 0-bits elsewhere, as described in Section 3.3.13, "Fixed-Point Rotate and Shift Instructions," on page 115.

MB (21:26)

Field used in MD-form and MDS-form instructions to specify the first 1-bit of a 64-bit mask, as described in Section 3.3.13, "Fixed-Point Rotate and Shift Instructions," on page 115. This field is defined in 64-bit implementations only.

ME (21:26)

Field used in MD-form and MDS-form instructions to specify the last 1-bit of a 64-bit mask, as described in Section 3.3.13, "Fixed-Point Rotate and Shift Instructions," on page 115. This field is defined in 64-bit implementations only.

NB (16:20)

Field used to specify the number of bytes to move in an immediate string load or store.

OPCD (0:5)

Primary opcode field.

OE (21)

Used for extended arithmetic to enable setting OV and SO in the XER.

RA (11:15)

Field used to specify a GPR to be used as a source or as a target.

RB (16:20)

Field used to specify a GPR to be used as a source.

Rc (31)

RECORD bit

0 Do not alter the Condition Register.

1 Set Condition Register Field 0 or Field 1 as described in Section 2.3.1, "Condition Register," on page 32.

RS (6:10)

Field used to specify a GPR to be used as a source.

RT (6:10)

Field used to specify a GPR to be used as a target.

SH (16:20, or 16:20 and 30)

Field used to specify a shift amount. Location 16:20 and 30 pertains to 64-bit implementations only.

SI (16:31)

Immediate field used to specify a 16-bit signed integer.

SPR (11:20)

Field used to specify a Special Purpose Register for the *mtspr* and *mfspr* instructions. The encoding is described in Section 3.3.14, "Move to/ from System Register Instructions," on page 128.

SR (12:15)

See Book III, Section 1.5.1, "Instruction Fields," on page 370.

TBR (11:20)

See Book II, Section 4.1, "Time Base Instructions," on page 352.

TO (6:10)

Field used to specify the conditions on which to trap. The encoding is described in Section 3.3.11, "Fixed-Point Trap Instructions," on page 101.

U (16:19)

Immediate field used as the data to be placed into a field in the FPSCR.

UI (16:31)

Immediate field used to specify a 16-bit unsigned integer.

XO (21:29, 21:30, 22:30, 26:30, 27:29, 27:30, or 30:31)

Extended opcode field. Locations 21:29, 27:29, 27:30, and 30:31 pertain to 64-bit implementations only.

1.8 Classes of Instructions

An instruction falls into exactly one of the following three classes:

- Defined

- Illegal

- Reserved

The class is determined by examining the opcode, and the extended opcode if any. If the opcode, or combination of opcode and extended opcode, is not that of a defined instruction or of a reserved instruction, the instruction is illegal.

Some instructions are defined only for 64-bit implementations and a few are defined only for 32-bit implementations (see Section 1.8.2, "Illegal Instruction Class," on page 24). With the exception of these, a given instruction is in the same class for all implementations of the PowerPC Architecture. In future versions of this architecture, instructions that are now illegal may become defined (by being added to the architecture) or reserved (by being assigned to one of the special purposes described in Appendix J, "Reserved Instructions," on page 293). Similarly, instructions that are now reserved may become defined.

1.8.1 Defined Instruction Class

This class of instructions contains all the instructions defined in the PowerPC User Instruction Set Architecture, PowerPC Virtual Environment Architecture, and PowerPC Operating Environment Architecture.

Defined instructions are guaranteed to be supported in all implementations, except as stated in the instruction descriptions. (The exceptions are instructions that are supported only in 64-bit implementations or only in 32-bit implementations.)

A defined instruction can have preferred and/or invalid forms, as described in Section 1.9.1, "Preferred Instruction Forms," on page 25, and Section 1.9.2, "Invalid Instruction Forms," on page 25.

1.8.2 Illegal Instruction Class

This class of instructions contains the set of instructions described in Appendix I, "Illegal Instructions," on page 291. For 64-bit implementations, this class includes all instructions that are defined only for 32-bit implementations. For 32-bit implementations, it includes all instructions that are defined only for 64-bit implementations.

Excluding instructions that are defined for one type of implementation but not the other, illegal instructions are available for future extensions of the PowerPC Architecture: that is, some future version of the PowerPC Architecture may define any of these instructions to perform new functions.

Any attempt to execute an illegal instruction will cause the system illegal instruction error handler to be invoked and will have no other effect.

An instruction consisting entirely of binary 0s is guaranteed always to be an illegal instruction. This increases the probability that an attempt to execute data or uninitialized storage will result in the invocation of the system illegal instruction error handler.

1.8.3 Reserved Instruction Class

This class of instructions contains the set of instructions described in Appendix J, "Reserved Instructions," on page 293.

Reserved instructions are allocated to specific purposes that are outside the scope of the PowerPC Architecture.

Any attempt to execute a reserved instruction will:

■ perform the actions described in the Book IV, *PowerPC Implementation Features* for the implementation if the instruction is implemented; or

■ cause the system illegal instruction error handler to be invoked if the instruction is not implemented.

1.9 Forms of Defined Instructions

1.9.1 Preferred Instruction Forms

Some of the defined instructions have preferred forms. For such an instruction, the preferred form will execute in an efficient manner, but any other form may take significantly longer to execute than the preferred form.

Instructions having preferred forms are:

■ the *Load/Store Multiple* instructions

■ the *Load/Store String* instructions

■ the *Or Immediate* instruction (preferred form of no-op)

1.9.2 Invalid Instruction Forms

Some of the defined instructions have invalid forms. An instruction form is invalid if one or more fields of the instruction, excluding the opcode field(s), are coded incorrectly in a manner that can be deduced by examining only the instruction encoding.

Any attempt to execute an invalid form of an instruction will either cause the system illegal instruction error handler to be invoked or yield boundedly undefined results. Exceptions to this rule are stated in the instruction descriptions.

Some kinds of invalid form can be deduced from the instruction layout. These are listed below.

■ Field shown as '/'(s) but coded as nonzero.

■ Field shown as containing a particular value but coded as some other value.

These invalid forms are not discussed further.

Instructions having invalid forms that cannot be so deduced are listed below. These kinds of invalid form are identified in the instruction descriptions.

■ the *Branch Conditional* instructions

■ the *Load/Store with Update* instructions

■ the *Load Multiple* instruction

Assembler Note

To the extent possible, the Assembler should report uses of invalid instruction forms as errors.

- the *Load String* instructions

- the *Fixed-Point Compare* instructions (invalid form exists only in 32-bit implementations)

- the *Load/Store Floating-Point with Update* instructions

1.9.3 Optional Instructions

Some of the defined instructions are optional. The optional instructions are defined in Appendix A, "Optional Instructions," on page 197, and also in Book III, Section 4.11.3, "Lookaside Buffer Management Instructions (Optional)," on page 442 and Book III, Appendix A, "Optional Facilities and Instructions," on page 489.

Any attempt to execute an optional instruction that is not provided by the implementation will cause the system illegal instruction error handler to be invoked. Exceptions to this rule are stated in the instruction descriptions.

1.10 Exceptions

There are two kinds of exception, those caused directly by the execution of an instruction and those caused by an asynchronous event. In either case, the exception may cause one of several components of the system software to be invoked.

The exceptions that can be caused directly by the execution of an instruction include the following:

- an attempt to execute an illegal instruction, or an attempt by an application program to execute a "privileged" instruction [see Book III, Section 5.5.7, "Program Interrupt," on page 467 (system illegal instruction error handler or system privileged instruction error handler)]

- the execution of a defined instruction using an invalid form (system illegal instruction error handler or system privileged instruction error handler)

- the execution of an optional instruction that is not provided by the implementation (system illegal instruction error handler)

- an attempt to access a storage location that is unavailable (system error handler)

- an attempt to access storage with an effective address alignment that is invalid for the instruction (system alignment error handler)

- the execution of a *System Call* instruction (system service program)

- the execution of a *Trap* instruction that traps (system trap handler)

- the execution of a floating-point instruction when floating-point instructions are unavailable (system floating-point unavailable error handler)

- the execution of a floating-point instruction that causes a floating-point exception that is enabled (system floating-point enabled exception error handler)

- the execution of a floating-point instruction that requires system software assistance (system floating-point assist error handler; the conditions under which such software assistance is required are implementation-dependent)

The exceptions that can be caused by an asynchronous event are described in Book III, Chapter 5, "Interrupts," on page 453.

The invocation of the system error handler is precise, except that if one of the imprecise modes for invoking the system floating-point enabled exception error handler is in effect (see page 153) then the invocation of the system floating-point enabled exception error handler may be imprecise. When the system error handler is invoked imprecisely, the excepting instruction does not appear to complete before the next instruction starts (because one of the effects of the excepting instruction, namely the invocation of the system error handler, has not yet occurred).

Additional information about exception handling can be found in Book III, Chapter 5.

1.11 Storage Addressing

A program references storage using the effective address computed by the processor when it executes a *Storage Access* or *Branch* instruction (or certain other instructions described in Book II, *PowerPC Virtual Environment Architecture*, and Book III, *PowerPC Operating Environment Architecture*) or when it fetches the next sequential instruction.

1.11.1 Storage Operands

Bytes in storage are numbered consecutively starting with 0. Each number is the address of the corresponding byte.

Storage operands may be bytes, halfwords, words, or doublewords, or, for the *Load/Store Multiple* and *Move Assist* instructions, a sequence of bytes or words. The address of a storage operand is the address of its first byte (i.e., of its lowest-numbered byte). Byte ordering is Big-Endian by default, but PowerPC can be operated in a mode in which byte ordering is Little-Endian.   See Appendix D, "Little-Endian Byte Ordering," on page 233.

Operand length is implicit for each instruction.

The operand of a single-register *Storage Access* instruction has a "natural" alignment boundary equal to the operand length. In other words, the "natural" address of an operand is an integral multiple of the operand length. A storage operand is said to be "aligned" if it is aligned at its natural boundary; otherwise it is said to be "unaligned."

Storage operands for single-register *Storage Access* instructions have the following characteristics. (Although not permitted as storage operands, quadwords are shown because quadword alignment is desirable for certain storage operands.)

Operand	Length	Addr$_{60:63}$ if aligned
Byte	8 bits	xxxx
Halfword	2 bytes	xxx0
Word	4 bytes	xx00
Doubleword	8 bytes	x000
Quadword	16 bytes	0000

Note: An "x" in an address bit position indicates that the bit can be 0 or 1 independent of the state of other bits in the address.

The concept of alignment is also applied more generally, to any datum in storage. For example, a 12-byte datum in storage is said to be word-aligned if its address is an integral multiple of 4.

Some instructions require their storage operands to have certain alignments. In addition, alignment may affect performance. For single-register *Storage Access* instructions, the best performance is obtained when storage operands are aligned. Additional effects of data placement on performance are described in Book II, Chapter 2, "Effect of Operand Placement on Performance," on page 339.

Instructions are always four bytes long and word-aligned.

1.11.2 Effective Address Calculation

The 64- or 32-bit address computed by the processor when executing a *Storage Access* or *Branch* instruction (or certain other instructions described in Book II, *PowerPC Virtual Environment Architecture*, and Book III, *PowerPC Operating Environment Architecture*) or when fetching the next sequential instruction is called the "effective address" and specifies a byte in storage. For a *Storage Access* instruction, if the sum of the effective address and the operand length exceeds the maximum effective address, the storage operand is considered to wrap around from the maximum effective address to effective address 0, as described below.

Effective address computations, for both data and instruction accesses, use 64{32}-bit unsigned binary arithmetic regardless of mode. A carry from bit 0 is ignored. In a 64-bit implementation, the 64-bit current instruction address and next instruction address are not affected by a change from 32-bit mode to 64-bit mode, but they are affected by a change from 64-bit mode to 32-bit mode (the high-order 32 bits are set to 0).

In 64-bit mode, the entire 64-bit result is used as the 64-bit effective address. The effective address arithmetic wraps around from the maximum address, $2^{64}-1$, to address 0.

In 32-bit mode, the low-order 32 bits of the 64-bit result are used as the effective address for the purpose of addressing storage. The high-order 32 bits of the 64-bit effective address are ignored for the purpose of accessing data, but are included whenever a 64-bit effective address is placed into a GPR by *Load with Update* and *Store with Update* instructions. The high-order 32 bits of the 64-bit effective address are set to 0 for the purpose of fetching instructions, and whenever a 64-bit effective address is placed into the Link Register by *Branch* instructions having LK=1. The high-order 32 bits of the 64-bit effective address are set to 0 in Special Purpose Registers when the system error handler is invoked. As used to address storage, the effective address arithmetic appears to wrap around from the maximum address, $2^{32}-1$, to address 0.

A zero in the RA field indicates the absence of the corresponding address component. For the absent component, a value of zero is used for the address. This is shown in the instruction descriptions as (RA|0).

In both 64-bit and 32-bit modes, the calculated effective address may be modified in its three low-order bits before accessing storage if the PowerPC system is operating in Little-Endian mode. See Appendix D, "Little-Endian Byte Ordering," on page 233.

Effective addresses are computed as follows. In the descriptions below, it should be understood that "the contents of a GPR" refers to the entire

64-bit contents, independent of mode, but that in 32-bit mode only bits 32:63 of the 64-bit result of the computation are used to address storage.

■ With X-form instructions, in computing the effective address of a data element, the contents of the GPR designated by RB are added to the contents of the GPR designated by RA or to zero if RA=0.

■ With D-form instructions, the 16-bit D field is sign-extended to form a 64-bit address component. In computing the effective address of a data element, this address component is added to the contents of the GPR designated by RA or to zero if RA=0.

■ With DS-form instructions, the 14-bit DS field is concatenated on the right with 0b00 and sign-extended to form a 64-bit address component. In computing the effective address of a data element, this address component is added to the contents of the GPR designated by RA or to zero if RA=0.

■ With I-form *Branch* instructions, the 24-bit LI field is concatenated on the right with 0b00 and sign-extended to form a 64-bit address component. If AA=0, this address component is added to the address of the branch instruction to form the effective address of the next instruction. If AA=1, this address component is the effective address of the next instruction.

■ With B-form *Branch* instructions, the 14-bit BD field is concatenated on the right with 0b00 and sign-extended to form a 64-bit address component. If AA=0, this address component is added to the address of the branch instruction to form the effective address of the next instruction. If AA=1, this address component is the effective address of the next instruction.

■ With XL-form *Branch* instructions, bits 0:61 of the Link Register or the Count Register are concatenated on the right with 0b00 to form the effective address of the next instruction.

■ With sequential instruction fetching, the value 4 is added to the address of the current instruction to form the effective address of the next instruction.

Branch Processor

2.1 Branch Processor Overview

This chapter describes the registers and instructions that make up the Branch Processor facility. Section 2.3, "Branch Processor Registers," on page 32 describes the registers associated with the Branch Processor. Section 2.4, "Branch Processor Instructions," on page 35 describes the instructions associated with the Branch Processor.

2.2 Instruction Fetching

In general, instructions appear to execute sequentially, in the order in which they appear in storage. The exceptions to this rule are listed below.

- *Branch* instructions for which the branch is taken cause execution to continue at the target address generated by the *Branch* instruction.

- *Trap* and *System Call* instructions cause the appropriate system handler to be invoked.

- Exceptions can cause the system error handler to be invoked, as described in Section 1.10, "Exceptions," on page 26.

- The *Return From Interrupt* instruction, described in Book III, "Return From Interrupt XL-form," on page 379, causes execution to continue at the address contained in a Special Purpose Register.

In general, from the view of the processor executing the instructions, each instruction appears to complete before the next instruction starts. For the instructions and facilities defined in Book I, the only exceptions to this rule are the following.

■ The system error handler is invoked imprecisely. The instruction that causes the system error handler to be invoked does not complete before the next instruction starts: see Section 1.10, "Exceptions," on page 26.

Programming Note

If a program modifies the instructions it intends to execute, it should call the appropriate system library program before attempting to execute the modified instructions, to ensure that the modifications have taken effect with respect to instruction fetching.

■ A *Store* instruction modifies a storage location that contains an instruction. Software synchronization is required to ensure that subsequent instruction fetches from that location obtain the modified version of the instruction: see Book II, Section 3.2.1, "Instruction Cache Instructions," on page 344.

2.3 Branch Processor Registers

2.3.1 Condition Register

The Condition Register (CR) is a 32-bit register which reflects the result of certain operations, and provides a mechanism for testing (and branching).

CR
0   31

Figure 18.   Condition Register

The bits in the Condition Register are grouped into eight 4-bit fields, named CR Field 0 (CR0), ..., CR Field 7 (CR7), which are set in one of the following ways:

■ Specified fields of the CR can be set by a move to the CR from a GPR (*mtcrf*).

■ A specified field of the CR can be set by a move to the CR from another CR field (*mcrf*), from the XER (*mcrxr*), or from the FPSCR (*mcrfs*).

■ CR Field 0 can be set as the implicit result of a fixed-point instruction.

■ CR Field 1 can be set as the implicit result of a floating-point instruction.

■ A specified CR field can be set as the result of either a fixed-point or a floating-point *Compare* instruction.

Instructions are provided to perform logical operations on individual CR bits and to test individual CR bits.

For all fixed-point instructions in which Rc=1, and for *addic., andi.,* and *andis.,* the first three bits of CR Field 0 (bits 0:2 of the Condition Register) are set by signed comparison of the result to zero, and the fourth bit of CR Field 0 (bit 3 of the Condition Register) is copied from the SO field of the XER. "Result" here refers to the entire 64-bit value placed into the target register in 64-bit mode, and to bits 32:63 of the 64-bit value placed into the target register in 32-bit mode.

```
if (64-bit implementation) & (64-bit mode)
    then M ← 0
    else M ← 32
if      (target_register)M:63 < 0 then   c ← 0b100
else if (target_register)M:63 > 0 then   c ← 0b010
else                                     c ← 0b001
CR0 ← c || XERSO
```

If any portion of the result is undefined, then the value placed into the first three bits of CR Field 0 is undefined.

The bits of CR Field 0 are interpreted as follows.

Bit	Description
0	*Negative (LT)* The result is negative.
1	*Positive (GT)* The result is positive.
2	*Zero (EQ)* The result is zero.
3	*Summary Overflow (SO)* This is a copy of the final state of XER_{SO} at the completion of the instruction.

Programming Note

CR Field 0 may not reflect the "true" (infinitely precise) result if overflow occurs: see Section 3.3.9, "Fixed-Point Arithmetic Instructions," on page 81.

The fixed-point instructions *stwcx.* and *stdcx.* also set CR Field 0.

For all floating-point instructions in which Rc=1, CR Field 1 (bits 4:7 of the Condition Register) is set to the Floating-Point exception status, copied from bits 0:3 of the Floating-Point Status and Control Register. These bits are interpreted as follows.

Bit	Description

4   *Floating-Point Exception Summary (FX)*
    This is a copy of the final state of $FPSCR_{FX}$ at the completion of the instruction.

5   *Floating-Point Enabled Exception Summary (FEX)*
    This is a copy of the final state of $FPSCR_{FEX}$ at the completion of the instruction.

6   *Floating-Point Invalid Operation Exception Summary (VX)*
    This is a copy of the final state of $FPSCR_{VX}$ at the completion of the instruction.

7   *Floating-Point Overflow Exception (OX)*
    This is a copy of the final state of $FPSCR_{OX}$ at the completion of the instruction.

For *Compare* instructions, a specified CR field is set to reflect the result of the comparison. The bits of the specified CR field are interpreted as follows. A complete description of how the bits are set is given in the instruction descriptions in Section 3.3.10, "Fixed-Point Compare Instructions," on page 98, and Section 4.6.7, "Floating-Point Compare Instructions," on page 191.

Bit	Description

0   *Less Than, Floating-Point Less Than (LT, FL)*
    For fixed-point *Compare* instructions, (RA) < SI or (RB) (signed comparison) or (RA) $\not<$ UI or (RB) (unsigned comparison). For floating-point *Compare* instructions, (FRA) < (FRB).

1   *Greater Than, Floating-Point Greater Than (GT, FG)*
    For fixed-point *Compare* instructions, (RA) > SI or (RB) (signed comparison) or (RA) $\not>$ UI or (RB) (unsigned comparison). For floating-point *Compare* instructions, (FRA) > (FRB).

2   *Equal, Floating-Point Equal (EQ, FE)*
    For fixed-point *Compare* instructions, (RA) = SI, UI, or (RB). For floating-point *Compare* instructions, (FRA) = (FRB).

3   *Summary Overflow, Floating-Point Unordered (SO, FU)*
     For fixed-point *Compare* instructions, this is a copy of the final
     state of XER_{SO} at the completion of the instruction. For floating-
     point *Compare* instructions, one or both of (FRA) and (FRB) is a
     NaN.

2.3.2 Link Register

The Link Register (LR) is a 64-bit {32-bit} register. It can be used to provide the branch target address for the *Branch Conditional to Link Register* instruction, and it holds the return address after *Branch and Link*
instructions.

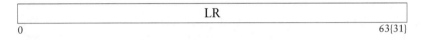

LR

0   63{31}

Figure 19.   **Link Register**

2.3.3 Count Register

The Count Register (CTR) is a 64-bit {32-bit} register. It can be used to
hold a loop count that can be decremented during execution of *Branch*
instructions that contain an appropriately coded BO field. If the value in
the Count Register is 0 before being decremented, it is −1 afterward. The
Count Register can also be used to provide the branch target address for
the *Branch Conditional to Count Register* instruction.

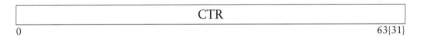

CTR

0   63{31}

Figure 20.   **Count Register**

2.4 Branch Processor Instructions

2.4.1 Branch Instructions

The sequence of instruction execution can be changed by the *Branch*
instructions. Because all instructions are on word boundaries, bits 62
and 63 of the generated branch target address are ignored by the processor in performing the branch.

The *Branch* instructions compute the effective address (EA) of the target in one of the following four ways, as described in Section 1.11.2, "Effective Address Calculation," on page 29.

1. Adding a displacement to the address of the branch instruction (*Branch* or *Branch Conditional* with AA=0).

2. Specifying an absolute address (*Branch* or *Branch Conditional* with AA=1).

3. Using the address contained in the Link Register (*Branch Conditional to Link Register*).

4. Using the address contained in the Count Register (*Branch Conditional to Count Register*).

In all four cases, in 32-bit mode of 64-bit implementations, the final step in the address computation is setting the high-order 32 bits of the target address to 0.

For the first two methods, the target addresses can be computed sufficiently ahead of the branch instruction that instructions can be prefetched along the target path. For the third and fourth methods, prefetching instructions along the target path is also possible, provided the Link Register or the Count Register is loaded sufficiently ahead of the branch instruction.

Branching can be conditional or unconditional, and the return address can optionally be provided. If the return address is to be provided (LK=1), the effective address of the instruction following the branch instruction is placed into the Link Register after the branch target address has been computed. This is done whether or not the branch is taken.

In *Branch Conditional* instructions, the BO field specifies the conditions under which the branch is taken. The first four bits of the BO field specify how the branch is affected by or affects the Condition Register and the Count Register. The fifth bit, shown below as having the value "y", may be used by some implementations as described below.

The encoding for the BO field is as follows. Here $M=0$ in 64-bit mode and $M=32$ in 32-bit mode. If the BO field specifies that the CTR is to be decremented, the entire 64-bit CTR is decremented regardless of the mode.

BO	Description
0000y	Decrement the CTR, then branch if the decremented $CTR_{M:63} \neq 0$ and the condition is FALSE.
0001y	Decrement the CTR, then branch if the decremented $CTR_{M:63} = 0$ and the condition is FALSE.
001zy	Branch if the condition is FALSE.
0100y	Decrement the CTR, then branch if the decremented $CTR_{M:63} \neq 0$ and the condition is TRUE.
0101y	Decrement the CTR, then branch if the decremented $CTR_{M:63} = 0$ and the condition is TRUE.
011zy	Branch if the condition is TRUE.
1z00y	Decrement the CTR, then branch if the decremented $CTR_{M:63} \neq 0$.
1z01y	Decrement the CTR, then branch if the decremented $CTR_{M:63} = 0$.
1z1zz	Branch always.

Above, "z" denotes a bit that is ignored.

The "y" bit provides a hint about whether a conditional branch is likely to be taken, and may be used by some implementations to improve performance.

The "branch always" encoding of the BO field does not have a "y" bit.

For *Branch Conditional* instructions that have a "y" bit, using y=0 indicates that the following behavior is likely.

- If the instruction is *bc[l][a]* with a negative value in the displacement field, the branch is taken.

- In all other cases (*bc[l][a]* with a nonnegative value in the displacement field, *bclr[l]*, or *bcctr[l]*), the branch falls through (is not taken).

Using y=1 reverses the preceding indications.

The displacement field is used as described above even if the target is an absolute address.

Extended mnemonics for branches

Many extended mnemonics are provided so that *Branch Conditional* instructions can be coded with the condition as part of the instruction mnemonic rather than as a numeric operand. Some of these are shown as examples with the *Branch* instructions. See Appendix C, "Assembler Extended Mnemonics," on page 215 for additional extended mnemonics.

Programming Note

The "z" bits should be set to 0, as they may be assigned a meaning in some future version of the architecture.

The default value for the "y" bit should be 0: the value 1 should be used only if software has determined that the prediction corresponding to y=1 is more likely to be correct than the prediction corresponding to y=0.

Branch   I-form

b	target_addr	(AA=0 LK=0)
ba	target_addr	(AA=1 LK=0)
bl	target_addr	(AA=0 LK=1)
bla	target_addr	(AA=1 LK=1)

18	LI	AA	LK
0	6	30	31

```
if AA then NIA ←iea EXTS(LI || 0b00)
else          NIA ←iea CIA + EXTS(LI || 0b00)
if LK then LR ←iea CIA + 4
```

target_addr specifies the branch target address.

If AA=0 then the branch target address is the sum of LI || 0b00 sign-extended and the address of this instruction, with the high-order 32 bits of the branch target address set to 0 in 32-bit mode of 64-bit implementations.

If AA=1 then the branch target address is the value LI || 0b00 sign-extended, with the high-order 32 bits of the branch target address set to 0 in 32-bit mode of 64-bit implementations.

If LK=1 then the effective address of the instruction following the *Branch* instruction is placed into the Link Register.

Special Registers Altered

    LR   (if LK=1)

Branch Conditional   B-form

bc	BO,BI,target_addr	(AA=0 LK=0)
bca	BO,BI,target_addr	(AA=1 LK=0)
bcl	BO,BI,target_addr	(AA=0 LK=1)
bcla	BO,BI,target_addr	(AA=1 LK=1)

16	BO	BI	BD	AA	LK
0	6	11	16	30	31

```
if (64-bit implementation) & (64-bit mode)
   then M ← 0
   else M ← 32
if ¬BO2 then CTR ← CTR - 1
ctr_ok ← BO2 | ((CTRM:63 ≠ 0) ⊕ BO3)
cond_ok ← BO0 | (CRBI ≡ BO1)
```

```
if ctr_ok & cond_ok then
   if AA then NIA ←ᵢₑₐ EXTS(BD || 0b00)
   else        NIA ←ᵢₑₐ CIA + EXTS(BD || 0b00)
if LK then LR ←ᵢₑₐ CIA + 4
```

The BI field specifies the bit in the Condition Register to be used as the condition of the branch. The BO field is used as described above. *target_addr* specifies the branch target address.

If AA=0 then the branch target address is the sum of BD || 0b00 sign-extended and the address of this instruction, with the high-order 32 bits of the branch target address set to 0 in 32-bit mode of 64-bit implementations.

If AA=1 then the branch target address is the value BD || 0b00 sign-extended, with the high-order 32 bits of the branch target address set to 0 in 32-bit mode of 64-bit implementations.

If LK=1 then the effective address of the instruction following the *Branch* instruction is placed into the Link Register.

Special Registers Altered

```
CTR                                              (if BO₂=0)
LR                                               (if LK=1)
```

Extended Mnemonics:

Examples of extended mnemonics for *Branch Conditional*:

Extended:		*Equivalent to:*	
blt	target	bc	12,0,target
bne	cr2,target	bc	4,10,target
bdnz	target	bc	16,0,target

Branch Conditional to Link Register   XL-form

bclr	BO,BI	(LK=0)
bclrl	BO,BI	(LK=1)

[POWER mnemonics: bcr, bcrl]

19	BO	BI	///	16	LK
0	6	11	16	21	31

```
if (64-bit implementation) & (64-bit mode)
   then M ← 0
   else M ← 32
if ¬BO₂ then CTR ← CTR - 1
```

Here A calls B and B returns to A. The two branches should be as follows.

—A calls B: use a *Branch* instruction that sets the Link Register (LK=1).

—B returns to A: use the *bclr* instruction (LK=0) (the return address is in, or can be restored to, the Link Register).

■ Indirect subroutine linkage:

Here A calls Glue, Glue calls B, and B returns to A rather than to Glue. (Such a calling sequence is common in linkage code used when the subroutine that the programmer wants to call, here B, is in a different module from the caller: the Binder inserts "glue" code to mediate the branch.) The three branches should be as follows.

—A calls Glue: use a *Branch* instruction that sets the Link Register (LK=1).

—Glue calls B: place the address of B in the Count Register, and use the *bcctr* instruction (LK=0).

—B returns to A: use the *bclr* instruction (LK=0) (the return address is in, or can be restored to, the Link Register).

```
ctr_ok ← BO₂ | ((CTR_M:63 ≠ 0) ⊕ BO₃)
cond_ok ← BO₀ | (CR_BI ≡ BO₁)
if ctr_ok & cond_ok then NIA ←_iea LR₀:61 || 0b00
if LK then LR ←_iea CIA + 4
```

The BI field specifies the bit in the Condition Register to be used as the condition of the branch. The BO field is used as described above, and the branch target address is $LR_{0:61}$ ‖ 0b00, with the high-order 32 bits of the branch target address set to 0 in 32-bit mode of 64-bit implementations.

If LK=1 then the effective address of the instruction following the *Branch* instruction is placed into the Link Register.

Special Registers Altered

```
CTR                                              (if BO₂=0)
LR                                               (if LK=1)
```

Extended Mnemonics:

Examples of extended mnemonics for *Branch Conditional to Link Register*:

Extended:	*Equivalent to:*	
bltlr	bclr	12,0
bnelr cr2	bclr	4,10
bdnzlr	bclr	16,0

Branch Conditional to Count Register   XL-form

bcctr	BO,BI	(LK=0)
bcctrl	BO,BI	(LK=1)

[POWER mnemonics: bcc, bccl]

19	BO	BI	///	528	LK
0	6	11	16	21	31

```
cond_ok ← BO₀ | (CR_BI ≡ BO₁)
if cond_ok then NIA ←_iea CTR₀:61 || 0b00
if LK then LR ←_iea CIA + 4
```

The BI field specifies the bit in the Condition Register to be used as the condition of the branch. The BO field is used as described above, and the branch target address is $CTR_{0:61}$ ‖ 0b00, with the high-order 32 bits of the branch target address set to 0 in 32-bit mode of 64-bit implementations.

If LK=1 then the effective address of the instruction following the *Branch* instruction is placed into the Link Register.

If the "decrement and test CTR" option is specified (BO_2=0), the instruction form is invalid.

Special Registers Altered

    LR   (if LK=1)

Extended Mnemonics:

Examples of extended mnemonics for *Branch Conditional to Count Register*:

Extended:	*Equivalent to:*
bltctr	bcctr 12,0
bnectr cr2	bcctr 4,10

2.4.2 System Call Instruction

This instruction provides the means by which a program can call upon the system to perform a service.

System Call   SC-form

sc

[POWER mnemonic: svca]

17	///	///	///	1	/
0	6	11	16	30	31

This instruction calls the system to perform a service. A complete description of this instruction can be found in Book III, Section 2.3.1, "System Linkage Instructions," on page 378.

When control is returned to the program that executed the *System Call*, the content of the registers will depend on the register conventions used by the program providing the system service.

This instruction is context synchronizing; see Book III, Section 1.7.1, "Context Synchronization," on page 371.

Special Registers Altered

    Dependent on the system service.

Compatibility Note

For a discussion of Power compatibility with respect to instruction bits 16:29, please refer to Appendix G, "Incompatibilities with the POWER Architecture," on page 271. For compatibility with future versions of this architecture, these bits should be coded as zero.

2.4.3 Condition Register Logical Instructions

Extended mnemonics for Condition Register logical operations

A set of extended mnemonics is provided that allow Condition Register logical operations, beyond those provided by the basic *Condition Register Logical* instructions, to be coded easily. Some of these are shown as examples with the *Condition Register Logical* instructions. See Appendix C, "Assembler Extended Mnemonics," on page 215 for additional extended mnemonics.

Condition Register AND   XL-form

crand   BT,BA,BB

19	BT	BA	BB	257	/
0	6	11	16	21	31

$CR_{BT} \leftarrow CR_{BA}\ \&\ CR_{BB}$

The bit in the Condition Register specified by BA is ANDed with the bit in the Condition Register specified by BB, and the result is placed into the bit in the Condition Register specified by BT.

Special Registers Altered

    CR

Condition Register OR   XL-form

cror   BT,BA,BB

19	BT	BA	BB	449	/
0	6	11	16	21	31

$CR_{BT} \leftarrow CR_{BA}\ |\ CR_{BB}$

The bit in the Condition Register specified by BA is ORed with the bit in the Condition Register specified by BB, and the result is placed into the bit in the Condition Register specified by BT.

Special Registers Altered

    CR

Extended Mnemonics:

Example of extended mnemonics for *Condition Register OR:*

Extended:	*Equivalent to:*
crmove Bx,By	cror Bx,By,By

Condition Register XOR   XL-form

crxor   BT,BA,BB

19	BT	BA	BB	193	/
0	6	11	16	21	31

$$CR_{BT} \leftarrow CR_{BA} \oplus CR_{BB}$$

The bit in the Condition Register specified by BA is XORed with the bit in the Condition Register specified by BB, and the result is placed into the bit in the Condition Register specified by BT.

Special Registers Altered

CR

Extended Mnemonics:

Example of extended mnemonics for *Condition Register XOR:*

Extended:	*Equivalent to:*
crclr Bx	crxor Bx,Bx,Bx

Condition Register NAND   XL-form

crnand   BT,BA,BB

19	BT	BA	BB	225	/
0	6	11	16	21	31

$$CR_{BT} \leftarrow \neg(CR_{BA} \& CR_{BB})$$

The bit in the Condition Register specified by BA is ANDed with the bit in the Condition Register specified by BB, and the complemented result is placed into the bit in the Condition Register specified by BT.

Special Registers Altered

CR

Condition Register NOR   XL-form

crnor   BT,BA,BB

19	BT	BA	BB	33	/
0	6	11	16	21	31

$$CR_{BT} \leftarrow \neg(CR_{BA} \mid CR_{BB})$$

The bit in the Condition Register specified by BA is ORed with the bit in the Condition Register specified by BB, and the complemented result is placed into the bit in the Condition Register specified by BT.

Special Registers Altered

CR

Extended Mnemonics:

Example of extended mnemonics for *Condition Register NOR:*

Extended:	*Equivalent to:*
crnot Bx,By	crnor Bx,By,By

Condition Register Equivalent   XL-form

creqv   BT,BA,BB

19	BT	BA	BB	289	/
0	6	11	16	21	31

$$CR_{BT} \leftarrow CR_{BA} \equiv CR_{BB}$$

The bit in the Condition Register specified by BA is XORed with the bit in the Condition Register specified by BB, and the complemented result is placed into the bit in the Condition Register specified by BT.

Special Registers Altered

CR

Extended Mnemonics:

Example of extended mnemonics for *Condition Register Equivalent:*

Extended:	*Equivalent to:*
crset Bx	creqv Bx,Bx,Bx

Condition Register AND with Complement   XL-form

crandc   BT,BA,BB

19	BT	BA	BB	129	/
0	6	11	16	21	31

$CR_{BT} \leftarrow CR_{BA} \; \& \; \neg CR_{BB}$

The bit in the Condition Register specified by BA is ANDed with the complement of the bit in the Condition Register specified by BB, and the result is placed into the bit in the Condition Register specified by BT.

Special Registers Altered

CR

Condition Register OR with Complement   XL-form

crorc   BT,BA,BB

19	BT	BA	BB	417	/
0	6	11	16	21	31

$CR_{BT} \leftarrow CR_{BA} \; | \; \neg CR_{BB}$

The bit in the Condition Register specified by BA is ORed with the complement of the bit in the Condition Register specified by BB, and the result is placed into the bit in the Condition Register specified by BT.

Special Registers Altered

CR

2.4.4 Condition Register Field Instruction

Move Condition Register Field   XL-form

mcrf   BF,BFA

19	BF	//	BFA	//	///	0	/
0	6	9	11	14	16	21	31

$$CR_{4\times BF:4\times BF+3} \leftarrow CR_{4\times BFA:4\times BFA+3}$$

The contents of Condition Register field BFA are copied into Condition Register field BF.

Special Registers Altered

CR

Fixed-Point Processor 3

3.1 Fixed-Point Processor Overview

This chapter describes the registers and instructions that make up the Fixed-Point Processor facility. Section 3.2, "Fixed-Point Processor Registers," describes the registers associated with the Fixed-Point Processor. Section 3.3, "Fixed-Point Processor Instructions," on page 49 describes the instructions associated with the Fixed-Point Processor.

3.2 Fixed-Point Processor Registers

3.2.1 General Purpose Registers

All manipulation of information is done in registers internal to the Fixed-Point Processor. The principal storage internal to the Fixed-Point Processor is a set of 32 general purpose registers (GPRs). See Figure 21.

Each GPR is a 64-bit {32-bit} register.

GPR 00
GPR 01
...
GPR 30
GPR 31

0   63 {31}

Figure 21. **General purpose registers**

3.2.2 Fixed-Point Exception Register

The Fixed-Point Exception Register (XER) is a 32-bit register.

<table>
<tr><td colspan="2" align="center">XER</td></tr>
<tr><td>0</td><td align="right">31</td></tr>
</table>

Figure 22.   **Fixed-Point Exception Register**

The bit definitions for the Fixed-Point Exception Register are as shown below. Here $M=0$ in 64-bit mode and $M=32$ in 32-bit mode.

The bits are set based on the operation of an instruction considered as a whole, not on intermediate results (e.g., the *Subtract From Carrying* instruction, the result of which is specified as the sum of three values, sets bits in the Fixed-Point Exception Register based on the entire operation, not on an intermediate sum).

Bit(s)	Description

0   *Summary Overflow* (SO)

The Summary Overflow bit is set to 1 whenever an instruction (except *mtspr*) sets the Overflow bit. Once set, the SO bit remains set until it is cleared by an *mtspr* instruction (specifying the XER) or an *mcrxr* instruction. It is not altered by *Compare* instructions, nor by other instructions (except *mtspr* to the XER, and *mcrxr*) that cannot overflow. Executing an *mtspr* instruction to the XER, supplying the values 0 for SO and 1 for OV, causes SO to be set to 0 and OV to be set to 1.

1   *Overflow* (OV)

The Overflow bit is set to indicate that an overflow has occurred during execution of an instruction. XO-form *Add, Subtract From,* and *Negate* instructions having OE=1 set it to 1 if the carry out of bit M is not equal to the carry out of bit $M+1$, and set it to 0 otherwise. XO-form *Multiply Low* and *Divide* instructions having OE=1 set it to 1 if the result cannot be represented in 64 bits (*mulld, divd, divdu*) or in 32 bits (*mullw, divw, divwu*), and set it to 0 otherwise. The OV bit is not altered by *Compare* instructions, nor by other instructions (except *mtspr* to the XER, and *mcrxr*) that cannot overflow.

2   *Carry* (CA)

The Carry bit is set as follows, during execution of certain instructions. *Add Carrying, Subtract From Carrying, Add Extended,* and

Subtract From Extended instructions set it to 1 if there is a carry out of bit M, and set it to 0 otherwise. *Shift Right Algebraic* instructions set it to 1 if any 1-bits have been shifted out of a negative operand, and set it to 0 otherwise. The CA bit is not altered by *Compare* instructions, nor by other instructions (except *Shift Right Algebraic*, *mtspr* to the XER, and *mcrxr*) that cannot carry.

3:24   Reserved

25:31   This field specifies the number of bytes to be transferred by a *Load String Indexed* or *Store String Indexed* instruction.

Compatibility Note

For a discussion of POWER compatibility with respect to XER bits 16:23, please refer to Appendix G, "Incompatibilities with the POWER Architecture," on page 271. For compatibility with future versions of this architecture, these bits should be set to zero.

3.3 Fixed-Point Processor Instructions

This section describes the instructions executed by the Fixed-Point processor.

3.3.1 Storage Access Instructions

The *Storage Access* instructions compute the effective address (EA) of the storage to be accessed as described in Section 1.11.2, "Effective Address Calculation," on page 29.

The order of bytes accessed by halfword, word, and doubleword loads and stores is Big-Endian, unless Little-Endian storage ordering is selected as described in Appendix D, "Little-Endian Byte Ordering," on page 233.

Programming Note

The "la" extended mnemonic permits computing an effective address as a *Load* or *Store* instruction would, but loads the address itself into a GPR rather than loading the value that is in storage at that address. This extended mnemonic is described in "Load Address," on page 232.

Storage Access Exceptions

Storage accesses will cause the system error handler to be invoked if the program is not allowed to modify the target storage (*Store* only) or if the program attempts to access storage that is unavailable.

3.3.2 Fixed-Point Load Instructions

The byte, halfword, word, or doubleword in storage addressed by EA is loaded into register RT.

Byte order of PowerPC is Big-Endian by default; see Appendix D, "Little-Endian Byte Ordering," on page 233 for PowerPC systems operated with Little-Endian byte ordering.

Many of the *Load* instructions have an "update" form, in which register RA is updated with the effective address. For these forms, if RA≠0

Programming Note

In some
implementations, the
Load Algebraic and *Load
with Update* instructions
may have greater latency
than other types of *Load*
instructions. Moreover,
Load with Update
instructions may take
longer to execute in
some implementations
than the corresponding
pair of a non-update
Load instruction and an
Add instruction.

and RA≠RT, the effective address is placed into register RA and the storage element (byte, halfword, word, or doubleword) addressed by EA is loaded into RT.

Load Byte and Zero D-form

lbz   RT,D(RA)

34	RT	RA	D
0	6	11	16 31

```
if RA = 0 then b ← 0
else             b ← (RA)
EA ← b + EXTS(D)
RT ← 56 0 ‖ MEM(EA, 1)
```

Let the effective address (EA) be the sum (RA|0)+D. The byte in storage addressed by EA is loaded into $RT_{56:63}$. $RT_{0:55}$ are set to 0.

Special Registers Altered

```
None
```

Load Byte and Zero Indexed X-form

lbzx   RT,RA,RB

31	RT	RA	RB	87	/
0	6	11	16	21	31

```
if RA = 0 then b ← 0
else             b ← (RA)
EA ← b + (RB)
RT ← 56 0 ‖ MEM(EA, 1)
```

Let the effective address (EA) be the sum (RA|0)+(RB). The byte in storage addressed by EA is loaded into $RT_{56:63}$. $RT_{0:55}$ are set to 0.

Special Registers Altered

```
None
```

Load Byte and Zero with Update D-form

lbzu   RT,D(RA)

35	RT	RA	D
0	6	11	16 31

```
EA ← (RA) + EXTS(D)
RT ← 56 0 || MEM(EA, 1)
RA ← EA
```

Let the effective address (EA) be the sum (RA)+D. The byte in storage addressed by EA is loaded into $RT_{56:63}$. $RT_{0:55}$ are set to 0.

EA is placed into register RA.

If RA=0 or RA=RT, the instruction form is invalid.

Special Registers Altered

```
None
```

Load Byte and Zero with Update Indexed X-form

lbzux   RT,RA,RB

31	RT	RA	RB	119	/
0	6	11	16	21	31

```
EA ← (RA) + (RB)
RT ← 56 0 || MEM(EA, 1)
RA ← EA
```

Let the effective address (EA) be the sum (RA)+(RB). The byte in storage addressed by EA is loaded into $RT_{56:63}$. $RT_{0:55}$ are set to 0.

EA is placed into register RA.

If RA=0 or RA=RT, the instruction form is invalid.

Special Registers Altered

```
None
```

Load Halfword and Zero D-form

lhz   RT,D(RA)

40	RT	RA	D
0	6	11	16 31

```
if RA = 0 then b ← 0
else            b ← (RA)
EA ← b + EXTS(D)
RT ← 48 0 ‖ MEM(EA, 2)
```

Let the effective address (EA) be the sum $(RA|0)+D$. The halfword in storage addressed by EA is loaded into $RT_{48:63}$. $RT_{0:47}$ are set to 0.

Special Registers Altered

```
None
```

Load Halfword and Zero Indexed X-form

lhzx   RT,RA,RB

31	RT	RA	RB	279	/
0	6	11	16	21	31

```
if RA = 0 then b ← 0
else            b ← (RA)
EA ← b + (RB)
RT ← 48 0 ‖ MEM(EA, 2)
```

Let the effective address (EA) be the sum $(RA|0)+(RB)$. The halfword in storage addressed by EA is loaded into $RT_{48:63}$. $RT_{0:47}$ are set to 0.

Special Registers Altered

```
None
```

Load Halfword and Zero with Update D-form

lhzu   RT,D(RA)

41	RT	RA	D
0	6	11	16 31

```
EA ← (RA) + EXTS(D)
RT ← 48 0 ‖ MEM(EA, 2)
RA ← EA
```

Let the effective address (EA) be the sum (RA)+D. The halfword in storage addressed by EA is loaded into $RT_{48:63}$. $RT_{0:47}$ are set to 0.

EA is placed into register RA.

If RA=0 or RA=RT, the instruction form is invalid.

Special Registers Altered

None

Load Halfword and Zero with Update Indexed X-form

lhzux   RT,RA,RB

31	RT	RA	RB	311	/
0	6	11	16	21	31

```
EA ← (RA) + (RB)
RT ← 48 0 ‖ MEM(EA, 2)
RA ← EA
```

Let the effective address (EA) be the sum (RA)+(RB). The halfword in storage addressed by EA is loaded into $RT_{48:63}$. $RT_{0:47}$ are set to 0.

EA is placed into register RA.

If RA=0 or RA=RT, the instruction form is invalid.

Special Registers Altered

None

Load Halfword Algebraic D-form

lha   RT,D(RA)

42	RT	RA	D
0	6	11	16 31

```
if RA = 0 then b ← 0
else            b ← (RA)
EA ← b + EXTS(D)
RT ← EXTS(MEM(EA, 2))
```

Let the effective address (EA) be the sum (RA|0)+D. The halfword in storage addressed by EA is loaded into $RT_{48:63}$. $RT_{0:47}$ are filled with a copy of bit 0 of the loaded halfword.

Special Registers Altered

None

Load Halfword Algebraic Indexed X-form

lhax   RT,RA,RB

31	RT	RA	RB	343	/
0	6	11	16	21	31

```
if RA = 0 then b ← 0
else            b ← (RA)
EA ← b + (RB)
RT ← EXTS(MEM(EA, 2))
```

Let the effective address (EA) be the sum (RA|0)+(RB). The halfword in storage addressed by EA is loaded into $RT_{48:63}$. $RT_{0:47}$ are filled with a copy of bit 0 of the loaded halfword.

Special Registers Altered

None

Load Halfword Algebraic with Update D-form

lhau   RT,D(RA)

43	RT	RA	D
0	6	11	16 31

```
EA ← (RA) + EXTS(D)
RT ← EXTS(MEM(EA, 2))
RA ← EA
```

Let the effective address (EA) be the sum (RA)+D. The halfword in storage addressed by EA is loaded into $RT_{48:63}$. $RT_{0:47}$ are filled with a copy of bit 0 of the loaded halfword.

EA is placed into register RA.

If RA=0 or RA=RT, the instruction form is invalid.

Special Registers Altered

```
None
```

Load Halfword Algebraic with Update Indexed X-form

lhaux   RT,RA,RB

31	RT	RA	RB	375	/
0	6	11	16	21	31

```
EA ← (RA) + (RB)
RT ← EXTS(MEM(EA, 2))
RA ← EA
```

Let the effective address (EA) be the sum (RA)+(RB). The halfword in storage addressed by EA is loaded into $RT_{48:63}$. $RT_{0:47}$ are filled with a copy of bit 0 of the loaded halfword.

EA is placed into register RA.

If RA=0 or RA=RT, the instruction form is invalid.

Special Registers Altered

```
None
```

Load Word and Zero D-form

lwz   RT,D(RA)

[Power mnemonic: l]

32	RT	RA	D
0	6	11	16	31

```
if RA = 0 then b ← 0
else            b ← (RA)
EA ← b + EXTS(D)
RT ← 320 || MEM(EA, 4)
```

Let the effective address (EA) be the sum (RA|0)+D. The word in storage addressed by EA is loaded into $RT_{32:63}$. $RT_{0:31}$ are set to 0.

Special Registers Altered

```
None
```

Load Word and Zero Indexed X-form

lwzx   RT,RA,RB

[Power mnemonic: lx]

31	RT	RA	RB	23	/
0	6	11	16	21	31

```
if RA = 0 then b ← 0
else              b ← (RA)
EA ← b + (RB)
RT ← 320 ‖ MEM(EA, 4)
```

Let the effective address (EA) be the sum (RA|0)+(RB). The word in storage addressed by EA is loaded into $RT_{32:63}$. $RT_{0:31}$ are set to 0.

Special Registers Altered

```
None
```

Load Word and Zero with Update D-form

lwzu   RT,D(RA)

[Power mnemonic: lu]

33	RT	RA	D
0	6	11	16 31

```
EA ← (RA) + EXTS(D)
RT ← 320 ‖ MEM(EA, 4)
RA ← EA
```

Let the effective address (EA) be the sum (RA)+D. The word in storage addressed by EA is loaded into $RT_{32:63}$. $RT_{0:31}$ are set to 0.
EA is placed into register RA.
If RA=0 or RA=RT, the instruction form is invalid.

Special Registers Altered

```
None
```

Load Word and Zero with Update Indexed X-form

lwzux   RT,RA,RB

[Power mnemonic: lux]

31	RT	RA	RB	55	/
0	6	11	16	21	31

```
EA ← (RA) + (RB)
RT ← 32 0 || MEM(EA, 4)
RA ← EA
```

Let the effective address (EA) be the sum (RA)+(RB). The word in storage addressed by EA is loaded into $RT_{32:63}$. $RT_{0:31}$ are set to 0.

EA is placed into register RA.

If RA=0 or RA=RT, the instruction form is invalid.

Special Registers Altered

```
None
```

Load Word Algebraic DS-form

lwa   RT,DS(RA)

58	RT	RA	DS	2
0	6	11	16	30 31

```
if RA = 0 then b ← 0
else          b ← (RA)
EA ← b + EXTS(DS||0b00)
RT ← EXTS(MEM(EA, 4))
```

Let the effective address (EA) be the sum (RA|0)+(DS||0b00). The word in storage addressed by EA is loaded into $RT_{32:63}$. $RT_{0:31}$ are filled with a copy of bit 0 of the loaded word.

This instruction is defined only for 64-bit implementations. Using it on a 32-bit implementation will cause the system illegal instruction error handler to be invoked.

Special Registers Altered

```
None
```

Load Word Algebraic Indexed X-form

lwax   RT,RA,RB

31	RT	RA	RB	341	/
0	6	11	16	21	31

```
if RA = 0 then b ← 0
else             b ← (RA)
EA ← b + (RB)
RT ← EXTS(MEM(EA, 4))
```

Let the effective address (EA) be the sum (RA|0)+(RB). The word in storage addressed by EA is loaded into $RT_{32:63}$. $RT_{0:31}$ are filled with a copy of bit 0 of the loaded word.

This instruction is defined only for 64-bit implementations. Using it on a 32-bit implementation will cause the system illegal instruction error handler to be invoked.

Special Registers Altered

```
None
```

Load Word Algebraic with Update Indexed X-form

lwaux   RT,RA,RB

31	RT	RA	RB	373	/
0	6	11	16	21	31

```
EA ← (RA) + (RB)
RT ← EXTS(MEM(EA, 4))
RA ← EA
```

Let the effective address (EA) be the sum (RA)+(RB). The word in storage addressed by EA is loaded into $RT_{32:63}$. $RT_{0:31}$ are filled with a copy of bit 0 of the loaded word.

EA is placed into register RA.

If RA=0 or RA=RT, the instruction form is invalid.

This instruction is defined only for 64-bit implementations. Using it on a 32-bit implementation will cause the system illegal instruction error handler to be invoked.

Special Registers Altered

```
None
```

Load Doubleword DS-form

ld   RT,DS(RA)

58	RT	RA	DS	0
0	6	11	16	30 31

```
if RA = 0 then b ← 0
else           b ← (RA)
EA ← b + EXTS(DS||0b00)
RT ← MEM(EA, 8)
```

Let the effective address (EA) be the sum (RA|0)+(DS||0b00). The doubleword in storage addressed by EA is loaded into RT.

This instruction is defined only for 64-bit implementations. Using it on a 32-bit implementation will cause the system illegal instruction error handler to be invoked.

Special Registers Altered

    None

Load Doubleword Indexed X-form

ldx   RT,RA,RB

31	RT	RA	RB	21	/
0	6	11	16	21	31

```
if RA = 0 then b ← 0
else           b ← (RA)
EA ← b + (RB)
RT ← MEM(EA, 8)
```

Let the effective address (EA) be the sum (RA|0)+(RB). The doubleword in storage addressed by EA is loaded into RT.

This instruction is defined only for 64-bit implementations. Using it on a 32-bit implementation will cause the system illegal instruction error handler to be invoked.

Special Registers Altered

    None

Load Doubleword with Update DS-form

ldu   RT,DS(RA)

58	RT	RA	DS	1
0	6	11	16	30 31

```
EA ← (RA) + EXTS(DS∥0b00)
RT ← MEM(EA, 8)
RA ← EA
```

Let the effective address (EA) be the sum (RA)+(DS∥0b00). The doubleword in storage addressed by EA is loaded into RT.

EA is placed into register RA.

If RA=0 or RA=RT, the instruction form is invalid.

This instruction is defined only for 64-bit implementations. Using it on a 32-bit implementation will cause the system illegal instruction error handler to be invoked.

Special Registers Altered

```
None
```

Load Doubleword with Update Indexed X-form

ldux   RT,RA,RB

31	RT	RA	RB	53	/
0	6	11	16	21	31

```
EA ← (RA) + (RB)
RT ← MEM(EA, 8)
RA ← EA
```

Let the effective address (EA) be the sum (RA)+(RB). The doubleword in storage addressed by EA is loaded into RT.

EA is placed into register RA.

If RA=0 or RA=RT, the instruction form is invalid.

This instruction is defined only for 64-bit implementations. Using it on a 32-bit implementation will cause the system illegal instruction error handler to be invoked.

Special Registers Altered

```
None
```

3.3.3 Fixed-Point Store Instructions

The contents of register RS are stored into the byte, halfword, word, or doubleword in storage addressed by EA.

   Byte order of PowerPC is Big-Endian by default; see Appendix D, "Little-Endian Byte Ordering," on page 233 for PowerPC systems operated with Little-Endian byte ordering.

   Many of the *Store* instructions have an "update" form, in which register RA is updated with the effective address. For these forms, the following rules apply.

■ If RA≠0, the effective address is placed into register RA.

■ If RS=RA, the contents of register RS are copied to the target storage element, and then EA is placed into RA (RS).

Store Byte D-form

stb   RS,D(RA)

38	RS	RA	D
0	6	11	16 31

```
if RA = 0 then b ← 0
else            b ← (RA)
EA ← b + EXTS(D)
MEM(EA, 1) ← (RS)₅₆:₆₃
```

   Let the effective address (EA) be the sum (RA|0)+D. $(RS)_{56:63}$ are stored into the byte in storage addressed by EA.

Special Registers Altered

   None

Store Byte Indexed X-form

stbx   RS,RA,RB

31	RS	RA	RB	215	/
0	6	11	16	21	31

```
if RA = 0 then b ← 0
else            b ← (RA)
EA ← b + (RB)
MEM(EA, 1) ← (RS)₅₆:₆₃
```

Let the effective address (EA) be the sum (RA|0)+(RB). $(RS)_{56:63}$ are stored into the byte in storage addressed by EA.

Special Registers Altered

    None

Store Byte with Update D-form

stbu   RS,D(RA)

39	RS	RA	D
0	6	11	16 31

```
EA ← (RA) + EXTS(D)
MEM(EA, 1) ← (RS)₅₆:₆₃
RA ← EA
```

Let the effective address (EA) be the sum (RA)+D. $(RS)_{56:63}$ are stored into the byte in storage addressed by EA.
    EA is placed into register RA.
    If RA=0, the instruction form is invalid.

Special Registers Altered

    None

Store Byte with Update Indexed X-form

stbux   RS,RA,RB

31	RS	RA	RB	247	/
0	6	11	16	21	31

```
EA ← (RA) + (RB)
MEM(EA, 1) ← (RS)₅₆:₆₃
RA ← EA
```

Let the effective address (EA) be the sum (RA)+(RB). $(RS)_{56:63}$ are stored into the byte in storage addressed by EA.
    EA is placed into register RA.
    If RA=0, the instruction form is invalid.

Special Registers Altered

    None

Store Halfword D-form

sth   RS,D(RA)

44	RS	RA	D
0	6	11	16 31

```
if RA = 0 then b ← 0
else             b ← (RA)
EA ← b + EXTS(D)
MEM(EA, 2) ← (RS)48:63
```

Let the effective address (EA) be the sum (RA|0)+D. $(RS)_{48:63}$ are stored into the halfword in storage addressed by EA.

Special Registers Altered

```
None
```

Store Halfword Indexed X-form

sthx   RS,RA,RB

31	RS	RA	RB	407	/
0	6	11	16	21	31

```
if RA = 0 then b ← 0
else             b ← (RA)
EA ← b + (RB)
MEM(EA, 2) ← (RS)48:63
```

Let the effective address (EA) be the sum (RA|0)+(RB). $(RS)_{48:63}$ are stored into the halfword in storage addressed by EA.

Special Registers Altered

```
None
```

Store Halfword with Update D-form

sthu   RS,D(RA)

45	RS	RA	D
0	6	11	16 31

```
EA ← (RA) + EXTS(D)
MEM(EA, 2) ← (RS)48:63
RA ← EA
```

Let the effective address (EA) be the sum (RA)+D. $(RS)_{48:63}$ are stored into the halfword in storage addressed by EA.

EA is placed into register RA.

If RA=0, the instruction form is invalid.

Special Registers Altered

```
None
```

Store Halfword with Update Indexed X-form

sthux   RS,RA,RB

31	RS	RA	RB	439	/
0	6	11	16	21	31

```
EA ← (RA) + (RB)
MEM(EA, 2) ← (RS)48:63
RA ← EA
```

Let the effective address (EA) be the sum (RA)+(RB). $(RS)_{48:63}$ are stored into the halfword in storage addressed by EA.

EA is placed into register RA.

If RA=0, the instruction form is invalid.

Special Registers Altered

```
None
```

Store Word D-form

stw   RS,D(RA)

[Power mnemonic: st]

36	RS	RA	D
0	6	11	16	31

```
if RA = 0 then b ← 0
else            b ← (RA)
EA ← b + EXTS(D)
MEM(EA, 4) ← (RS)32:63
```

Let the effective address (EA) be the sum (RA|0)+D. $(RS)_{32:63}$ are stored into the word in storage addressed by EA.

Special Registers Altered

```
None
```

Store Word Indexed   X-form

stwx   RS,RA,RB

[Power mnemonic: stx]

31	RS	RA	RB	151	/
0	6	11	16	21	31

```
if RA = 0 then b ← 0
else             b ← (RA)
EA ← b + (RB)
MEM(EA, 4) ← (RS)32:63
```

Let the effective address (EA) be the sum (RA|0)+(RB). $(RS)_{32:63}$ are stored into the word in storage addressed by EA.

Special Registers Altered

```
None
```

Store Word with Update   D-form

stwu   RS,D(RA)

[Power mnemonic: stu]

37	RS	RA	D	
0	6	11	16	31

```
EA ← (RA) + EXTS(D)
MEM(EA, 4) ← (RS)32:63
RA ← EA
```

Let the effective address (EA) be the sum (RA)+D. $(RS)_{32:63}$ are stored into the word in storage addressed by EA.

EA is placed into register RA.

If RA=0, the instruction form is invalid.

Special Registers Altered

```
None
```

Store Word with Update Indexed X-form

stwux   RS,RA,RB

[Power mnemonic: stux]

31	RS	RA	RB	183	/
0	6	11	16	21	31

```
EA ← (RA) + (RB)
MEM(EA, 4) ← (RS)32:63
RA ← EA
```

Let the effective address (EA) be the sum (RA)+(RB). $(RS)_{32:63}$ are stored into the word in storage addressed by EA.

EA is placed into register RA.

If RA=0, the instruction form is invalid.

Special Registers Altered

```
None
```

Store Doubleword DS-form

std   RS,DS(RA)

62	RS	RA	DS	0
0	6	11	16	30 31

```
if RA = 0 then b ← 0
else            b ← (RA)
EA ← b + EXTS(DS||0b00)
MEM(EA, 8) ← (RS)
```

Let the effective address (EA) be the sum (RA|0)+(DS||0b00). (RS) is stored into the doubleword in storage addressed by EA.

This instruction is defined only for 64-bit implementations. Using it on a 32-bit implementation will cause the system illegal instruction error handler to be invoked.

Special Registers Altered

```
None
```

Store Doubleword Indexed X-form

stdx   RS,RA,RB

31	RS	RA	RB	149	/
0	6	11	16	21	31

```
if RA = 0 then b ← 0
else             b ← (RA)
EA ← b + (RB)
MEM(EA, 8) ← (RS)
```

Let the effective address (EA) be the sum (RA|0)+(RB). (RS) is stored into the doubleword in storage addressed by EA.

This instruction is defined only for 64-bit implementations. Using it on a 32-bit implementation will cause the system illegal instruction error handler to be invoked.

Special Registers Altered

None

Store Doubleword with Update DS-form

stdu   RS,DS(RA)

62	RS	RA	DS	1
0	6	11	16	30 31

```
EA ← (RA) + EXTS(DS||0b00)
MEM(EA, 8) ← (RS)
RA ← EA
```

Let the effective address (EA) be the sum (RA)+(DS||0b00). (RS) is stored into the doubleword in storage addressed by EA.

EA is placed into register RA.

If RA=0, the instruction form is invalid.

This instruction is defined only for 64-bit implementations. Using it on a 32-bit implementation will cause the system illegal instruction error handler to be invoked.

Special Registers Altered

None

Store Doubleword with Update Indexed X-form

stdux   RS,RA,RB

31	RS	RA	RB	181	/
0	6	11	16	21	31

```
EA ← (RA) + (RB)
MEM(EA, 8) ← (RS)
RA ← EA
```

Let the effective address (EA) be the sum (RA)+(RB). (RS) is stored into the doubleword in storage addressed by EA.

EA is placed into register RA.

If RA=0, the instruction form is invalid.

This instruction is defined only for 64-bit implementations. Using it on a 32-bit implementation will cause the system illegal instruction error handler to be invoked.

Special Registers Altered

```
None
```

Programming Note

In some implementations, the *Load Byte-Reverse* instructions may have greater latency than other *Load* instructions.

3.3.4 Fixed-Point Load and Store with Byte Reversal Instructions

When used in a PowerPC system operating with Big-Endian byte order (the default), these instructions have the effect of loading and storing data in Little-Endian order. Likewise, when used in a PowerPC system operating with Little-Endian byte order, these instructions have the effect of loading and storing data in Big-Endian order. See Appendix D, "Little-Endian Byte Ordering," on page 233 for a discussion of byte order.

Load Halfword Byte-Reverse Indexed X-form

lhbrx   RT,RA,RB

31	RT	RA	RB	790	/
0	6	11	16	21	31

```
if RA = 0 then b ← 0
else            b ← (RA)
EA ← b + (RB)
RT ← 48_0 ∥ MEM(EA+1, 1) ∥ MEM(EA, 1)
```

Let the effective address (EA) be the sum (RA|0)+(RB). Bits 0:7 of the halfword in storage addressed by EA are loaded into $RT_{56:63}$. Bits 8:15 of the halfword in storage addressed by EA are loaded into $RT_{48:55}$. $RT_{0:47}$ are set to 0.

Special Registers Altered

    None

Load Word Byte-Reverse Indexed X-form

lwbrx   RT,RA,RB

[Power mnemonic: lbrx]

31	RT	RA	RB	534	/
0	6	11	16	21	31

```
if RA = 0 then b ← 0
else             b ← (RA)
EA ← b + (RB)
RT ← 32 0 ‖ MEM(EA+3, 1) ‖ MEM(EA+2, 1)
          ‖ MEM(EA+1, 1) ‖ MEM(EA, 1)
```

Let the effective address (EA) be the sum (RA|0)+(RB). Bits 0:7 of the word in storage addressed by EA are loaded into $RT_{56:63}$. Bits 8:15 of the word in storage addressed by EA are loaded into $RT_{48:55}$. Bits 16:23 of the word in storage addressed by EA are loaded into $RT_{40:47}$. Bits 24:31 of the word in storage addressed by EA are loaded into $RT_{32:39}$. $RT_{0:31}$ are set to 0.

Special Registers Altered

    None

Store Halfword Byte-Reverse Indexed X-form

sthbrx   RS,RA,RB

31	RS	RA	RB	918	/
0	6	11	16	21	31

```
if RA = 0 then b ← 0
else             b ← (RA)
EA ← b + (RB)
MEM(EA, 2) ← (RS)56:63 ‖ (RS)48:55
```

Let the effective address (EA) be the sum (RA|0)+(RB). $(RS)_{56:63}$ are stored into bits 0:7 of the halfword in storage addressed by EA. $(RS)_{48:55}$ are stored into bits 8:15 of the halfword in storage addressed by EA.

Special Registers Altered

    None

Store Word Byte-Reverse Indexed X-form

stwbrx   RS,RA,RB

[Power mnemonic: stbrx]

31	RS	RA	RB	662	/
0	6	11	16	21	31

```
if RA = 0 then b ← 0
else            b ← (RA)
EA ← b + (RB)
MEM(EA, 4) ← (RS)56:63 ‖ (RS)48:55 ‖ (RS)40:47 ‖ (RS)32:39
```

Let the effective address (EA) be the sum (RA|0)+(RB). $(RS)_{56:63}$ are stored into bits 0:7 of the word in storage addressed by EA. $(RS)_{48:55}$ are stored into bits 8:15 of the word in storage addressed by EA. $(RS)_{40:47}$ are stored into bits 16:23 of the word in storage addressed by EA. $(RS)_{32:39}$ are stored into bits 24:31 of the word in storage addressed by EA.

Special Registers Altered

    None

3.3.5 Fixed-Point Load and Store Multiple Instructions

The *Load/Store Multiple* instructions have preferred forms: see Section 1.9.1, "Preferred Instruction Forms," on page 25. In the preferred forms, storage alignment satisfies the following rule.

■ The combination of the EA and RT (RS) is such that the low-order byte of GPR 31 is loaded (stored) from (into) the last byte of an aligned quadword in storage.

Compatibility Note

For a discussion of POWER compatibility with respect to the alignment of the EA for the *Load Multiple Word* and *Store Multiple Word* instructions, please refer to Appendix G, "Incompatibilities with the POWER Architecture," on page 271. For compatibility with future versions of this architecture, these EAs should be word-aligned.

On PowerPC systems operating with Little-Endian byte order, execution of a *Load Multiple* or *Store Multiple* instruction causes the system alignment error handler to be invoked. See Appendix D, "Little-Endian Byte Ordering," on page 233.

Load Multiple Word D-form

lmw   RT,D(RA)

[Power mnemonic: lm]

46	RT	RA	D
0	6	11	16 31

```
if RA = 0 then b ← 0
else              b ← (RA)
EA ← b + EXTS(D)
r ← RT
do while r ≤ 31
   GPR(r) ← ³²0 ‖ MEM(EA, 4)
   r ← r + 1
   EA ← EA + 4
```

Let n = (32–RT). Let the effective address (EA) be the sum (RA|0)+D.

n consecutive words starting at EA are loaded into the low-order 32 bits of GPRs RT through 31. The high-order 32 bits of these GPRs are set to zero.

EA must be a multiple of 4. If it is not, either the system alignment error handler is invoked or the results are boundedly undefined.

If RA is in the range of registers to be loaded or RT=RA=0, the instruction form is invalid.

Special Registers Altered

```
None
```

Store Multiple Word D-form

stmw   RS,D(RA)

[Power mnemonic: stm]

47	RS	RA	D
0	6	11	16 31

```
if RA = 0 then b ← 0
else            b ← (RA)
EA ← b + EXTS(D)
r ← RS
do while r ≤ 31
  MEM(EA, 4) ← GPR(r)₃₂:₆₃
  r ← r + 1
  EA ← EA + 4
```

Let n = (32–RS). Let the effective address (EA) be the sum (RA|0)+D.

n consecutive words starting at EA are stored from the low-order 32 bits of GPRs RS through 31.

EA must be a multiple of 4. If it is not, either the system alignment error handler is invoked or the results are boundedly undefined.

Special Registers Altered

```
None
```

3.3.6 Fixed-Point Move Assist Instructions

The *Move Assist* instructions allow movement of data from storage to registers or from registers to storage without concern for alignment. These instructions can be used for a short move between arbitrary storage locations or to initiate a long move between unaligned storage fields.

The *Load/Store String* instructions have preferred forms: see Section 1.9.1, "Preferred Instruction Forms," on page 25. In the preferred forms, register usage satisfies the following rules.

- RS = 5

- RT = 5

- last register loaded/stored ≤ 12

On PowerPC systems operating with Little-Endian byte order, execution of a *Load/Store String* instruction causes the system alignment error handler to be invoked. See Appendix D, "Little-Endian Byte Ordering," on page 233.

Load String Word Immediate X-form

lswi   RT,RA,NB

[Power mnemonic: lsi]

31	RT	RA	NB	597	/
0	6	11	16	21	31

```
if RA = 0 then EA ← 0
else            EA ← (RA)
if NB = 0 then n ← 32
else            n ← NB
r ← RT - 1
i ← 32
do while n > 0
   if i = 32 then
     r ← r + 1 (mod 32)
     GPR(r) ← 0
   GPR(r)_{i:i+7} ← MEM(EA, 1)
   i ← i + 8
   if i = 64 then i ← 32
   EA ← EA + 1
   n ← n - 1
```

Let the effective address (EA) be (RA|0). Let n = NB if NB≠0, n = 32 if NB=0: n is the number of bytes to load. Let nr = CEIL(n÷4): nr is the number of registers to receive data.

n consecutive bytes starting at EA are loaded into GPRs RT through RT+nr−1. Data are loaded into the low-order four bytes of each GPR; the high-order four bytes are set to 0.

Bytes are loaded left to right in each register. The sequence of registers wraps around to GPR 0 if required. If the low-order four bytes of register RT+nr−1 are only partially filled, the unfilled low-order byte(s) of that register are set to 0.

If RA is in the range of registers to be loaded or RT=RA=0, the instruction form is invalid.

Special Registers Altered

```
None
```

Load String Word Indexed X-form

lswx   RT,RA,RB

[Power mnemonic: lsx]

31	RT	RA	RB	533	/
0	6	11	16	21	31

```
if RA = 0 then b ← 0
else          b ← (RA)
EA ← b + (RB)
n ← XER25:31
r ← RT - 1
i ← 32
RT ← undefined
do while n > 0
  if i = 32 then
     r ← r + 1 (mod 32)
     GPR(r) ← 0
  GPR(r)i:i+7 ← MEM(EA, 1)
  i ← i + 8
  if i = 64 then i ← 32
  EA ← EA + 1
  n ← n - 1
```

Let the effective address (EA) be the sum (RA|0)+(RB). Let n = $XER_{25:31}$: n is the number of bytes to load. Let nr = CEIL(n÷4): nr is the number of registers to receive data.

If n>0, n consecutive bytes starting at EA are loaded into GPRs RT through RT+nr−1. Data are loaded into the low-order four bytes of each GPR; the high-order four bytes are set to 0.

Bytes are loaded left to right in each register. The sequence of registers wraps around to GPR 0 if required. If the low-order four bytes of register RT+nr−1 are only partially filled, the unfilled low-order byte(s) of that register are set to 0.

If n=0, the content of register RT is undefined.

If RA or RB is in the range of registers to be loaded, either the system illegal instruction error handler is invoked or the results are boundedly undefined. If RT=RA=0, the instruction form is invalid.

Special Registers Altered
```
None
```

Store String Word Immediate X-form

stswi   RS,RA,NB

[Power mnemonic: stsi]

31	RS	RA	NB	725	/
0	6	11	16	21	31

```
if RA = 0 then EA ← 0
else            EA ← (RA)
if NB = 0 then n ← 32
else            n ← NB
r ← RS - 1
i ← 32
do while n > 0
  if i = 32 then r ← r + 1 (mod 32)
  MEM(EA, 1) ← GPR(r)_{i:i+7}
  i ← i + 8
  if i = 64 then i ← 32
  EA ← EA + 1
  n ← n - 1
```

Let the effective address (EA) be (RA|0). Let n = NB if NB≠0, n = 32 if NB=0: n is the number of bytes to store. Let nr = CEIL(n÷4): nr is the number of registers to supply data.

n consecutive bytes starting at EA are stored from GPRs RS through RS+nr−1. Data are stored from the low-order four bytes of each GPR.

Bytes are stored left to right from each register. The sequence of registers wraps around to GPR 0 if required.

Special Registers Altered
None

Store String Word Indexed X-form

stswx   RS,RA,RB

[Power mnemonic: stsx]

31	RS	RA	RB	661	/
0	6	11	16	21	31

```
if RA = 0 then b ← 0
else          b ← (RA)
EA ← b + (RB)
n ← XER25:31
r ← RS - 1
i ← 32
do while n > 0
   if i = 32 then r ← r + 1 (mod 32)
   MEM(EA, 1) ← GPR(r)i:i+7
   i ← i + 8
   if i = 64 then i ← 32
   EA ← EA + 1
   n ← n - 1
```

Let the effective address (EA) be the sum (RA|0)+(RB). Let n = $XER_{25:31}$: n is the number of bytes to store. Let nr = CEIL(n÷4): nr is the number of registers to supply data.

n consecutive bytes starting at EA are stored from GPRs RS through RS+nr−1. Data are stored from the low-order four bytes of each GPR.

Bytes are stored left to right from each register. The sequence of registers wraps around to GPR 0 if required.

If n = 0, no bytes are stored.

Special Registers Altered

None

3.3.7 Storage Synchronization Instructions

Programming Note

Because the *Storage Synchronization* instructions have implementation dependencies (e.g., the granularity at which reservations are managed), they must be

The *Storage Synchronization* instructions can be used to control the order in which storage operations are completed with respect to asynchronous events, and the order in which storage operations are seen by other processors and by other mechanisms that access storage. Additional information about these instructions and about related aspects of storage management can be found in Book II, Sections 1.8.1, "Storage Access Ordering," on page 333 and 1.8.2, "Atomic Update Primitives," on page 336, and Book III, Chapter 4, "Storage Control," on page 391.

On a PowerPC system operating with Little-Endian byte order the three low-order bits of the effective address computed by *Load And Reserve* and *Store Conditional* are modified before accessing storage. See Appendix D, "Little-Endian Byte Ordering," on page 233.

Load Word And Reserve Indexed X-form

lwarx   RT,RA,RB

31	RT	RA	RB	20	/
0	6	11	16	21	31

```
if RA = 0 then b ← 0
else            b ← (RA)
EA ← b + (RB)
RESERVE ← 1
RESERVE_ADDR ← func(EA)
RT ← 32 0 ‖ MEM(EA, 4)
```

Let the effective address (EA) be the sum (RA|0)+(RB). The word in storage addressed by EA is loaded into $RT_{32:63}$. $RT_{0:31}$ are set to 0.

This instruction creates a reservation for use by a *Store Word Conditional* instruction. An address computed from the EA is associated with the reservation and replaces any address previously associated with the reservation: the manner in which the address to be associated with the reservation is computed from the EA is described in Book II, Section 1.8.2, "Atomic Update Primitives," on page 336.

EA must be a multiple of 4. If it is not, either the system alignment error handler is invoked or the results are boundedly undefined.

Special Registers Altered

```
None
```

Load Doubleword And Reserve Indexed X-form

ldarx   RT,RA,RB

31	RT	RA	RB	84	/
0	6	11	16	21	31

```
if RA = 0 then b ← 0
else            b ← (RA)
EA ← b + (RB)
RESERVE ← 1
RESERVE_ADDR ← func(EA)
RT ← MEM(EA, 8)
```

used with care. The operating system should provide system library programs that use these instructions to implement the high-level synchronization functions (Test and Set, Compare and Swap, etc.) needed by application programs. Application programs should use these library programs, rather than use the *Storage Synchronization* instructions directly.

Programming Note

The granularity with which reservations are managed is implementation-dependent. Therefore the storage to be accessed by the *Load And Reserve* and *Store Conditional* instructions should be allocated by a system library program. Additional information can be found in Book II, Section 1.8.2, "Atomic Update Primitives," on page 336.

When correctly used, the *Load And Reserve* and *Store Conditional* instructions can provide an atomic update function for a single aligned word (*Load Word And Reserve* and *Store Word Conditional*) or doubleword (*Load Doubleword And Reserve* and *Store Doubleword Conditional*) of storage.

One of the requirements for correct use is that *Load Word And Reserve* be paired with *Store Word Conditional*, and *Load DoubleWord And Reserve* with *Store Doubleword Conditional*, with the same effective address used for both instructions of the pair. Examples of correct uses of these instructions to emulate primitives such as "Fetch and Add," "Test and Set," and "Compare and Swap" can be found in Appendix E.1, "Synchronization," on page 249.

At most one reservation exists on any given processor: there are not separate reservations for words and for doublewords.

The conditionality of the *Store Conditional* instruction's store is based only on whether a

Let the effective address (EA) be the sum (RA|0)+(RB). The doubleword in storage addressed by EA is loaded into RT.

This instruction creates a reservation for use by a *Store Doubleword Conditional* instruction. An address computed from the EA is associated with the reservation and replaces any address previously associated with the reservation: the manner in which the address to be associated with the reservation is computed from the EA is described in Book II, Section 1.8.2, "Atomic Update Primitives," on page 336.

EA must be a multiple of 8. If it is not, either the system alignment error handler is invoked or the results are boundedly undefined.

This instruction is defined only for 64-bit implementations. Using it on a 32-bit implementation will cause the system illegal instruction error handler to be invoked.

Special Registers Altered

    None

Store Word Conditional Indexed X-form

stwcx.   RS,RA,RB

31	RS	RA	RB	150	1
0	6	11	16	21	31

```
if RA = 0 then b ← 0
else             b ← (RA)
EA ← b + (RB)
if RESERVE then
   MEM(EA, 4) ← (RS)32:63
   RESERVE ← 0
   CR0 ← 0b00 || 0b1 || XERSO
else
   CR0 ← 0b00 || 0b0 || XERSO
```

Let the effective address (EA) be the sum (RA|0)+(RB).

If a reservation exists, $(RS)_{32:63}$ are stored into the word in storage addressed by EA and the reservation is cleared.

If a reservation does not exist, the instruction completes without altering storage.

CR Field 0 is set to reflect whether the store operation was performed (i.e., whether a reservation existed when the *stwcx.* instruction commenced execution), as follows.

$$CR0_{LT\ GT\ EQ\ SO}= 0b00 \parallel store\_performed \parallel XER_{SO}$$

EA must be a multiple of 4. If it is not, either the system alignment error handler is invoked or the results are boundedly undefined.

Special Registers Altered

    CR0

Store Doubleword Conditional Indexed X-form

stdcx.   RS,RA,RB

31	RS	RA	RB	214	1
0	6	11	16	21	31

```
if RA = 0 then b ← 0
else             b ← (RA)
EA ← b + (RB)
if RESERVE then
  MEM(EA, 8) ← (RS)
  RESERVE ← 0
  CR0 ← 0b00 ∥ 0b1 ∥ XER_SO
else
  CR0 ← 0b00 ∥ 0b0 ∥ XER_SO
```

Let the effective address (EA) be the sum $(RA|0)+(RB)$.

If a reservation exists, (RS) is stored into the doubleword in storage addressed by EA and the reservation is cleared.

If a reservation does not exist, the instruction completes without altering storage.

CR Field 0 is set to reflect whether the store operation was performed (i.e., whether a reservation existed when the *stdcx.* instruction commenced execution), as follows.

$$CR0_{LT\ GT\ EQ\ SO} = 0b00 \parallel \text{store\_performed} \parallel XER_{SO}$$

EA must be a multiple of 8. If it is not, either the system alignment error handler is invoked or the results are boundedly undefined.

This instruction is defined only for 64-bit implementations. Using it on a 32-bit implementation will cause the system illegal instruction error handler to be invoked.

Special Registers Altered

    CR0

reservation exists, not on a match between the address associated with the reservation and the address computed from the EA of the *Store Conditional* instruction.

A reservation is cleared if any of the following events occurs.

- The processor holding the reservation executes another *Load And Reserve* instruction; this clears the first reservation and establishes a new one.

- The processor holding the reservation executes a *Store Conditional* instruction to *any* address.

- Another processor executes any *Store* instruction to the address associated with the reservation.

- Any mechanism, other than the processor holding the reservation, stores to the address associated with the reservation.

See Book II, Section 1.8.2, "Atomic Update Primitives," on page 336 for additional information.

Programming Note

The *sync* instruction can be used to ensure that the results of all stores into a data structure that are performed in a "critical section" of a program are seen by other processors before the data structure is seen as unlocked.

The functions performed by the *sync* instruction will normally take a significant amount of time to complete, so indiscriminate use of this instruction may adversely affect performance. In addition, the time required to execute *sync* may vary from one execution to another.

The *Enforce In-order Execution of I/O* (*eieio*) instruction, described in Book II, Sections 1.8.1, "Storage Access Ordering," on page 333 and 3.3, "Enforce In-order Execution of I/O Instruction," on page 350 may be more appropriate than *sync* for cases in which the only requirement is to control the order in which storage references are seen by I/O devices.

Synchronize X-form

sync

[Power mnemonic: dcs]

31	///	///	///	598	/
0	6	11	16	21	31

The *sync* instruction provides an ordering function for the effects of all instructions executed by a given processor. Executing a *sync* instruction ensures that all instructions previously initiated by the given processor appear to have completed before the *sync* instruction completes, and that no subsequent instructions are initiated by the given processor until after the *sync* instruction completes. When the *sync* instruction completes, all storage accesses initiated by the given processor prior to the *sync* instruction will have been performed with respect to all other mechanisms that access storage. (See Book II, "Synchronize," on page 334 for a more complete description. See also Book III, Section 4.12, "Table Update Synchronization Requirements," on page 446 for an exception involving TLB invalidates.)

This instruction is execution synchronizing (see Book III, Section 1.7.2, "Execution Synchronization," on page 372).

Special Registers Altered
    None

3.3.8 Other Fixed-Point Instructions

The remainder of the fixed-point instructions use the contents of the General Purpose Registers (GPRs) as source operands, and place results into GPRs, into the Fixed-Point Exception Register (XER), and into Condition Register fields. In addition, the *Trap* instructions compare the contents of one GPR with a second GPR or immediate data and, if the conditions are met, invoke the system trap handler.

These instructions treat the source operands as signed integers unless the instruction is explicitly identified as performing an unsigned operation.

The X-form and XO-form instructions with Rc=1, and the D-form instructions *addic.*, *andi.*, and *andis.*, set the first three bits of CR Field 0 to characterize the result placed into the target register. In 64-bit mode, these bits are set by signed comparison of the result to zero. In 32-bit mode, these bits are set by signed comparison of the low-order 32 bits of the result to zero.

Unless otherwise noted and when appropriate, when CR Field 0 and the XER are set they reflect the value placed into the target register.

3.3.9 Fixed-Point Arithmetic Instructions

The XO-form *Arithmetic* instructions with Rc=1, and the D-form *Arithmetic* instruction *addic.*, set the first three bits of CR Field 0 as described in Section 3.3.8, "Other Fixed-Point Instructions," on page 80.

addic, addic., subfic, addc, subfc, adde, subfe, addme, subfme, addze, and *subfze* always set CA, to reflect the carry out of bit 0 in 64-bit mode and out of bit 32 in 32-bit mode. The XO-form *Arithmetic* instructions set SO and OV when OE=1 to reflect overflow of the result. Except for the *Multiply Low* and *Divide* instructions, the setting of these bits is mode-dependent, and reflects overflow of the 64-bit result in 64-bit mode and overflow of the low-order 32-bit result in 32-bit mode. For XO-form *Multiply Low* and *Divide* instructions, the setting of these bits is mode-independent, and reflects overflow of the 64-bit result for *mulld, divd,* and *divdu,* and overflow of the low-order 32-bit result for *mullw, divw,* and *divwu.*

Extended mnemonics for addition and subtraction

Several extended mnemonics are provided that use the *Add Immediate* and *Add Immediate Shifted* instructions to load an immediate value or an address into a target register. Some of these are shown as examples with the two instructions.

The PowerPC Architecture supplies *Subtract From* instructions, which subtract the second operand from the third. A set of extended mnemonics is provided that use the more "normal" order, in which the third operand is subtracted from the second, with the third operand being either an immediate field or a register. Some of these are shown as examples with the appropriate *Add* and *Subtract From* instructions.

See Appendix C, "Assembler Extended Mnemonics," on page 215 for additional extended mnemonics.

Programming Note

Instructions with the OE bit set or which set CA may execute slowly or may prevent the execution of subsequent instructions until the operation is completed.

Programming Note

Notice that CR Field 0 may not reflect the "true" (infinitely precise) result if overflow occurs.

Programming Note

addi, addis, add, and *subf* are the preferred instructions for addition and subtraction, because they set few status bits.

Notice that *addi* and *addis* use the value 0, not the contents of GPR 0, if RA=0.

Add Immediate D-form

addi   RT,RA,SI

[Power mnemonic: cal]

14	RT	RA	SI
0	6	11	16 31

```
if RA = 0 then RT ← EXTS(SI)
else            RT ← (RA) + EXTS(SI)
```

The sum (RA|0) + SI is placed into register RT.

Special Registers Altered
```
None
```

Extended Mnemonics:
Examples of extended mnemonics for *Add Immediate*:

Extended:		*Equivalent to:*	
li	Rx,value	addi	Rx,0,value
la	Rx,disp(Ry)	addi	Rx,Ry,disp
subi	Rx,Ry,value	addi	Rx,Ry,–value

Add Immediate Shifted D-form

addis   RT,RA,SI

[Power mnemonic: cau]

15	RT	RA	SI
0	6	11	16 31

```
if RA = 0 then RT ← EXTS(SI ‖ 16 0)
else            RT ← (RA) + EXTS(SI ‖ 16 0)
```

The sum (RA|0) + (SI ‖ 0x0000) is placed into register RT.

Special Registers Altered
```
None
```

Extended Mnemonics:

Examples of extended mnemonics for *Add Immediate Shifted:*

Extended:		*Equivalent to:*	
lis	Rx,value	addis	Rx,0,value
subis	Rx,Ry,value	addis	Rx,Ry,–value

Add XO-form

add	RT,RA,RB	(OE=0 Rc=0)
add.	RT,RA,RB	(OE=0 Rc=1)
addo	RT,RA,RB	(OE=1 Rc=0)
addo.	RT,RA,RB	(OE=1 Rc=1)

[Power mnemonics: cax, cax., caxo, caxo.]

31	RT	RA	RB	OE	266	Rc
0	6	11	16	21	22	31

RT ← (RA) + (RB)

The sum (RA) + (RB) is placed into register RT.

Special Registers Altered

```
CR0                                                      (if Rc=1)
SO OV                                                    (if OE=1)
```

Subtract From XO-form

subf	RT,RA,RB	(OE=0 Rc=0)
subf.	RT,RA,RB	(OE=0 Rc=1)
subfo	RT,RA,RB	(OE=1 Rc=0)
subfo.	RT,RA,RB	(OE=1 Rc=1)

31	RT	RA	RB	OE	40	Rc
0	6	11	16	21	22	31

RT ← ¬(RA) + (RB) + 1

The sum ¬(RA) + (RB) +1 is placed into register RT.

Special Registers Altered

```
CR0                                                      (if Rc=1)
SO OV                                                    (if OE=1)
```

Extended Mnemonics:

Example of extended mnemonics for *Subtract From:*

Extended:	*Equivalent to:*
sub Rx,Ry,Rz	subf Rx,Rz,Ry

Add Immediate Carrying D-form

addic   RT,RA,SI

[Power mnemonic: ai]

12		RT	RA	SI	
0		6	11	16	31

```
RT ← (RA) + EXTS(SI)
```

The sum (RA) + SI is placed into register RT.

Special Registers Altered

```
CA
```

Programming Note

The setting of CA by the *Add* and *Subtract From* instructions, including the Extended versions thereof, is mode-dependent. If a sequence of these instructions is used to perform extended-precision addition or subtraction, the same mode should be used throughout the sequence.

Extended Mnemonics:

Example of extended mnemonics for *Add Immediate Carrying:*

Extended:	*Equivalent to:*
subic Rx,Ry,value	addic Rx,Ry,–value

Add Immediate Carrying and Record D-form

addic.   RT,RA,SI

[Power mnemonic: ai.]

13		RT	RA	SI	
0		6	11	16	31

```
RT ← (RA) + EXTS(SI)
```

The sum (RA) + SI is placed into register RT.

Special Registers Altered

```
CR0 CA
```

Extended Mnemonics:

Example of extended mnemonics for *Add Immediate Carrying and Record:*

Extended: *Equivalent to:*
subic. Rx,Ry,value   addic. Rx,Ry,−value

Subtract From Immediate Carrying D-form

subfic   RT,RA,SI

[Power mnemonic: sfi]

8	RT	RA	SI
0	6	11	16 31

$$RT \leftarrow \neg(RA) + EXTS(SI) + 1$$

The sum $\neg(RA) + SI + 1$ is placed into register RT.

Special Registers Altered

CA

Add Carrying XO-form

addc   RT,RA,RB   (OE=0 Rc=0)
addc.   RT,RA,RB   (OE=0 Rc=1)
addco   RT,RA,RB   (OE=1 Rc=0)
addco.   RT,RA,RB   (OE=1 Rc=1)

[Power mnemonics: a, a., ao, ao.]

31	RT	RA	RB	OE	10	Rc
0	6	11	16	21	22	31

$$RT \leftarrow (RA) + (RB)$$

The sum $(RA) + (RB)$ is placed into register RT.

Special Registers Altered

CA
CRO   (if Rc=1)
SO OV   (if OE=1)

Subtract From Carrying XO-form

subfc	RT,RA,RB	(OE=0 Rc=0)
subfc.	RT,RA,RB	(OE=0 Rc=1)
subfco	RT,RA,RB	(OE=1 Rc=0)
subfco.	RT,RA,RB	(OE=1 Rc=1)

[Power mnemonics: sf, sf., sfo, sfo.]

31	RT	RA	RB	OE	8	Rc
0	6	11	16	21 22		31

$$RT \leftarrow \neg(RA) + (RB) + 1$$

The sum ¬(RA) + (RB) + 1 is placed into register RT.

Special Registers Altered

```
CA
CRO                                           (if Rc=1)
SO OV                                         (if OE=1)
```

Extended Mnemonics:

Example of extended mnemonics for *Subtract From Carrying:*

Extended:	*Equivalent to:*
subc Rx,Ry,Rz	subfc Rx,Rz,Ry

Add Extended XO-form

adde	RT,RA,RB	(OE=0 Rc=0)
adde.	RT,RA,RB	(OE=0 Rc=1)
addeo	RT,RA,RB	(OE=1 Rc=0)
addeo.	RT,RA,RB	(OE=1 Rc=1)

[Power mnemonics: ae, ae., aeo, aeo.]

31	RT	RA	RB	OE	138	Rc
0	6	11	16	21 22		31

$$RT \leftarrow (RA) + (RB) + CA$$

The sum (RA) + (RB) + CA is placed into register RT.

Special Registers Altered

```
CA
CRO                                           (if Rc=1)
SO OV                                         (if OE=1)
```

Subtract From Extended XO-form

subfe	RT,RA,RB	(OE=0 Rc=0)
subfe.	RT,RA,RB	(OE=0 Rc=1)
subfeo	RT,RA,RB	(OE=1 Rc=0)
subfeo.	RT,RA,RB	(OE=1 Rc=1)

[Power mnemonics: sfe, sfe., sfeo, sfeo.]

31	RT	RA	RB	OE	136	Rc
0	6	11	16	21	22	31

```
RT ← ¬(RA) + (RB) + CA
```

The sum ¬(RA) + (RB) + CA is placed into register RT.

Special Registers Altered

```
CA
CRO                                        (if Rc=1)
SO OV                                      (if OE=1)
```

Add to Minus One Extended XO-form

addme	RT,RA	(OE=0 Rc=0)
addme.	RT,RA	(OE=0 Rc=1)
addmeo	RT,RA	(OE=1 Rc=0)
addmeo.	RT,RA	(OE=1 Rc=1)

[Power mnemonics: ame, ame., ameo, ameo.]

31	RT	RA	///	OE	234	Rc
0	6	11	16	21	22	31

```
RT ← (RA) + CA - 1
```

The sum (RA) + CA + $^{64}1$ is placed into register RT.

Special Registers Altered

```
CA
CRO                                        (if Rc=1)
SO OV                                      (if OE=1)
```

Subtract From Minus One Extended XO-form

subfme	RT,RA	(OE=0 Rc=0)
subfme.	RT,RA	(OE=0 Rc=1)
subfmeo	RT,RA	(OE=1 Rc=0)
subfmeo.	RT,RA	(OE=1 Rc=1)

[Power mnemonics: sfme, sfme., sfmeo, sfmeo.]

31	RT	RA	///	OE	232	Rc
0	6	11	16	21	22	31

```
RT ← ¬(RA) + CA - 1
```

The sum $\neg(RA) + CA + ^{64}1$ is placed into register RT.

Special Registers Altered

```
CA
CR0                                            (if Rc=1)
SO OV                                          (if OE=1)
```

Add to Zero Extended XO-form

addze	RT,RA	(OE=0 Rc=0)
addze.	RT,RA	(OE=0 Rc=1)
addzeo	RT,RA	(OE=1 Rc=0)
addzeo.	RT,RA	(OE=1 Rc=1)

[Power mnemonics: aze, aze., azeo, azeo.]

31	RT	RA	///	OE	202	Rc
0	6	11	16	21	22	31

```
RT ← (RA) + CA
```

The sum (RA) + CA is placed into register RT.

Special Registers Altered

```
CA
CR0                                            (if Rc=1)
SO OV                                          (if OE=1)
```

Subtract From Zero Extended XO-form

subfze	RT,RA	(OE=0 Rc=0)
subfze.	RT,RA	(OE=0 Rc=1)
subfzeo	RT,RA	(OE=1 Rc=0)
subfzeo.	RT,RA	(OE=1 Rc=1)

[Power mnemonics: sfze, sfze., sfzeo, sfzeo.]

31	RT	RA	///	OE	200	Rc
0	6	11	16	21 22		31

```
RT ← ¬(RA) + CA
```

The sum ¬(RA) + CA is placed into register RT.

Special Registers Altered

```
CA
CRO                                                 (if Rc=1)
SO OV                                               (if OE=1)
```

Negate XO-form

neg	RT,RA	(OE=0 Rc=0)
neg.	RT,RA	(OE=0 Rc=1)
nego	RT,RA	(OE=1 Rc=0)
nego.	RT,RA	(OE=1 Rc=1)

31	RT	RA	///	OE	104	Rc
0	6	11	16	21 22		31

```
RT ← ¬(RA) + 1
```

The sum ¬(RA) + 1 is placed into register RT.

If executing in 64-bit mode and register RA contain the most negative 64-bit number (0x8000_0000_0000_0000), the result is the most negative number and, if OE=1, OV is set to 1. Similarly, if executing in 32-bit mode and $(RA)_{32:63}$ contains the most negative 32-bit number (0x8000_0000), the low-order 32 bits of the result contain the most negative 32-bit number and, if OE=1, OV is set to 1.

Special Registers Altered

```
CRO                                                 (if Rc=1)
SO OV                                               (if OE=1)
```

Programming Note

For *mulli* and *mullw*, the low-order 32 bits of the product are the correct 32-bit product for 32-bit mode.

For *mulli* and *mulld*, the low-order 64 bits of the product are independent of whether the operands are regarded as signed or unsigned 64-bit integers. For *mulli* and *mullw*, the low-order 32 bits of the product are independent of whether the operands are regarded as signed or unsigned 32-bit integers.

Multiply Low Immediate   D-form

mulli   RT,RA,SI

[Power mnemonic: muli]

7		RT		RA		SI	
0		6		11		16	31

$$\text{prod}_{0:127} \leftarrow (RA) \times EXTS(SI)$$
$$RT \leftarrow \text{prod}_{64:127}$$

The 64-bit first operand is (RA). The 64-bit second operand is the sign-extended value of the SI field. The low-order 64 bits of the 128-bit product of the operands are placed into register RT.

Both operands and the product are interpreted as signed integers.

Special Registers Altered

    None

Programming Note

The XO-form *Multiply* instructions may execute faster on some implementations if RB contains the operand having the smaller absolute value.

Multiply Low Doubleword   XO-form

mulld	RT,RA,RB	(OE=0 Rc=0)
mulld.	RT,RA,RB	(OE=0 Rc=1)
mulldo	RT,RA,RB	(OE=1 Rc=0)
mulldo.	RT,RA,RB	(OE=1 Rc=1)

31		RT		RA		RB		OE	233		Rc
0		6		11		16		21	22		31

$$\text{prod}_{0:127} \leftarrow (RA) \times (RB)$$
$$RT \leftarrow \text{prod}_{64:127}$$

The 64-bit operands are (RA) and (RB). The low-order 64 bits of the 128-bit product of the operands are placed into register RT.

If OE=1 then OV is set to 1 if the product cannot be represented in 64 bits.

Both operands and the product are interpreted as signed integers.

This instruction is defined only for 64-bit implementations. Using it on a 32-bit implementation will cause the system illegal instruction error handler to be invoked.

Special Registers Altered

    CR0   (if Rc=1)
    SO OV   (if OE=1)

Multiply Low Word   XO-form

mullw	RT,RA,RB	(OE=0 Rc=0)
mullw.	RT,RA,RB	(OE=0 Rc=1)
mullwo	RT,RA,RB	(OE=1 Rc=0)
mullwo.	RT,RA,RB	(OE=1 Rc=1)

[Power mnemonics: muls, muls., mulso, mulso.]

31	RT	RA	RB	OE	235	Rc
0	6	11	16	21 22		31

$$RT \leftarrow (RA)_{32:63} \times (RB)_{32:63}$$

The 32-bit operands are the low-order 32 bits of RA and of RB. The 64-bit product of the operands is placed into register RT.

If OE=1 then OV is set to 1 if the product cannot be represented in 32 bits.

Both operands and the product are interpreted as signed integers.

Special Registers Altered

CR0	(if Rc=1)
SO OV	(if OE=1)

Multiply High Doubleword   XO-form

mulhd	RT,RA,RB	(Rc=0)
mulhd.	RT,RA,RB	(Rc=1)

31	RT	RA	RB	/	73	Rc
0	6	11	16	21 22		31

$$prod_{0:127} \leftarrow (RA) \times (RB)$$
$$RT \leftarrow prod_{0:63}$$

The 64-bit operands are (RA) and (RB). The high-order 64 bits of the 128-bit product of the operands are placed into register RT.

Both operands and the product are interpreted as signed integers.

This instruction is defined only for 64-bit implementations. Using it on a 32-bit implementation will cause the system illegal instruction error handler to be invoked.

Special Registers Altered

CR0	(if Rc=1)

Multiply High Word   XO-form

mulhw	RT,RA,RB
mulhw.	RT,RA,RB

(Rc=0)
(Rc=1)

31	RT	RA	RB	/	75	Rc
0	6	11	16	21 22		31

```
prod0:63 ← (RA)32:63 × (RB)32:63
RT32:63 ← prod0:31
RT0:31 ← undefined
```

$$prod_{0:63} \leftarrow (RA)_{32:63} \times (RB)_{32:63}$$
$$RT_{32:63} \leftarrow prod_{0:31}$$
$$RT_{0:31} \leftarrow undefined$$

The 32-bit operands are the low-order 32 bits of RA and of RB. The high-order 32 bits of the 64-bit product of the operands are placed into $RT_{32:63}$. $(RT)_{0:31}$ are undefined.

Both operands and the product are interpreted as signed integers.

Special Registers Altered

    CR0   (if Rc=1)

Multiply High Doubleword Unsigned   XO-form

mulhdu	RT,RA,RB
mulhdu.	RT,RA,RB

(Rc=0)
(Rc=1)

31	RT	RA	RB	/	9	Rc
0	6	11	16	21 22		31

$$prod_{0:127} \leftarrow (RA) \times (RB)$$
$$RT \leftarrow prod_{0:63}$$

The 64-bit operands are (RA) and (RB). The high-order 64 bits of the 128-bit product of the operands are placed into register RT.

Both operands and the product are interpreted as unsigned integers, except that if Rc=1 the first three bits of CR Field 0 are set by signed comparison of the result to zero.

This instruction is defined only for 64-bit implementations. Using it on a 32-bit implementation will cause the system illegal instruction error handler to be invoked.

Special Registers Altered

    CR0   (if Rc=1)

Multiply High Word Unsigned   XO-form

| mulhwu | RT,RA,RB | (Rc=0) |
| mulhwu. | RT,RA,RB | (Rc=1) |

31	RT	RA	RB	/	11	Rc
0	6	11	16	21 22		31

```
prod_{0:63} ← (RA)_{32:63} × (RB)_{32:63}
RT_{32:63} ← prod_{0:31}
RT_{0:31} ← undefined
```

The 32-bit operands are the low-order 32 bits of RA and of RB. The high-order 32 bits of the 64-bit product of the operands are placed into $RT_{32:63}$. $(RT)_{0:31}$ are undefined.

Both operands and the product are interpreted as unsigned integers, except that if Rc=1 the first three bits of CR Field 0 are set by signed comparison of the result to zero.

Special Registers Altered

    CR0   (if Rc=1)

Programming Note

The 64-bit signed remainder of dividing (RA) by (RB) can be computed as follows, except in the case that (RA) = -2^{63} and (RB) = -1.

```
divd    RT,RA,RB
# RT = quotient
mulld   RT,RT,RB
# RT = quotient*divisor
subf    RT,RT,RA
# RT = remainder
```

Divide Doubleword XO-form

divd	RT,RA,RB	(OE=0 Rc=0)
divd.	RT,RA,RB	(OE=0 Rc=1)
divdo	RT,RA,RB	(OE=1 Rc=0)
divdo.	RT,RA,RB	(OE=1 Rc=1)

31	RT	RA	RB	OE	489	Rc
0	6	11	16	21	22	31

```
dividend_{0:63} ← (RA)
divisor_{0:63} ← (RB)
RT ← dividend ÷ divisor
```

The 64-bit dividend is (RA). The 64-bit divisor is (RB). The 64-bit quotient of the dividend and divisor is placed into RT. The remainder is not supplied as a result.

Both operands and the quotient are interpreted as signed integers. The quotient is the unique signed integer that satisfies

dividend = (*quotient* × *divisor*) + *r*

where $0 \le r < |divisor|$ if the dividend is nonnegative, and $-|divisor| < r \le 0$ if the dividend is negative.

If an attempt is made to perform any of the divisions

0x8000_0000_0000_0000 ÷ −1
<anything> ÷ 0

then the contents of register RT are undefined as are (if Rc=1) the contents of the LT, GT, and EQ bits of CR Field 0. In these cases, if OE=1 then OV is set to 1.

This instruction is defined only for 64-bit implementations. Using it on a 32-bit implementation will cause the system illegal instruction error handler to be invoked.

Special Registers Altered

```
CR0                                          (if Rc=1)
SO OV                                        (if OE=1)
```

Divide Word XO-form

Programming Note

The 32-bit signed remainder of dividing $(RA)_{32:63}$ by $(RB)_{32:63}$ can be computed as follows, except in the case that $(RA) = -2^{31}$ and $(RB) = -1$.

divw	RT,RA,RB	(OE=0 Rc=0)
divw.	RT,RA,RB	(OE=0 Rc=1)
divwo	RT,RA,RB	(OE=1 Rc=0)
divwo.	RT,RA,RB	(OE=1 Rc=1)

31	RT	RA	RB	OE	491	Rc
0	6	11	16	21 22		31

```
divw   RT,RA,RB
# RT = quotient
mullw  RT,RT,RB
# RT = quotient*divisor
subf   RT,RT,RA
# RT = remainder
```

```
dividend_{0:63} ← EXTS((RA)_{32:63})
divisor_{0:63} ← EXTS((RB)_{32:63})
RT_{32:63} ← dividend ÷ divisor
RT_{0:31} ← undefined
```

The 64-bit dividend is the sign-extended value of $(RA)_{32:63}$. The 64-bit divisor is the sign-extended value of $(RB)_{32:63}$. The 64-bit quotient is formed. The low-order 32 bits of the 64-bit quotient are placed into $RT_{32:63}$. $(RT)_{0:31}$ are undefined. The remainder is not supplied as a result.

Both operands and the quotient are interpreted as signed integers. The quotient is the unique signed integer that satisfies

$$dividend = (quotient \times divisor) + r$$

where $0 \le r < |divisor|$ if the dividend is nonnegative, and $-|divisor| < r \le 0$ if the dividend is negative.

If an attempt is made to perform any of the divisions

0x8000_0000 ÷ −1
<anything> ÷ 0

then the contents of register RT are undefined as are (if Rc=1) the contents of the LT, GT, and EQ bits of CR Field 0. In these cases, if OE=1 then OV is set to 1.

Special Registers Altered

```
CR0                                      (if Rc=1)
SO OV                                    (if OE=1)
```

Programming Note

The 64-bit unsigned remainder of dividing (RA) by (RB) can be computed as follows.

```
divdu  RT,RA,RB
# RT = quotient
mulld  RT,RT,RB
# RT = quotient*divisor
subf   RT,RT,RA
# RT = remainder
```

Divide Doubleword Unsigned XO-form

divdu	RT,RA,RB	(OE=0 Rc=0)
divdu.	RT,RA,RB	(OE=0 Rc=1)
divduo	RT,RA,RB	(OE=1 Rc=0)
divduo.	RT,RA,RB	(OE=1 Rc=1)

31	RT	RA	RB	OE	457	Rc
0	6	11	16	21	22	31

$dividend_{0:63} \leftarrow (RA)$
$divisor_{0:63} \leftarrow (RB)$
$RT \leftarrow dividend \div divisor$

The 64-bit dividend is (RA). The 64-bit divisor is (RB). The 64-bit quotient of the dividend and divisor is placed into RT. The remainder is not supplied as a result.

Both operands and the quotient are interpreted as unsigned integers, except that if Rc=1 the first three bits of CR Field 0 are set by signed comparison of the result to zero. The quotient is the unique unsigned integer that satisfies

$$dividend = (quotient \times divisor) + r$$

where $0 \le r < divisor$.

If an attempt is made to perform the division

<anything> ÷ 0

then the contents of register RT are undefined as are (if Rc=1) the contents of the LT, GT, and EQ bits of CR Field 0. In this case, if OE=1 then OV is set to 1.

This instruction is defined only for 64-bit implementations. Using it on a 32-bit implementation will cause the system illegal instruction error handler to be invoked.

Special Registers Altered

```
CR0                                          (if Rc=1)
SO OV                                        (if OE=1)
```

Divide Word Unsigned XO-form

divwu	RT,RA,RB	(OE=0 Rc=0)
divwu.	RT,RA,RB	(OE=0 Rc=1)
divwuo	RT,RA,RB	(OE=1 Rc=0)
divwuo.	RT,RA,RB	(OE=1 Rc=1)

31	RT	RA	RB	OE	459	Rc
0	6	11	16	21	22	31

Programming Note

The 32-bit unsigned remainder of dividing $(RA)_{32:63}$ by $(RB)_{32:63}$ can be computed as follows.

```
divwu  RT,RA,RB
# RT = quotient
mullw  RT,RT,RB
# RT = quotient*divisor
subf   RT,RT,RA
# RT = remainder
```

$$\text{dividend}_{0:63} \leftarrow {}^{32}0 \parallel (RA)_{32:63}$$
$$\text{divisor}_{0:63} \leftarrow {}^{32}0 \parallel (RB)_{32:63}$$
$$RT_{32:63} \leftarrow \text{dividend} \div \text{divisor}$$
$$RT_{0:31} \leftarrow \text{undefined}$$

The 64-bit dividend is the zero-extended value of $(RA)_{32:63}$. The 64-bit divisor is the zero-extended value of $(RB)_{32:63}$. The 64-bit quotient is formed. The low-order 32 bits of the 64-bit quotient are placed into $RT_{32:63}$. $(RT)_{0:31}$ are undefined. The remainder is not supplied as a result.

Both operands and the quotient are interpreted as unsigned integers, except that if Rc=1 the first three bits of CR Field 0 are set by signed comparison of the result to zero. The quotient is the unique unsigned integer that satisfies

dividend = (quotient × divisor) + r

where $0 \leq r < divisor$.

If an attempt is made to perform the division

<anything> ÷ 0

then the contents of register RT are undefined as are (if Rc=1) the contents of the LT, GT, and EQ bits of CR Field 0. In this case, if OE=1 then OV is set to 1.

Special Registers Altered

| CR0 | (if Rc=1) |
| SO OV | (if OE=1) |

3.3.10 Fixed-Point Compare Instructions

The fixed-point *Compare* instructions compare the contents of register RA with (1) the sign-extended value of the SI field, (2) the zero-extended value of the UI field, or (3) the contents of register RB. The comparison is signed for *cmpi* and *cmp*, and unsigned for *cmpli* and *cmpl*.

For 64-bit implementations, the L field controls whether the operands are treated as 64- or 32-bit quantities, as follows:

L	Operand length
0	32-bit operands
1	64-bit operands

When the operands are treated as 32-bit signed quantities, bit 32 of the register (RA or RB) is the sign bit.

For 32-bit implementations, the L field must be zero.

The *Compare* instructions set one bit in the leftmost three bits of the designated CR field to 1, and the other two to 0. XER_{SO} is copied into bit 3 of the designated CR field.

The CR field is set as follows.

Bit	Name	Description
0	LT	(RA) < SI or (RB) (signed comparison) (RA) $\overset{u}{<}$ UI or (RB) (unsigned comparison)
1	GT	(RA) > SI or (RB) (signed comparison) (RA) $\overset{u}{>}$ UI or (RB) (unsigned comparison)
2	EQ	(RA) = SI, UI, or (RB)
3	SO	Summary Overflow from the XER

Extended mnemonics for compares

A set of extended mnemonics is provided so that compares can be coded with the operand length as part of the instruction mnemonic rather than as a numeric operand. Some of these are shown as examples with the *Compare* instructions. The extended mnemonics for doubleword comparisons are available only in 64-bit implementations. See Appendix C, "Assembler Extended Mnemonics," on page 215 for additional extended mnemonics.

Compare Immediate D-form

cmpi   BF,L,RA,SI

11	BF	/	L	RA	SI
0	6	9	10	11	16 31

```
if L = 0 then a ← EXTS((RA)32:63)
         else a ← (RA)
if       a < EXTS(SI) then c ← 0b100
else if a > EXTS(SI) then c ← 0b010
else                       c ← 0b001
CR4×BF:4×BF+3 ← c ‖ XERSO
```

The contents of register RA ($(RA)_{32:63}$ sign-extended to 64 bits if L=0) are compared with the sign-extended value of the SI field, treating the operands as signed integers. The result of the comparison is placed into CR field BF.

In 32-bit implementations, if L=1 the instruction form is invalid.

Special Registers Altered

```
CR field BF
```

Extended Mnemonics:

Examples of extended mnemonics for *Compare Immediate*:

Extended:	*Equivalent to:*
cmpdi Rx,value	cmpi 0,1,Rx,value
cmpwi cr3,Rx,value	cmpi 3,0,Rx,value

Compare X-form

cmp   BF,L,RA,RB

31	BF	/	L	RA	RB	0	/
0	6	9	10	11	16	21	31

```
if L = 0 then a ← EXTS((RA)32:63)
              b ← EXTS((RB)32:63)
         else a ← (RA)
              b ← (RB)
if       a < b then c ← 0b100
else if a > b then c ← 0b010
else                c ← 0b001
CR4×BF:4×BF+3 ← c ‖ XERSO
```

The contents of register RA ($(RA)_{32:63}$ if L=0) are compared with the contents of register RB ($(RB)_{32:63}$ if L=0), treating the operands as signed integers. The result of the comparison is placed into CR field BF.

In 32-bit implementations, if L=1 the instruction form is invalid.

Special Registers Altered

```
CR field BF
```

Extended Mnemonics:

Examples of extended mnemonics for *Compare:*

Extended:	*Equivalent to:*
cmpd Rx,Ry	cmp 0,1,Rx,Ry
cmpw cr3,Rx,Ry	cmp 3,0,Rx,Ry

Compare Logical Immediate D-form

cmpli   BF,L,RA,UI

10	BF	/	L	RA	UI
0	6	9	10 11	16	31

```
if L = 0 then a ←  ³²0 ∥ (RA)₃₂:₆₃
          else a ← (RA)
if        a ≮ (⁴⁸0 ∥ UI) then c ← 0b100
else if a ≯ (⁴⁸0 ∥ UI) then c ← 0b010
else                        c ← 0b001
CR₄ₓBF:₄ₓBF₊₃ ← c ∥ XERₛₒ
```

The contents of register RA ($(RA)_{32:63}$ zero-extended to 64 bits if L=0) are compared with $^{48}0 \parallel UI$, treating the operands as unsigned integers. The result of the comparison is placed into CR field BF.

In 32-bit implementations, if L=1 the instruction form is invalid.

Special Registers Altered

```
CR field BF
```

Extended Mnemonics:

Examples of extended mnemonics for *Compare Logical Immediate:*

Extended:	*Equivalent to:*
cmpldi Rx,value	cmpli 0,1,Rx,value
cmplwi cr3,Rx,value	cmpli 3,0,Rx,value

Compare Logical X-form

cmpl   BF,L,RA,RB

31	BF	/	L	RA	RB	32	/
0	6	9	10 11	16	21		31

```
if L = 0 then a ← ³²0 ‖ (RA)₃₂:₆₃
              b ← ³²0 ‖ (RB)₃₂:₆₃
         else a ← (RA)
              b ← (RB)
if      a <ᵘ b then c ← 0b100
else if a >ᵘ b then c ← 0b010
else              c ← 0b001
CR₄ₓBF:₄ₓBF+3 ← c ‖ XERₛₒ
```

The contents of register RA ($(RA)_{32:63}$ if L=0) are compared with the contents of register RB ($(RB)_{32:63}$ if L=0), treating the operands as unsigned integers. The result of the comparison is placed into CR field BF.

In 32-bit implementations, if L=1 the instruction form is invalid.

Special Registers Altered

```
CR field BF
```

Extended Mnemonics:

Examples of extended mnemonics for *Compare Logical*:

Extended:	*Equivalent to*:
cmpld Rx,Ry	cmpl 0,1,Rx,Ry
cmplw cr3,Rx,Ry	cmpl 3,0,Rx,Ry

3.3.11 Fixed-Point Trap Instructions

The *Trap* instructions are provided to test for a specified set of conditions. If any of the conditions tested by a *Trap* instruction are met, the system trap handler is invoked. If none of the tested conditions are met, instruction execution continues normally.

The contents of register RA are compared with either the sign-extended value of the SI field or the contents of register RB, depending on the *Trap* instruction. For **tdi** and **td**, the entire contents of RA (and RB) participate in the comparison; for **twi** and **tw**, only the contents of the low-order 32 bits of RA (and RB) participate in the comparison.

This comparison results in five conditions which are ANDed with TO.

If the result is not 0 the system trap handler is invoked. These conditions are:

TO bit	ANDed with Condition
0	Less Than, using signed comparison
1	Greater Than, using signed comparison
2	Equal
3	Less Than, using unsigned comparison
4	Greater Than, using unsigned comparison

Extended mnemonics for traps

A set of extended mnemonics is provided so that traps can be coded with the condition as part of the instruction mnemonic rather than as a numeric operand. Some of these are shown as examples with the *Trap* instructions. See Appendix C, "Assembler Extended Mnemonics," on page 215 for additional extended mnemonics.

Trap Doubleword Immediate D-form

tdi   TO,RA,SI

2	TO	RA	SI
0	6	11	16 31

```
a ← (RA)
if (a < EXTS(SI)) & TO_0 then TRAP
if (a > EXTS(SI)) & TO_1 then TRAP
if (a = EXTS(SI)) & TO_2 then TRAP
if (a ≮ EXTS(SI)) & TO_3 then TRAP
if (a ≯ EXTS(SI)) & TO_4 then TRAP
```

The contents of register RA are compared with the sign-extended value of the SI field. If any bit in the TO field is set to 1 and its corresponding condition is met by the result of the comparison, then the system trap handler is invoked.

This instruction is defined only for 64-bit implementations. Using it on a 32-bit implementation will cause the system illegal instruction error handler to be invoked.

Special Registers Altered
```
None
```

Extended Mnemonics:

Examples of extended mnemonics for *Trap Doubleword Immediate*:

Extended:		*Equivalent to:*	
tdlti	Rx,value	tdi	16,Rx,value
tdnei	Rx,value	tdi	24,Rx,value

Trap Word Immediate D-form

twi   TO,RA,SI

[Power mnemonic: ti]

3	TO	RA	SI
0	6	11	16 31

```
a ← EXTS((RA)32:63)
if (a < EXTS(SI)) & TO0 then TRAP
if (a > EXTS(SI)) & TO1 then TRAP
if (a = EXTS(SI)) & TO2 then TRAP
if (a ≮ EXTS(SI)) & TO3 then TRAP
if (a ≯ EXTS(SI)) & TO4 then TRAP
```

The contents of $RA_{32:63}$ are compared with the sign-extended value of the SI field. If any bit in the TO field is set to 1 and its corresponding condition is met by the result of the comparison, then the system trap handler is invoked.

Special Registers Altered

    None

Extended Mnemonics:

Examples of extended mnemonics for *Trap Word Immediate*:

Extended:		*Equivalent to:*	
twgti	Rx,value	twi	8,Rx,value
twllei	Rx,value	twi	6,Rx,value

Trap Doubleword X-form

td   TO,RA,RB

31	TO	RA	RB	68	/
0	6	11	16	21	31

```
a ← (RA)
b ← (RB)
if (a < b) & TO₀ then TRAP
if (a > b) & TO₁ then TRAP
if (a = b) & TO₂ then TRAP
if (a ≮ b) & TO₃ then TRAP
if (a ≯ b) & TO₄ then TRAP
```

The contents of register RA are compared with the contents of register RB. If any bit in the TO field is set to 1 and its corresponding condition is met by the result of the comparison, then the system trap handler is invoked.

This instruction is defined only for 64-bit implementations. Using it on a 32-bit implementation will cause the system illegal instruction error handler to be invoked.

Special Registers Altered

None

Extended Mnemonics:

Examples of extended mnemonics for *Trap Doubleword*:

Extended:		*Equivalent to:*	
tdge	Rx,Ry	td	12,Rx,Ry
tdlnl	Rx,Ry	td	5,Rx,Ry

Trap Word X-form

tw   TO,RA,RB

[Power mnemonic: t]

31	TO	RA	RB	4	/
0	6	11	16	21	31

```
a ← EXTS((RA)32:63)
b ← EXTS((RB)32:63)
if (a < b) & TO0 then TRAP
if (a > b) & TO1 then TRAP
if (a = b) & TO2 then TRAP
if (a ≰ b) & TO3 then TRAP
if (a ≱ b) & TO4 then TRAP
```

The contents of $RA_{32:63}$ are compared with the contents of $RB_{32:63}$. If any bit in the TO field is set to 1 and its corresponding condition is met by the result of the comparison, then the system trap handler is invoked.

Special Registers Altered

```
None
```

Extended Mnemonics:

Examples of extended mnemonics for *Trap Word*:

Extended:		*Equivalent to:*	
tweq	Rx,Ry	tw	4,Rx,Ry
twlge	Rx,Ry	tw	5,Rx,Ry
trap		tw	31,0,0

3.3.12 Fixed-Point Logical Instructions

The *Logical* instructions perform bit-parallel operations on 64-bit operands.

The X-form *Logical* instructions with Rc=1, and the D-form *Logical* instructions **andi.** and **andis.**, set the first three bits of CR Field 0 as described in Section 3.3.8, "Other Fixed-Point Instructions," on page 80. The *Logical* instructions do not change the SO, OV, and CA bits in the XER.

Extended mnemonics for logical operations

An extended mnemonic is provided that generates the preferred form of "no-op" (an instruction that does nothing). This is shown as an example with the *OR Immediate* instruction.

Extended mnemonics are provided that use the *OR* and *NOR* instructions to copy the contents of one register to another, with and without complementing. These are shown as examples with the two instructions.

See Appendix C, "Assembler Extended Mnemonics," on page 215 for additional extended mnemonics.

AND Immediate D-form

andi.   RA,RS,UI

[Power mnemonic: andil.]

28		RS	RA	UI	
0		6	11	16	31

$$RA \leftarrow (RS) \,\&\, (^{48}0 \parallel UI)$$

The contents of register RS are ANDed with $^{48}0 \parallel UI$ and the result is placed into register RA.

Special Registers Altered
    CR0

AND Immediate Shifted D-form

andis.   RA,RS,UI

[Power mnemonic: andiu.]

29		RS	RA	UI	
0		6	11	16	31

$$RA \leftarrow (RS) \,\&\, (^{32}0 \parallel UI \parallel {}^{16}0)$$

The contents of register RS are ANDed with $^{32}0 \parallel UI \parallel {}^{16}0$ and the result is placed into register RA.

Special Registers Altered
    CR0

OR Immediate   D-form

ori   RA,RS,UI

[Power mnemonic: oril]

24	RS	RA	UI
0	6	11	16 31

$$RA \leftarrow (RS) \mid (^{48}0 \parallel UI)$$

The contents of register RS are ORed with $^{48}0 \parallel UI$ and the result is placed into register RA.

The preferred "no-op" (an instruction that does nothing) is:

        ori   0,0,0

Special Registers Altered

None

Extended Mnemonics:

Example of extended mnemonics for *OR Immediate*:

Extended:	*Equivalent to:*
nop	ori 0,0,0

OR Immediate Shifted D-form

oris   RA,RS,UI

[Power mnemonic: oriu]

25	RS	RA	UI
0	6	11	16 31

$$RA \leftarrow (RS) \mid (^{32}0 \parallel UI \parallel {}^{16}0)$$

The contents of register RS are ORed with $^{32}0 \parallel UI \parallel {}^{16}0$ and the result is placed into register RA.

Special Registers Altered

None

XOR Immediate D-form

xori   RA,RS,UI

[Power mnemonic: xoril]

26	RS	RA	UI
0	6	11	16 31

RA ← (RS) ⊕ (^{48}0 ‖ UI)

The contents of register RS are XORed with ^{48}0 ‖ UI and the result is placed into register RA.

Special Registers Altered

None

XOR Immediate Shifted D-form

xoris   RA,RS,UI

[Power mnemonic: xoriu]

27	RS	RA	UI
0	6	11	16 31

RA ← (RS) ⊕ (^{32}0 ‖ UI ‖ ^{16}0)

The contents of register RS are XORed with ^{32}0 ‖ UI ‖ ^{16}0 and the result is placed into register RA.

Special Registers Altered

None

AND X-form

and	RA,RS,RB	(Rc=0)
and.	RA,RS,RB	(Rc=1)

31	RS	RA	RB	28	Rc
0	6	11	16	21	31

RA ← (RS) & (RB)

The contents of register RS are ANDed with the contents of register RB and the result is placed into register RA.

Special Registers Altered

    CR0   (if Rc=1)

OR X-form

or	RA,RS,RB	(Rc=0)
or.	RA,RS,RB	(Rc=1)

31	RS	RA	RB	444	Rc
0	6	11	16	21	31

RA ← (RS) | (RB)

The contents of register RS are ORed with the contents of register RB and the result is placed into register RA.

Special Registers Altered

    CR0   (if Rc=1)

Extended Mnemonics:

Example of extended mnemonics for *OR*:

Extended:		*Equivalent to:*	
mr	Rx,Ry	or	Rx,Ry,Ry

XOR X-form

xor	RA,RS,RB	(Rc=0)
xor.	RA,RS,RB	(Rc=1)

31	RS	RA	RB	316	Rc
0	6	11	16	21	31

```
RA ← (RS) ⊕ (RB)
```

The contents of register RS are XORed with the contents of register RB and the result is placed into register RA.

Special Registers Altered
```
CRO
```
(if Rc=1)

NAND X-form

nand	RA,RS,RB	(Rc=0)
nand.	RA,RS,RB	(Rc=1)

31	RS	RA	RB	476	Rc
0	6	11	16	21	31

```
RA ← ¬((RS) & (RB))
```

The contents of register RS are ANDed with the contents of register RB and the complemented result is placed into register RA.

Special Registers Altered
```
CRO
```
(if Rc=1)

NOR X-form

nor	RA,RS,RB	(Rc=0)
nor.	RA,RS,RB	(Rc=1)

31	RS	RA	RB	124	Rc
0	6	11	16	21	31

```
RA ← ¬((RS) | (RB))
```

The contents of register RS are ORed with the contents of register RB and the complemented result is placed into register RA.

Special Registers Altered
```
CRO
```
(if Rc=1)

Programming Note

nand or *nor* with RA=RB can be used to obtain the one's complement.

Extended Mnemonics:

Example of extended mnemonics for *NOR:*

Extended:	*Equivalent to:*
not Rx,Ry	nor Rx,Ry,Ry

Equivalent X-form

eqv	RA,RS,RB	(Rc=0)
eqv.	RA,RS,RB	(Rc=1)

31	RS	RA	RB	284	Rc
0	6	11	16	21	31

RA ← (RS) ≡ (RB)

The contents of register RS are XORed with the contents of register RB and the complemented result is placed into register RA.

Special Registers Altered

CR0   (if Rc=1)

AND with Complement X-form

andc	RA,RS,RB	(Rc=0)
andc.	RA,RS,RB	(Rc=1)

31	RS	RA	RB	60	Rc
0	6	11	16	21	31

RA ← (RS) & ¬(RB)

The contents of register RS are ANDed with the complement of the contents of register RB and the result is placed into register RA.

Special Registers Altered

CR0   (if Rc=1)

OR with Complement X-form

| orc | RA,RS,RB | (Rc=0) |
| orc. | RA,RS,RB | (Rc=1) |

31	RS	RA	RB	412	Rc
0	6	11	16	21	31

$RA \leftarrow (RS) \mid \neg(RB)$

The contents of register RS are ORed with the complement of the contents of register RB and the result is placed into register RA.

Special Registers Altered

CR0   (if Rc=1)

Extend Sign Byte X-form

| extsb | RA,RS | (Rc=0) |
| extsb. | RA,RS | (Rc=1) |

31	RS	RA	///	954	Rc
0	6	11	16	21	31

$s \leftarrow (RS)_{56}$
$RA_{56:63} \leftarrow (RS)_{56:63}$
$RA_{0:55} \leftarrow {}^{56}s$

$(RS)_{56:63}$ are placed into $RA_{56:63}$. Bit 56 of register RS is placed into $RA_{0:55}$.

Special Registers Altered

CR0   (if Rc=1)

Extend Sign Halfword X-form

| extsh | RA,RS | (Rc=0) |
| extsh. | RA,RS | (Rc=1) |

[Power mnemonics: exts, exts.]

31		RS		RA		///		922		Rc
0		6		11		16		21		31

$$s \leftarrow (RS)_{48}$$
$$RA_{48:63} \leftarrow (RS)_{48:63}$$
$$RA_{0:47} \leftarrow {}^{48}s$$

$(RS)_{48:63}$ are placed into $RA_{48:63}$. Bit 48 of register RS is placed into $RA_{0:47}$.

Special Registers Altered

    CR0   (if Rc=1)

Extend Sign Word X-form

| extsw | RA,RS | (Rc=0) |
| extsw. | RA,RS | (Rc=1) |

31		RS		RA		///		986		Rc
0		6		11		16		21		31

$$s \leftarrow (RS)_{32}$$
$$RA_{32:63} \leftarrow (RS)_{32:63}$$
$$RA_{0:31} \leftarrow {}^{32}s$$

$(RS)_{32:63}$ are placed into $RA_{32:63}$. Bit 32 of register RS is placed into $RA_{0:31}$.

This instruction is defined only for 64-bit implementations. Using it on a 32-bit implementation will cause the system illegal instruction error handler to be invoked.

Special Registers Altered

    CR0   (if Rc=1)

Count Leading Zeros Doubleword X-form

cntlzd   RA,RS   (Rc=0)
cntlzd.   RA,RS   (Rc=1)

31	RS	RA	///	58	Rc
0	6	11	16	21	31

```
n ← 0
do while n < 64
   if (RS)_n = 1 then leave
   n ← n + 1
RA ← n
```

Programming Note

For both *Count Leading Zeros* instructions, if Rc=1 then LT is set to 0 in CR Field 0.

A count of the number of consecutive zero bits starting at bit 0 of register RS is placed into RA. This number ranges from 0 to 64, inclusive.

If Rc=1, CR Field 0 is set to reflect the result.

This instruction is defined only for 64-bit implementations. Using it on a 32-bit implementation will cause the system illegal instruction error handler to be invoked.

Special Registers Altered
```
CR0                                                      (if Rc=1)
```

Count Leading Zeros Word X-form

cntlzw   RA,RS   (Rc=0)
cntlzw.   RA,RS   (Rc=1)

[Power mnemonics: cntlz, cntlz.]

31	RS	RA	///	26	Rc
0	6	11	16	21	31

```
n ← 32
do while n < 64
   if (RS)_n = 1 then leave
   n ← n + 1
RA ← n - 32
```

A count of the number of consecutive zero bits starting at bit 32 of register RS is placed into RA. This number ranges from 0 to 32, inclusive.

If Rc=1, CR Field 0 is set to reflect the result.

Special Registers Altered
```
CR0                                                      (if Rc=1)
```

3.3.13 Fixed-Point Rotate and Shift Instructions

The Fixed-Point Processor performs rotation operations on data from a GPR and returns the result, or a portion of the result, to a GPR.

The rotation operations rotate a 64-bit quantity left by a specified number of bit positions.   Bits that exit from position 0 enter at position 63.

Two types of rotation operation are supported.

For the first type, denoted $rotate_{64}$ or $ROTL_{64}$, the value rotated is the given 64-bit value. The $rotate_{64}$ operation is used to rotate a given 64-bit quantity.

For the second type, denoted $rotate_{32}$ or $ROTL_{32}$, the value rotated consists of two copies of bits 32:63 of the given 64-bit value, one copy in bits 0:31 and the other in bits 32:63. The $rotate_{32}$ operation is used to rotate a given 32-bit quantity.

The *Rotate and Shift* instructions employ a mask generator. The mask is 64 bits long, and consists of 1-bits from a start bit, *mstart,* through and including a stop bit, *mstop,* and 0-bits elsewhere. The values of *mstart* and *mstop* range from 0 to 63. If *mstart > mstop*, the 1-bits wrap around from position 63 to position 0. Thus the mask is formed as follows:

```
if mstart ≤ mstop then
    mask_mstart:mstop = ones
    mask_all other bits = zeros
else
    mask_mstart:63 = ones
    mask_0:mstop = ones
    mask_all other bits = zeros
```

There is no way to specify an all-zero mask.

For instructions that use the $rotate_{32}$ operation, the mask start and stop positions are always in the low-order 32 bits of the mask.

The use of the mask is described in following sections.

The *Rotate and Shift* instructions with Rc=1 set the first three bits of CR field 0 as described in Section 3.3.8, "Other Fixed-Point Instructions," on page 80. *Rotate and Shift* instructions do not change the OV and SO bits. *Rotate and Shift* instructions, except algebraic right shifts, do not change the CA bit.

Extended Mnemonics for Rotates and Shifts

The *Rotate and Shift* instructions, while powerful, can be complicated to code (they have up to five operands). A set of extended mnemonics is provided that allow simpler coding of often-used functions such as clearing the leftmost or rightmost bits of a register, left justifying or right justifying an arbitrary field, and performing simple rotates and shifts. Some of these extended mnemonics are shown as examples with the *Rotate* instructions. See Appendix C, "Assembler Extended Mnemonics," on page 215 for additional extended mnemonics.

Fixed-Point Rotate Instructions

These instructions rotate the contents of a register. The result of the rotation is

■ inserted into the target register under control of a mask (if a mask bit is 1 the associated bit of the rotated data are placed into the target register, and if the mask bit is 0 the associated bit in the target register remains unchanged); or

■ ANDed with a mask before being placed into the target register.

The *Rotate Left* instructions allow right-rotation of the contents of a register to be performed (in concept) by a left-rotation of $64-n$, where n is the number of bits by which to rotate right. They allow right-rotation of the contents of the low-order 32 bits of a register to be performed (in concept) by a left-rotation of $32-n$, where n is the number of bits by which to rotate right.

Rotate Left Doubleword Immediate then Clear Left   MD-form

rldicl	RA,RS,SH,MB	(Rc=0)
rldicl.	RA,RS,SH,MB	(Rc=1)

30	RS	RA	sh	mb	0	sh	Rc
0	6	11	16	21	27	30	31

```
n ← sh5 || sh0:4
r ← ROTL64((RS), n)
b ← mb5 || mb0:4
m ← MASK(b, 63)
RA ← r & m
```

The contents of register RS are rotated$_{64}$ left SH bits. A mask is generated having 1-bits from bit MB through bit 63 and 0-bits elsewhere. The rotated data are ANDed with the generated mask and the result is placed into register RA.

This instruction is defined only for 64-bit implementations. Using it on a 32-bit implementation will cause the system illegal instruction error

Programming Note

rldicl can be used to extract an n-bit field that starts at bit position b in register RS, right-justified into register RA (clearing the remaining $64-n$ bits of RA), by setting SH=$b+n$ and MB=$64-n$. It can be used to rotate the contents of a register left (right) by n bits by setting SH=n ($64-n$) and MB=0. It can be used to shift the contents of a register right by n bits by setting SH=$64-n$ and MB=n. It can be used to clear the high-order n bits of a register by setting SH=0 and MB=n.

Extended mnemonics are provided for all of these uses: see Appendix C, "Assembler Extended Mnemonics," on page 215.

handler to be invoked.

Special Registers Altered

CR0   (if Rc=1)

Extended Mnemonics:

Examples of extended mnemonics for *Rotate Left Doubleword Immediate then Clear Left*:

Extended:		*Equivalent to:*	
extrdi	Rx,Ry,n,b	rldicl	Rx,Ry,b+n,64−n
srdi	Rx,Ry,n	rldicl	Rx,Ry,64−n,n
clrldi	Rx,Ry,n	rldicl	Rx,Ry,0,n

Programming Note

rldicr can be used to extract an *n*-bit field that starts at bit position *b* in register RS, left-justified into register RA (clearing the remaining 64−*n* bits of RA), by setting SH=*b* and ME=*n*−1. It can be used to rotate the contents of a register left (right) by *n* bits by setting SH=*n* (64−*n*) and ME=63. It can be used to shift the contents of a register left by *n* bits by setting SH=*n* and ME=63−*n*. It can be used to clear the low-order *n* bits of a register by setting SH=0 and ME=63−*n*.

Extended mnemonics are provided for all of these uses (some devolve to *rldicl*): see Appendix C, "Assembler Extended Mnemonics," on page 215.

Rotate Left Doubleword Immediate then Clear Right MD-form

rldicr	RA,RS,SH,ME	(Rc=0)
rldicr.	RA,RS,SH,ME	(Rc=1)

30		RS		RA		sh		me		1		sh	Rc
0		6		11		16		21		27		30	31

```
n ← sh₅ ‖ sh₀:₄
r ← ROTL₆₄((RS), n)
e ← me₅ ‖ me₀:₄
m ← MASK(0, e)
RA ← r & m
```

$$n \leftarrow sh_5 \,\|\, sh_{0:4}$$
$$r \leftarrow ROTL_{64}((RS), n)$$
$$e \leftarrow me_5 \,\|\, me_{0:4}$$
$$m \leftarrow MASK(0, e)$$
$$RA \leftarrow r \,\&\, m$$

The contents of register RS are rotated$_{64}$ left SH bits. A mask is generated having 1-bits from bit 0 through bit ME and 0-bits elsewhere. The rotated data are ANDed with the generated mask and the result is placed into register RA.

This instruction is defined only for 64-bit implementations. Using it on a 32-bit implementation will cause the system illegal instruction error handler to be invoked.

Special Registers Altered

CR0   (if Rc=1)

Extended Mnemonics:

Examples of extended mnemonics for *Rotate Left Doubleword Immediate then Clear Right*:

Extended:	*Equivalent to:*
extldi Rx,Ry,n,b	rldicr Rx,Ry,b,n−1
sldi Rx,Ry,n	rldicr Rx,Ry,n,63−n
clrrdi Rx,Ry,n	rldicr Rx,Ry,0,63−n

Rotate Left Doubleword Immediate then Clear MD-form

rldic	RA,RS,SH,MB	(Rc=0)
rldic.	RA,RS,SH,MB	(Rc=1)

30	RS	RA	sh	mb	2	sh	Rc
0	6	11	16	21	27	30	31

$n \leftarrow sh_5 \parallel sh_{0:4}$
$r \leftarrow ROTL_{64}((RS), n)$
$b \leftarrow mb_5 \parallel mb_{0:4}$
$m \leftarrow MASK(b, \neg n)$
$RA \leftarrow r \& m$

The contents of register RS are rotated$_{64}$ left SH bits. A mask is generated having 1-bits from bit MB through bit 63−SH and 0-bits elsewhere. The rotated data are ANDed with the generated mask and the result is placed into register RA.

This instruction is defined only for 64-bit implementations. Using it on a 32-bit implementation will cause the system illegal instruction error handler to be invoked.

Special Registers Altered
```
CR0                                                      (if Rc=1)
```

Extended Mnemonics:

Example of extended mnemonics for *Rotate Left Doubleword Immediate then Clear*:

Extended:	*Equivalent to:*
clrlsldi Rx,Ry,b,n	rldic Rx,Ry,n,b−n

Programming Note

rldic can be used to clear the high-order *b* bits of the contents of a register and then shift the result left by *n* bits by setting SH=*n* and MB=*b*−*n*. It can be used to clear the high-order *n* bits of a register by setting SH=0 and MB=*n*.

Extended mnemonics are provided for both of these uses (the second devolves to *rldicl*): see Appendix C, "Assembler Extended Mnemonics," on page 215.

Rotate Left Word Immediate then AND with Mask   M-form

| rlwinm | RA,RS,SH,MB,ME | (Rc=0) |
| rlwinm. | RA,RS,SH,MB,ME | (Rc=1) |

[Power mnemonics: rlinm, rlinm.]

21	RS	RA	SH	MB	ME	Rc
0	6	11	16	21	26	31

```
n ← SH
r ← ROTL32((RS)32:63, n)
m ← MASK(MB+32, ME+32)
RA ← r & m
```

The contents of register RS are rotated$_{32}$ left SH bits. A mask is generated having 1-bits from bit MB+32 through bit ME+32 and 0-bits elsewhere. The rotated data are ANDed with the generated mask and the result is placed into register RA.

Special Registers Altered

```
CR0                                                            (if Rc=1)
```

Extended Mnemonics:

Examples of extended mnemonics for *Rotate Left Word Immediate then AND with Mask:*

Extended:		*Equivalent to:*	
extlwi	Rx,Ry,n,b	rlwinm	Rx,Ry,b,0,n−1
srwi	Rx,Ry,n	rlwinm	Rx,Ry,32−n,n,31
clrrwi	Rx,Ry,n	rlwinm	Rx,Ry,0,0,31−n

Rotate Left Doubleword then Clear Left   MDS-form

| rldcl | RA,RS,RB,MB | (Rc=0) |
| rldcl. | RA,RS,RB,MB | (Rc=1) |

30	RS	RA	RB	mb	8	Rc
0	6	11	16	21	27	31

```
n ← (RB)58:63
r ← ROTL64((RS), n)
b ← mb5 ‖ mb0:4
m ← MASK(b, 63)
RA ← r & m
```

Programming Note

Let RSL represent the low-order 32 bits of register RS, with the bits numbered from 0 through 31.

rlwinm can be used to extract an *n*-bit field that starts at bit position *b* in RSL, right-justified into the low-order 32 bits of register RA (clearing the remaining 32−*n* bits of the low-order 32 bits of RA), by setting SH=*b*+*n*, MB=32−*n*, and ME=31. It can be used to extract an *n*-bit field that starts at bit position *b* in RSL, left-justified into the low-order 32 bits of register RA (clearing the remaining 32−*n* bits of the low-order 32 bits of RA), by setting SH=*b*, MB = 0, and ME=*n*−1. It can be used to rotate the contents of the low-order 32 bits of a register left (right) by *n* bits by setting SH=*n* (32−*n*), MB=0, and ME=31. It can be used to shift the contents of the low-order 32 bits of a register right by *n* bits by setting SH=32−*n*, MB=*n*, and ME=31. It can be used to clear the high-order *b* bits of the low-order 32 bits of the contents of a register and then shift the result left by *n* bits by setting SH=*n*, MB=*b*−*n* and ME=31−*n*. It can be used to clear the low-order *n* bits of the low-order 32 bits of a register by setting SH=0, MB=0, and ME=31−*n*.

For all the uses given

above, the high-order 32 bits of register RA are cleared.

Extended mnemonics are provided for all of these uses: see Appendix C, "Assembler Extended Mnemonics," on page 215.

Programming Note

rldcl can be used to extract an n-bit field that starts at variable bit position b in register RS, right-justified into register RA (clearing the remaining $64-n$ bits of RA), by setting $RB_{58:63}=b+n$ and $MB=64-n$. It can be used to rotate the contents of a register left (right) by variable n bits by setting $RB_{58:63}=n$ $(64-n)$ and $MB=0$.

Extended mnemonics are provided for some of these uses: see Appendix C, "Assembler Extended Mnemonics," on page 215.

Programming Note

rldcr can be used to extract an n-bit field that starts at variable bit position b in register RS, left-justified into register RA (clearing the remaining $64-n$ bits of RA), by setting $RB_{58:63}=b$ and $ME=n-1$. It can be used to rotate the contents of a register left (right) by variable n bits by setting $RB_{58:63}=n$ $(64-n)$ and $ME=63$.

Extended mnemonics are

The contents of register RS are rotated$_{64}$ left the number of bits specified by $(RB)_{58:63}$. A mask is generated having 1-bits from bit MB through bit 63 and 0-bits elsewhere. The rotated data are ANDed with the generated mask and the result is placed into register RA.

This instruction is defined only for 64-bit implementations. Using it on a 32-bit implementation will cause the system illegal instruction error handler to be invoked.

Special Registers Altered

```
CR0                                                          (if Rc=1)
```

Extended Mnemonics:

Example of extended mnemonics for *Rotate Left Doubleword then Clear Left*:

Extended:	*Equivalent to:*
rotld Rx,Ry,Rz	rldcl Rx,Ry,Rz,0

Rotate Left Doubleword then Clear Right MDS-form

rldcr	RA,RS,RB,ME	(Rc=0)
rldcr.	RA,RS,RB,ME	(Rc=1)

30		RS	RA	RB	me	9	Rc
0	6	11	16	21		27	31

```
n ← (RB)58:63
r ← ROTL64((RS), n)
e ← me5 ‖ me0:4
m ← MASK(0, e)
RA ← r & m
```

The contents of register RS are rotated$_{64}$ left the number of bits specified by $(RB)_{58:63}$. A mask is generated having 1-bits from bit 0 through bit ME and 0-bits elsewhere. The rotated data are ANDed with the generated mask and the result is placed into register RA.

This instruction is defined only for 64-bit implementations. Using it on a 32-bit implementation will cause the system illegal instruction error handler to be invoked.

Special Registers Altered

```
CR0                                                          (if Rc=1)
```

provided for some of these uses (some devolve to *rldcl*): see Appendix C, "Assembler Extended Mnemonics," on page 215.

Programming Note

Let RSL represent the low-order 32 bits of register RS, with the bits numbered from 0 through 31.

rlwnm can be used to extract an *n*-bit field that starts at variable bit position *b* in RSL, right-justified into the low-order 32 bits of register RA (clearing the remaining 32−*n* bits of the low-order 32 bits of RA), by setting $RB_{59:63}=b+n$, MB=32−*n*, and ME=31. It can be used to extract an *n*-bit field that starts at variable bit position *b* in RSL, left-justified into the low-order 32 bits of register RA (clearing the remaining 32−*n* bits of the low-order 32 bits of RA), by setting $RB_{59:63}=b$, MB = 0, and ME=*n*−1. It can be used to rotate the contents of the low-order 32 bits of a register left (right) by variable *n* bits by setting $RB_{59:63}=n$ (32−*n*), MB=0, and ME=31.

For all the uses given above, the high-order 32 bits of register RA are cleared.

Extended mnemonics are provided for some of these uses: see Appendix C, "Assembler Extended

Rotate Left Word then AND with Mask M-form

| rlwnm | RA,RS,RB,MB,ME | (Rc=0) |
| rlwnm. | RA,RS,RB,MB,ME | (Rc=1) |

[Power mnemonics: rlnm, rlnm.]

23		RS		RA		RB		MB		ME		Rc
0		6		11		16		21		26		31

```
n ← (RB)59:63
r ← ROTL32((RS)32:63, n)
m ← MASK(MB+32, ME+32)
RA ← r & m
```

The contents of register RS are rotated$_{32}$ left the number of bits specified by $(RB)_{59:63}$. A mask is generated having 1-bits from bit MB+32 through bit ME+32 and 0-bits elsewhere. The rotated data are ANDed with the generated mask and the result is placed into register RA.

Special Registers Altered

```
CRO                                        (if Rc=1)
```

Extended Mnemonics:

Example of extended mnemonics for *Rotate Left Word then AND with Mask:*

| *Extended:* | *Equivalent to:* |
| rotlw   Rx,Ry,Rz | rlwnm   Rx,Ry,Rz,0,31 |

Rotate Left Doubleword Immediate then Mask Insert MD-form

| rldimi | RA,RS,SH,MB | (Rc=0) |
| rldimi. | RA,RS,SH,MB | (Rc=1) |

30		RS		RA		sh		mb		3		sh	Rc
0		6		11		16		21		27		30	31

```
n ← sh5 || sh0:4
r ← ROTL64((RS), n)
b ← mb5 || mb0:4
m ← MASK(b, ¬n)
RA ← r&m | (RA)&¬m
```

The contents of register RS are rotated$_{64}$ left SH bits. A mask is generated having 1-bits from bit MB through bit 63−SH and 0-bits else-

Mnemonics," on page 215.

Programming Note

rldimi can be used to insert an *n*-bit field that is right-justified in register RS into register RA starting at bit position *b* by setting SH=64–(*b+n*) and MB=*b*.

An extended mnemonic is provided for this use: see Appendix C, "Assembler Extended Mnemonics," on page 215.

Programming Note

Let RAL represent the low-order 32 bits of register RA, with the bits numbered from 0 through 31.

rlwimi can be used to insert an *n*-bit field that is left-justified in the low-order 32 bits of register RS into RAL starting at bit position *b* by setting SH=32–*b*, MB=*b*, and ME=(*b+n*)–1. It can be used to insert an *n*-bit field that is right-justified in the low-order 32 bits of register RS into RAL starting at bit position *b* by setting SH=32–(*b+n*), MB=*b*, and ME=(*b+n*)–1.

Extended mnemonics are provided for both of these uses: see Appendix C, "Assembler Extended Mnemonics," on page 215.

where. The rotated data are inserted into register RA under control of the generated mask.

This instruction is defined only for 64-bit implementations. Using it on a 32-bit implementation will cause the system illegal instruction error handler to be invoked.

Special Registers Altered

```
    CR0                                                      (if Rc=1)
```

Extended Mnemonics:

Example of extended mnemonics for *Rotate Left Doubleword Immediate then Mask Insert*:

Extended:	*Equivalent to:*
insrdi Rx,Ry,n,b	rldimi Rx,Ry,64–(b+n),b

Rotate Left Word Immediate then Mask Insert M-form

| rlwimi | RA,RS,SH,MB,ME | (Rc=0) |
| rlwimi. | RA,RS,SH,MB,ME | (Rc=1) |

[Power mnemonics: rlimi, rlimi.]

20	RS	RA	SH	MB	ME	Rc
0	6	11	16	21	26	31

```
n ← SH
r ← ROTL_32((RS)_{32:63}, n)
m ← MASK(MB+32, ME+32)
RA ← r&m | (RA)&¬m
```

The contents of register RS are rotated$_{32}$ left SH bits. A mask is generated having 1-bits from bit MB+32 through bit ME+32 and 0-bits elsewhere. The rotated data are inserted into register RA under control of the generated mask.

Special Registers Altered

```
    CR0                                                      (if Rc=1)
```

Extended Mnemonics:

Example of extended mnemonics for *Rotate Left Word Immediate then Mask Insert*:

Extended:	Equivalent to:
inslwi Rx,Ry,n,b	rlwimi Rx,Ry,32−b,b,b+n−1

Programming Note

Multiple-precision shifts
can be programmed as
shown in Appendix E.2,
"Multiple-Precision
Shifts," on page 256.

Fixed-Point Shift Instructions

The instructions in this section perform left and right shifts.

Extended Mnemonics for Shifts

Immediate-form logical (unsigned) shift operations are obtained by specifying appropriate masks and shift values for certain *Rotate* instructions. A set of extended mnemonics is provided to make coding of such shifts simpler and easier to understand. Some of these are shown as examples with the *Rotate* instructions. See Appendix C, "Assembler Extended Mnemonics," on page 215 for additional extended mnemonics.

Shift Left Doubleword X-form

sld	RA,RS,RB	(Rc=0)
sld.	RA,RS,RB	(Rc=1)

31	RS	RA	RB	27	Rc
0	6	11	16	21	31

```
n ← (RB)₅₈:₆₃
r ← ROTL₆₄((RS), n)
if (RB)₅₇ = 0 then
    m ← MASK(0, 63-n)
else m ← ⁶⁴0
RA ← r & m
```

The contents of register RS are shifted left the number of bits specified by $(RB)_{57:63}$. Bits shifted out of position 0 are lost. Zeros are supplied to the vacated positions on the right. The result is placed into register RA. Shift amounts from 64 to 127 give a zero result.

This instruction is defined only for 64-bit implementations. Using it on a 32-bit implementation will cause the system illegal instruction error handler to be invoked.

Special Registers Altered

```
CRO                                          (if Rc=1)
```

Shift Left Word X-form

| slw | RA,RS,RB | (Rc=0) |
| slw. | RA,RS,RB | (Rc=1) |

[Power mnemonics: sl, sl.]

31	RS	RA	RB	24	Rc
0	6	11	16	21	31

```
n ← (RB)59:63
r ← ROTL32((RS)32:63, n)
if (RB)58 = 0 then
      m ← MASK(32, 63-n)
else m ← 640
RA ← r & m
```

The contents of the low-order 32 bits of register RS are shifted left the number of bits specified by $(RB)_{58:63}$. Bits shifted out of position 32 are lost. Zeros are supplied to the vacated positions on the right. The 32-bit result is placed into $RA_{32:63}$. $RA_{0:31}$ are set to zero. Shift amounts from 32 to 63 give a zero result.

Special Registers Altered

        CR0   (if Rc=1)

Shift Right Doubleword X-form

| srd | RA,RS,RB | (Rc=0) |
| srd. | RA,RS,RB | (Rc=1) |

31	RS	RA	RB	539	Rc
0	6	11	16	21	31

```
n ← (RB)58:63
r ← ROTL64((RS), 64-n)
if (RB)57 = 0 then
      m ← MASK(n, 63)
else m ← 640
RA ← r & m
```

The contents of register RS are shifted right the number of bits specified by $(RB)_{57:63}$. Bits shifted out of position 63 are lost. Zeros are supplied to the vacated positions on the left. The result is placed into register RA. Shift amounts from 64 to 127 give a zero result.

This instruction is defined only for 64-bit implementations. Using it on a 32-bit implementation will cause the system illegal instruction error handler to be invoked.

Special Registers Altered

```
CR0                                                          (if Rc=1)
```

Shift Right Word X-form

srw	RA,RS,RB	(Rc=0)
srw.	RA,RS,RB	(Rc=1)

[Power mnemonics: sr, sr.]

31	RS	RA	RB	536	Rc
0	6	11	16	21	31

```
n ← (RB)59:63
r ← ROTL32((RS)32:63, 64-n)
if (RB)58 = 0 then
    m ← MASK(n+32, 63)
else m ← 640
RA ← r & m
```

The contents of the low-order 32 bits of register RS are shifted right the number of bits specified by $(RB)_{58:63}$. Bits shifted out of position 63 are lost. Zeros are supplied to the vacated positions on the left. The 32-bit result is placed into $RA_{32:63}$. $RA_{0:31}$ are set to zero. Shift amounts from 32 to 63 give a zero result.

Special Registers Altered

```
CR0                                                          (if Rc=1)
```

Shift Right Algebraic Doubleword Immediate XS-form

Programming Note

Any *Shift Right Algebraic* instruction, followed by **addze**, can be used to divide quickly by 2^N. The setting of the CA bit by the *Shift Right Algebraic* instructions is independent of mode.

| sradi | RA,RS,SH | (Rc=0) |
| sradi. | RA,RS,SH | (Rc=1) |

31	RS	RA	sh	413	sh	Rc
0	6	11	16	21	30	31

```
n ← sh₅ ∥ sh₀:₄
r ← ROTL₆₄((RS), 64-n)
m ← MASK(n, 63)
s ← (RS)₀
RA ← r&m | (⁶⁴s)&¬m
CA ← s & ((r&¬m)≠0)
```

$$n \leftarrow sh_5 \parallel sh_{0:4}$$
$$r \leftarrow ROTL_{64}((RS), 64-n)$$
$$m \leftarrow MASK(n, 63)$$
$$s \leftarrow (RS)_0$$
$$RA \leftarrow r\&m \mid (^{64}s)\&\neg m$$
$$CA \leftarrow s \& ((r\&\neg m)\neq0)$$

The contents of register RS are shifted right SH bits. Bits shifted out of position 63 are lost. Bit 0 of RS is replicated to fill the vacated positions on the left. The result is placed into register RA. CA is set to 1 if (RS) is negative and any 1-bits are shifted out of position 63; otherwise CA is set to 0. A shift amount of zero causes RA to be set equal to (RS), and CA to be set to 0.

This instruction is defined only for 64-bit implementations. Using it on a 32-bit implementation will cause the system illegal instruction error handler to be invoked.

Special Registers Altered

```
CA
CR0                                        (if Rc=1)
```

Shift Right Algebraic Word Immediate X-form

| srawi | RA,RS,SH | (Rc=0) |
| srawi. | RA,RS,SH | (Rc=1) |

[Power mnemonics: srai, srai.]

31	RS	RA	SH	824	Rc
0	6	11	16	21	31

$$n \leftarrow SH$$
$$r \leftarrow ROTL_{32}((RS)_{32:63}, 64-n)$$
$$m \leftarrow MASK(n+32, 63)$$
$$s \leftarrow (RS)_{32}$$
$$RA \leftarrow r\&m \mid (^{64}s)\&\neg m$$
$$CA \leftarrow s \& ((r\&\neg m)_{32:63}\neq0)$$

The contents of the low-order 32 bits of register RS are shifted right SH bits. Bits shifted out of position 63 are lost. Bit 32 of RS is replicated to fill the vacated positions on the left. The 32-bit result is placed into $RA_{32:63}$. Bit 32 of RS is replicated to fill $RA_{0:31}$. CA is set to 1 if the low-order 32 bits of (RS) contain a negative number and any 1-bits are shifted out of position 63; otherwise CA is set to 0. A shift amount of zero causes RA to receive $EXTS((RS)_{32:63})$, and CA to be set to 0.

Special Registers Altered

```
CA
CRO                                              (if Rc=1)
```

Shift Right Algebraic Doubleword X-form

srad	RA,RS,RB	(Rc=0)
srad.	RA,RS,RB	(Rc=1)

31	RS	RA	RB	794	Rc
0	6	11	16	21	31

```
n ← (RB)58:63
r ← ROTL64((RS), 64-n)
if (RB)57 = 0 then
      m ← MASK(n, 63)
else m ← 640
s ← (RS)0
RA ← r&m | (64s)&¬m
CA ← s & ((r&¬m)≠0)
```

The contents of register RS are shifted right the number of bits specified by $(RB)_{57:63}$. Bits shifted out of position 63 are lost. Bit 0 of RS is replicated to fill the vacated positions on the left. The result is placed into register RA. CA is set to 1 if (RS) is negative and any 1-bits are shifted out of position 63; otherwise CA is set to 0. A shift amount of zero causes RA to be set equal to (RS), and CA to be set to 0. Shift amounts from 64 to 127 give a result of 64 sign bits in RA, and cause CA to receive the sign bit of (RS).

This instruction is defined only for 64-bit implementations. Using it on a 32-bit implementation will cause the system illegal instruction error handler to be invoked.

Special Registers Altered

```
CA
CRO                                              (if Rc=1)
```

Shift Right Algebraic Word X-form

| sraw | RA,RS,RB | (Rc=0) |
| sraw. | RA,RS,RB | (Rc=1) |

[Power mnemonics: sra, sra.]

31	RS	RA	RB	792	Rc
0	6	11	16	21	31

```
n ← (RB)59:63
r ← ROTL32((RS)32:63, 64-n)
if (RB)58 = 0 then
      m ← MASK(n+32, 63)
else m ← 640
s ← (RS)32
RA ← r&m | (64s)&¬m
CA ← s & ((r&¬m)32:63≠0)
```

The contents of the low-order 32 bits of register RS are shifted right the number of bits specified by $(RB)_{58:63}$. Bits shifted out of position 63 are lost. Bit 32 of RS is replicated to fill the vacated positions on the left. The 32-bit result is placed into $RA_{32:63}$. Bit 32 of RS is replicated to fill $RA_{0:31}$. CA is set to 1 if the low-order 32 bits of (RS) contain a negative number and any 1-bits are shifted out of position 63; otherwise CA is set to 0. A shift amount of zero causes RA to receive $EXTS((RS)_{32:63})$, and CA to be set to 0. Shift amounts from 32 to 63 give a result of 64 sign bits, and cause CA to receive the sign bit of $(RS)_{32:63}$.

Special Registers Altered

```
CA
CRO                                            (if Rc=1)
```

3.3.14 Move to/from System Register Instructions

Extended Mnemonics:

A set of extended mnemonics is provided for the *mtspr* and *mfspr* instructions so that they can be coded with the SPR name as part of the mnemonic rather than as a numeric operand. Some of these are shown as examples with the two instructions. See Appendix C, "Assembler Extended Mnemonics," on page 215 for additional extended mnemonics.

Move To Special Purpose Register XFX-form

mtspr   SPR,RS

31	RS	spr	467	/
0	6	11	21	31

Compiler and Assembler Note

For the *mtspr* and *mfspr* instructions, the SPR number coded in assembler language does not appear directly as a 10-bit binary number in the instruction. The number coded is split into two 5-bit halves that are reversed in the instruction, with the high-order 5 bits appearing in bits 16:20 of the instruction and the low-order 5 bits in bits 11:15. This maintains compatibility with POWER SPR encodings, in which these two instructions have only a 5-bit SPR field occupying bits 11:15.

Compatibility Note

For a discussion of POWER compatibility with respect to SPR numbers not shown in the instruction descriptions for *mtspr* and *mfspr*, please refer to Appendix G, "Incompatibilities with the POWER Architecture," on page 271. For compatibility with future versions of this architecture, only SPR numbers discussed in these instruction descriptions should be used.

$n \leftarrow spr_{5:9} \parallel spr_{0:4}$
if length(SPREG(n)) = 64 then
    SPREG(n) $\leftarrow$ (RS)
else
    SPREG(n) $\leftarrow$ (RS)$_{32:63\{0:31\}}$

The SPR field denotes a Special Purpose Register, encoded as shown in the table below. The contents of register RS are placed into the designated Special Purpose Register. For Special Purpose Registers that are 32 bits long, the low-order 32 bits of RS are placed into the SPR.

decimal	SPR*		Register name
	$spr_{5:9}$	$spr_{0:4}$	
1	00000	00001	XER
8	00000	01000	LR
9	00000	01001	CTR

*Note that the order of the two 5-bit halves of the SPR number is reversed.

If the SPR field contains any value other than one of the values shown above then one of the following occurs.

- The system illegal instruction error handler is invoked.

- The system privileged instruction error handler is invoked.

- The results are boundedly undefined.

A complete description of this instruction can be found in Book III, Section 3.4.1, "Move to/from System Register Instructions," on page 384.

Special Registers Altered
    See above

Extended Mnemonics:

Examples of extended mnemonics for *Move To Special Purpose Register*:

Extended:	*Equivalent to:*
mtxer Rx	mtspr 1,Rx
mtlr Rx	mtspr 8,Rx
mtctr Rx	mtspr 9,Rx

Move From Special Purpose Register XFX-form

mfspr   RT,SPR

31	RT	spr	339	/
0	6	11	21	31

```
n ← spr5:9 ‖ spr0:4
if length(SPREG(n)) = 64 then
   RT ← SPREG(n)
else
   RT ← 320 ‖ SPREG(n)
```

The SPR field denotes a Special Purpose Register, encoded as shown in the table below. The contents of the designated Special Purpose Register are placed into register RT. For Special Purpose Registers that are 32 bits long, the low-order 32 bits of RT receive the contents of the Special Purpose Register and the high-order 32 bits of RT are set to zero.

decimal	SPR* $spr_{5:9}$ $spr_{0:4}$		Register name
1	00000	00001	XER
8	00000	01000	LR
9	00000	01001	CTR

*Note that the order of the two 5-bit halves of the SPR number is reversed.

If the SPR field contains any value other than one of the values shown above then one of the following occurs.

■ The system illegal instruction error handler is invoked.

■ The system privileged instruction error handler is invoked.

■ The results are boundedly undefined.

A complete description of this instruction can be found in Book III, Section 3.4.1, "Move to/from System Register Instructions," on page 384.

Compiler/Assembler/ Compatibility Notes

See the Notes that appear with *mtspr* in "Move To Special Purpose Register XFX-form," on page 129.

Special Registers Altered
```
None
```

Extended Mnemonics:
Examples of extended mnemonics for *Move From Special Purpose Register*:

Extended:		*Equivalent to:*
mfxer	Rx	mfspr Rx,1
mflr	Rx	mfspr Rx,8
mfctr	Rx	mfspr Rx,9

Move To Condition Register Fields XFX-form

mtcrf   FXM,RS

31	RS	/	FXM	/	144	/
0	6	11	12	20	21	31

```
mask ← 4(FXM0) || 4(FXM1) || ... 4(FXM7)
CR ← ((RS)32:63 & mask) | (CR & ¬mask)
```

The contents of bits 32:63 of register RS are placed into the Condition Register under control of the field mask specified by FXM. The field mask identifies the 4-bit fields affected. Let i be an integer in the range 0–7. If FXM(i) = 1 then CR field i (CR bits $4{\times}i$ through $4{\times}i{+}3$) is set to the contents of the corresponding field of the low-order 32 bits of RS.

Programming Note

Updating a proper subset of the eight fields of the Condition Register may result in substantially poorer performance on some implementations than updating all of the fields.

Special Registers Altered
```
CR fields selected by mask
```

Move to Condition Register from XER X-form

mcrxr   BF

31	BF	//	///	///	512	/
0	6	9	11	16	21	31

$CR_{4 \times BF:4 \times BF+3} \leftarrow XER_{0:3}$
$XER_{0:3} \leftarrow 0b0000$

The contents of $XER_{0:3}$ are copied into the Condition Register field designated by BF. $XER_{0:3}$ are set to zero.

Special Registers Altered

CR $XER_{0:3}$

Move From Condition Register X-form

mfcr   RT

31	RT	///	///	19	/
0	6	11	16	21	31

$RT \leftarrow {}^{32}0 \parallel CR$

The contents of the Condition Register are placed into $RT_{32:63}$. $RT_{0:31}$ are set to 0.

Special Registers Altered

None

Floating-Point Processor

4.1 Floating-Point Processor Overview

This chapter describes the registers and instructions that make up the Floating-Point Processor facility. Section 4.2, "Floating-Point Processor Registers," on page 135 describes the registers associated with the Floating-Point Processor. Section 4.6, "Floating-Point Processor Instructions," on page 167 describes the instructions associated with the Floating-Point Processor.

This architecture specifies that the processor implement a floating-point system as defined in ANSI/IEEE Standard 754-1985, "IEEE Standard for Binary Floating-Point Arithmetic" (hereafter referred to as "the IEEE standard"), but requires software support in order to conform fully with that standard. That standard defines certain required "operations" (addition, subtraction, etc.); the term "floating-point operation" is used in this chapter to refer to one of these required operations, or to the operation performed by one of the *Multiply-Add* or *Reciprocal Estimate* instructions. All floating-point operations conform to that standard, except if software sets the Floating-Point Non-IEEE Mode (NI) bit in the Floating-Point Status and Control Register to 1 (see page 140), in which case floating-point operations do not necessarily conform to that standard.

Instructions are provided to perform arithmetic, rounding, conversion, comparison, and other operations in floating-point registers; to move floating-point data between storage and these registers; and to manipulate the Floating-Point Status and Control Register explicitly.

These instructions are divided into two categories.

■ computational instructions

The computational instructions are those that perform addition, subtraction, multiplication, division, extracting the square root, rounding, conversion, comparison, and combinations of these operations. These instructions provide the floating-point operations. They place status information into the Floating-Point Status and Control Register. They are the instructions described in Sections 4.6.5 through 4.6.7 and Appendix A.1.2.

■ non-computational instructions

The non-computational instructions are those that perform loads and stores, move the contents of a floating-point register to another floating-point register possibly altering the sign, manipulate the Floating-Point Status and Control Register explicitly, and select the value from one of two floating-point registers based on the value in a third floating-point register. The operations performed by these instructions are not considered floating-point operations. With the exception of the instructions that manipulate the Floating-Point Status and Control Register explicitly, they do not alter the Floating-Point Status and Control Register. They are the instructions described in Sections 4.6.2 through 4.6.4, 4.6.8, and Appendix A.1.3.

A floating-point number consists of a signed exponent and a signed significand. The quantity expressed by this number is the product of the significand and the number $2^{exponent}$. Encodings are provided in the data format to represent finite numeric values, ± Infinity, and values that are "Not a Number" (NaN). Operations involving infinities produce results obeying traditional mathematical conventions. NaNs have no mathematical interpretation. Their encoding permits a variable diagnostic information field. They may be used to indicate such things as uninitialized variables and can be produced by certain invalid operations.

There is one class of exceptional events that occur during instruction execution that is unique to the Floating-Point Processor: the Floating-Point Exception. Floating-point exceptions are signaled with bits set in the Floating-Point Status and Control Register (FPSCR). They can cause the system floating-point enabled exception error handler to be invoked, precisely or imprecisely, if the proper control bits are set.

Floating-Point Exceptions

The following floating-point exceptions are detected by the processor:

- Invalid Operation Exception   (VX)
    - SNaN   (VXSNAN)
    - Infinity − Infinity   (VXISI)
    - Infinity ÷ Infinity   (VXIDI)
    - Zero ÷ Zero   (VXZDZ)
    - Infinity × Zero   (VXIMZ)
    - Invalid Compare   (VXVC)
    - Software Request   (VXSOFT)
    - Invalid Square Root   (VXSQRT)
    - Invalid Integer Convert   (VXCVI)
- Zero Divide Exception   (ZX)
- Overflow Exception   (OX)
- Underflow Exception   (UX)
- Inexact Exception(XX)

Each floating-point exception, and each category of Invalid Operation Exception, has an exception bit in the FPSCR. In addition, each floating-point exception has a corresponding enable bit in the FPSCR. See Section 4.2.2, "Floating-Point Status and Control Register," on page 137, for a description of these exception and enable bits, and Section 4.4, "Floating-Point Exceptions," on page 150, for a detailed discussion of floating-point exceptions, including the effects of the enable bits.

4.2 Floating-Point Processor Registers

4.2.1 Floating-Point Registers

Implementations of this architecture provide 32 floating-point registers (FPRs). The floating-point instruction formats provide 5-bit fields for specifying the FPRs to be used in the execution of the instruction. The FPRs are numbered 0–31. See Figure 23 on page 136.

Each FPR contains 64 bits that support the floating-point double format. Every instruction that interprets the contents of an FPR as a floating-point value uses the floating-point double format for this interpretation.

The computational instructions, and the *Move* and *Select* instructions, operate on data located in FPRs and, with the exception of the *Compare* instructions, place the result value into an FPR and optionally place status information into the Condition Register.

Load and store double instructions are provided that transfer 64 bits of data between storage and the FPRs with no conversion. Load single instructions are provided to transfer and convert floating-point values in floating-point single format from storage to the same value in floating-point double format in the FPRs. Store single instructions are provided to transfer and convert floating-point values in floating-point double format from the FPRs to the same value in floating-point single format in storage.

Instructions are provided that manipulate the Floating-Point Status and Control Register and the Condition Register explicitly. Some of these instructions copy data from an FPR to the Floating-Point Status and Control Register or vice versa.

The computational instructions and the *Select* instruction accept values from the FPRs in double format. For single-precision arithmetic instructions, all input values must be representable in single format. If they are not, the result placed into the target FPR, and the setting of status bits in the FPSCR and in the Condition Register (if Rc=1) are undefined.

The arithmetic, rounding, and conversion instructions produce intermediate results that may be regarded as being infinitely precise. After normalization or denormalization, if the infinitely precise intermediate result is not representable in the destination format (either 32-bit or 64-bit) then it is rounded. The final result is then placed into the FPR in the double format.

FPR 00
FPR 01
...
FPR 30
FPR 31

0   63

Figure 23. **Floating-point registers**

4.2.2 Floating-Point Status and Control Register

The Floating-Point Status and Control Register (FPSCR) controls the handling of floating-point exceptions and records status resulting from the floating-point operations. Bits 0:23 are status bits. Bits 24:31 are control bits.

The exception bits in the FPSCR (bits 0:12, 21:23) are sticky, with the exception of Floating-Point Enabled Exception Summary (FEX) and Floating-Point Invalid Operation Exception Summary (VX). That is, once set, the sticky bits remain set until they are cleared by an *mcrfs*, *mtfsfi*, *mtfsf*, or *mtfsb0* instruction.

FEX and VX are simply the ORs of other FPSCR bits. Therefore these two bits are not listed among the FPSCR bits affected by the various instructions.

FPCSR
0   31

Figure 24. **Floating-Point Status and Control Register**

The format of the FPSCR is:

Bit(s) Description

0 *Floating-Point Exception Summary* (FX)
Every floating-point instruction, except *mtfsfi* and *mtfsf*, implicitly sets FPSCR_{FX} to 1 if that instruction causes any of the floating-point exception bits in the FPSCR to change from 0 to 1. *mcrfs*, *mtfsfi*, *mtfsf*, *mtfsb0*, and *mtfsb1* can alter FPSCR_{FX} explicitly.

1 *Floating-Point Enabled Exception Summary* (FEX)
This bit indicates whether any enabled exceptions have occurred. It is the OR of all the floating-point exception bits masked by their respective enable bits. *mcrfs*, *mtfsfi*, *mtfsf*, *mtfsb0*, and *mtfsb1* cannot alter FPSCR_{FEX} explicitly.

2 *Floating-Point Invalid Operation Exception Summary* (VX)
This bit indicates whether any invalid operation exceptions have occurred. It is the OR of all the Invalid Operation exception bits. *mcrfs*, *mtfsfi*, *mtfsf*, *mtfsb0*, and *mtfsb1* cannot alter FPSCR_{VX} explicitly.

3   *Floating-Point Overflow Exception* (OX)
        See Section 4.4.3, "Overflow Exception," on page 159.

4   *Floating-Point Underflow Exception* (UX)
        See Section 4.4.4, "Underflow Exception," on page 160.

5   *Floating-Point Zero Divide Exception* (ZX)
        See Section 4.4.2, "Zero Divide Exception," on page 158.

6   *Floating-Point Inexact Exception* (XX)
        See Section 4.4.5, "Inexact Exception," on page 162.

        $FPSCR_{XX}$ is a sticky version of $FPSCR_{FI}$ (see below). Thus the
        following rules completely describe how $FPSCR_{XX}$ is set by a
        given instruction.

        ■ If the instruction affects $FPSCR_{FI}$, the new value of $FPSCR_{XX}$
          is obtained by ORing the old value of $FPSCR_{XX}$ with the new
          value of $FPSCR_{FI}$.

        ■ If the instruction does not affect $FPSCR_{FI}$, the value of
          $FPSCR_{XX}$ is unchanged.

7   *Floating-Point Invalid Operation Exception (SNaN)* (VXSNAN)
        See Section 4.4.1, "Invalid Operation Exception," on page 155.

8   *Floating-Point Invalid Operation Exception ($\infty - \infty$)* (VXISI)
        See Section 4.4.1, "Invalid Operation Exception," on page 155.

9   *Floating-Point Invalid Operation Exception ($\infty \div \infty$)* (VXIDI)
        See Section 4.4.1, "Invalid Operation Exception," on page 155.

10   *Floating-Point Invalid Operation Exception (0 ÷ 0)* (VXZDZ)
        See Section 4.4.1, "Invalid Operation Exception," on page 155.

11   *Floating-Point Invalid Operation Exception ($\infty \times 0$)* (VXIMZ)
        See Section 4.4.1, "Invalid Operation Exception," on page 155.

12   *Floating-Point Invalid Operation Exception (Invalid Compare)*
        (VXVC)
        See Section 4.4.1, "Invalid Operation Exception," on page 155.

13   *Floating-Point Fraction Rounded* (FR)
        The last *Arithmetic* or *Rounding and Conversion* instruction that
        rounded the intermediate result incremented the fraction. See Sec-
        tion 4.3.6, "Rounding," on page 149. This bit is not sticky.

14   *Floating-Point Fraction Inexact* (FI)
        The last *Arithmetic* or *Rounding and Conversion* instruction either
        rounded the intermediate result (producing an inexact fraction) or

caused a disabled Overflow Exception. See Section 4.3.6, "Rounding," on page 149. This bit is not sticky.

See the definition of $FPSCR_{XX}$, above, regarding the relationship between $FPSCR_{FI}$ and $FPSCR_{XX}$.

15:19 *Floating-Point Result Flags* (FPRF)
This field is set as described below. For arithmetic, rounding, and conversion instructions, the field is set based on the result placed into the target register, except that if any portion of the result is undefined then the value placed into FPRF is undefined.

15 *Floating-Point Result Class Descriptor* (C)
Arithmetic, rounding, and conversion instructions may set this bit with the FPCC bits, to indicate the class of the result as shown in Figure 25 on page 140.

16:19 *Floating-Point Condition Code* (FPCC)
Floating-point *Compare* instructions set one of the FPCC bits to 1 and the other three FPCC bits to 0. Arithmetic, rounding, and conversion instructions may set the FPCC bits with the C bit, to indicate the class of the result as shown in Figure 25 on page 140. Note that in this case the high-order three bits of the FPCC retain their relational significance indicating that the value is less than, greater than, or equal to zero.

16 *Floating-Point Less Than or Negative* (FL or <)

17 *Floating-Point Greater Than or Positive* (FG or >)

18 *Floating-Point Equal or Zero* (FE or =)

19 *Floating-Point Unordered or NaN* (FU or ?)

20 Reserved

21 *Floating-Point Invalid Operation Exception (Software Request)* (VXSOFT)
This bit can be altered only by *mcrfs, mtfsfi, mtfsf, mtfsb0,* or *mtfsb1.* See Section 4.4.1, "Invalid Operation Exception," on page 155.

22 *Floating-Point Invalid Operation Exception (Invalid Square Root)* (VXSQRT)
See Section 4.4.1, "Invalid Operation Exception," on page 155.

23 *Floating-Point Invalid Operation Exception (Invalid Integer Convert)* (VXCVI)
See Section 4.4.1, "Invalid Operation Exception," on page 155.

Programming Note

If the implementation does not support the *Floating Square Root* instruction or the *Floating Reciprocal Square Root Estimate* instruction, software can simulate the instruction and set $FPSCR_{VXSQRT}$ to reflect the exception.

Result Flags					Result Value Class
C	<	>	=	?	
1	0	0	0	1	Quiet NaN
0	1	0	0	1	–Infinity
0	1	0	0	0	–Normalized Number
1	1	0	0	0	–Denormalized Number
1	0	0	1	0	–Zero
0	0	0	1	0	+Zero
1	0	1	0	0	+Denormalized Number
0	0	1	0	0	+Normalized Number
0	0	1	0	1	+Infinity

Figure 25. **Floating-Point Result Flags**

24   *Floating-Point Invalid Operation Exception Enable* (VE)
See Section 4.4.1, "Invalid Operation Exception," on page 155.

25   *Floating-Point Overflow Exception Enable* (OE)
See Section 4.4.3, "Overflow Exception," on page 159.

26   *Floating-Point Underflow Exception Enable* (UE)
See Section 4.4.4, "Underflow Exception," on page 160.

27   *Floating-Point Zero Divide Exception Enable* (ZE)
See Section 4.4.2, "Zero Divide Exception," on page 158.

28   *Floating-Point Inexact Exception Enable* (XE)
See Section 4.4.5, "Inexact Exception," on page 162.

29   *Floating-Point Non-IEEE Mode* (NI)
If this bit is set to 1, the remaining FPSCR bits may have meanings other than those given in this document, and the results of floating-point operations need not conform to the IEEE standard. If the IEEE-conforming result of a floating-point operation would be a denormalized number, the result of that operation is 0 (with the same sign as the denormalized number) if $FPSCR_{NI}=1$ and other requirements specified in the Book IV, *PowerPC Implementation*

Features for the implementation are met. The other effects of setting this bit to 1 are described in Book IV and may differ between implementations.

30:31 *Floating-Point Rounding Control* (RN)
See Section 4.3.6, "Rounding," on page 149.

00   Round to Nearest

01   Round toward Zero

10   Round toward +Infinity

11   Round toward –Infinity

4.3 Floating-Point Data

4.3.1 Data Format

This architecture defines the representation of a floating-point value in two different binary fixed-length formats. The format may be a 32-bit single format for a single-precision value or a 64-bit double format for a double-precision value. The single format may be used for data in storage. The double format may be used for data in storage and for data in floating-point registers.

The lengths of the exponent and the fraction fields differ between these two formats. The structure of the single and double formats is shown below:

Figure 26. **Floating-point single format**

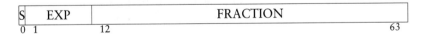

Figure 27. **Floating-point double format**

	Format	
	Single	Double
Exponent Bias	+127	+1023
Maximum Exponent	+127	+1023
Minimum Exponent	−126	−1022
Widths (bits)		
Format	32	64
Sign	1	1
Exponent	8	11
Fraction	23	52
Significand	24	53

Figure 28.   **IEEE floating-point fields**

Values in floating-point format are composed of three fields:

S   sign bit

EXP   exponent+bias

FRACTION   fraction

If only a portion of a floating-point data item in storage is accessed, such as with a load or store instruction for a byte or halfword (or word in the case of floating-point double format), the value affected will depend on whether the PowerPC system is operating with Big-Endian byte order (the default), or Little-Endian byte order. See Appendix D, "Little-Endian Byte Ordering," on page 233.

Representation of numeric values in the floating-point formats consists of a sign bit (S), a biased exponent (EXP), and the fraction portion FRACTION of the significand. The significand consists of a leading implied bit concatenated on the right with the FRACTION. This leading implied bit is 1 for normalized numbers and 0 for denormalized numbers and is located in the unit bit position (i.e., the first bit to the left of the binary point). Values representable within the two floating-point formats can be specified by the parameters listed in Figure 28 on page 142.

The architecture requires that the FPRs of the Floating-Point Processor support the floating-point double format only.

4.3.2 Value Representation

This architecture defines numeric and nonnumeric values representable within each of the two supported formats. The numeric values are approximations to the real numbers and include the normalized numbers, denormalized numbers, and zero values. The nonnumeric values representable are the infinities and the Not a Numbers (NaNs). The infinities are adjoined to the real numbers, but are not numbers themselves, and the standard rules of arithmetic do not hold when they are used in an operation. They are related to the real numbers by order alone. It is possible, however, to define restricted operations among numbers and infinities as defined below. The relative location on the real number line for each of the defined entities is shown in Figure 29.

Figure 29.   **Approximation to real numbers**

The NaNs are not related to the numeric values or infinities by order or value but are encodings used to convey diagnostic information such as the representation of uninitialized variables.

The following is a description of the different floating-point values defined in the architecture:

Binary floating-point numbers
Machine representable values used as approximations to real numbers. Three categories of numbers are supported: normalized numbers, denormalized numbers, and zero values.

Normalized numbers (± NOR)
These are values that have a biased exponent value in the range:

   1 to 254 in single format

   1 to 2046 in double format

They are values in which the implied unit bit is 1. Normalized numbers are interpreted as follows:

$$NOR = (-1)^s \times 2^E \times (1.\text{fraction})$$

where s is the sign, E is the unbiased exponent, and 1.fraction is the significand, which is composed of a leading unit bit (implied bit) and a fraction part.

The ranges covered by the magnitude (M) of a normalized floating-point number are approximately equal to:

Single Format:

$$1.2 \times 10^{-38} \leq M \leq 3.4 \times 10^{38}$$

Double Format:

$$2.2 \times 10^{-308} \leq M \leq 1.8 \times 10^{308}$$

Zero values $(\pm\,0)$

These are values that have a biased exponent value of zero and a fraction value of zero. Zeros can have a positive or negative sign. The sign of zero is ignored by comparison operations (i.e., comparison regards +0 as equal to −0).

Denormalized numbers $(\pm\,\text{DEN})$

These are values that have a biased exponent value of zero and a nonzero fraction value. They are nonzero numbers smaller in magnitude than the representable normalized numbers. They are values in which the implied unit bit is 0. Denormalized numbers are interpreted as follows:

$$DEN = (-1)^s \times 2^{\text{Emin}} \times (0.\text{fraction})$$

where Emin is the minimum representable exponent value (−126 for single-precision, −1022 for double-precision).

Infinities $(\pm\,\infty)$

These are values that have the maximum biased exponent value:

255 in the single format

2047 in the double format

and a zero fraction value. They are used to approximate values greater in magnitude than the maximum normalized value.

Infinity arithmetic is defined as the limiting case of real arithmetic, with restricted operations defined among numbers and infinities. Infinities and the real numbers can be related by ordering in the affine sense:

$-\infty <$ every finite number $< +\infty$

Arithmetic on infinities is always exact and does not signal any exception, except when an exception occurs due to the invalid operations as described in Section 4.4.1, "Invalid Operation Exception," on page 155.

Not a Numbers (NaNs)
These are values that have the maximum biased exponent value and a nonzero fraction value. The sign bit is ignored (i.e., NaNs are neither positive nor negative). If the high-order bit of the fraction field is 0 then the NaN is a *Signalling NaN*; otherwise it is a *Quiet NaN*.

Signalling NaNs are used to signal exceptions when they appear as operands of computational instructions.

Quiet NaNs are used to represent the results of certain invalid operations, such as invalid arithmetic operations on infinities or on NaNs, when Invalid Operation Exception is disabled (FPSCR$_{VE}$=0). Quiet NaNs propagate through all floating-point operations except ordered comparison, *Floating Round to Single-Precision,* and conversion to integer. Quiet NaNs do not signal exceptions, except for ordered comparison and conversion to integer operations. Specific encodings in QNaNs can thus be preserved through a sequence of floating-point operations, and used to convey diagnostic information to help identify results from invalid operations.

When a QNaN is the result of a floating-point operation because one of the operands is a NaN or because a QNaN was generated due to a disabled Invalid Operation Exception, then the following rule is applied to determine the NaN with the high-order fraction bit set to 1 that is to be stored as the result.

```
if (FRA) is a NaN
    then FRT ← (FRA)
    else if (FRB) is a NaN
        then if instruction is frsp
            then FRT ← (FRB)₀:₃₄ ‖ ²⁹0
            else FRT ← (FRB)
        else if (FRC) is a NaN
            then FRT ← (FRC)
            else if generated QNaN
                then FRT ← generated QNaN
```

If the operand specified by FRA is a NaN, then that NaN is stored as the result. Otherwise, if the operand specified by FRB is a NaN (if the instruction specifies an FRB operand), then that NaN is stored as the result, with the low-order 29 bits of the result set to 0 if the instruction is *frsp*. Otherwise, if the operand specified by FRC is a NaN (if the instruction specifies an FRC operand), then that NaN is stored as the result. Otherwise, if a QNaN was generated due to a disabled Invalid Operation Exception, then that QNaN is stored as the result. If a QNaN is to be generated as a result, then the QNaN generated has a sign bit of 0, an exponent field of all 1s, and a high-order fraction bit of 1 with all other fraction bits 0. Any instruction that generates a QNaN as the result of a disabled Invalid Operation must generate this QNaN (i.e., 0x7FF8_0000_0000_0000).

A double-precision NaN is considered to be representable in single format if and only if the low-order 29 bits of the double-precision NaN's fraction are zero.

4.3.3 Sign of Result

The following rules govern the sign of the result of an arithmetic, rounding, or conversion operation, when the operation does not yield an exception. They apply even when the operands or results are zeros or infinities.

■ The sign of the result of an add operation is the sign of the operand having the larger absolute value. If both operands have the same sign, the sign of the result of an add operation is the same as the sign of the operands. The sign of the result of the subtract operation x–y is the same as the sign of the result of the add operation x+(–y).

When the sum of two operands with opposite sign, or the difference of two operands with the same sign, is exactly zero, the sign of the result is positive in all rounding modes except Round toward –Infinity, in which mode the sign is negative.

■ The sign of the result of a multiply or divide operation is the Exclusive OR of the signs of the operands.

■ The sign of the result of a *Square Root* or *Reciprocal Square Root Estimate* operation is always positive, except that the square root of –0 is –0 and the reciprocal square root of –0 is –Infinity.

■ The sign of the result of a *Round to Single-Precision* or *Convert To/ From Integer* operation is the sign of the operand being converted.

For the *Multiply-Add* instructions, the rules given above are applied first to the multiply operation and then to the add or subtract operation (one of the inputs to the add or subtract operation is the result of the multiply operation).

4.3.4 Normalization and Denormalization

The intermediate result of an arithmetic or *frsp* instruction may require normalization and/or denormalization as described below. Normalization and denormalization do not affect the sign of the result.

When an arithmetic or *frsp* instruction produces an intermediate result, consisting of a sign bit, an exponent, and a nonzero significand with a 0 leading bit, it is not a normalized number and must be normalized before it is stored.

A number is normalized by shifting its significand left while decrementing its exponent by 1 for each bit shifted, until the leading significand bit becomes 1. The Guard bit and the Round bit (see Section 4.5.1, "Execution Model for IEEE Operations," on page 163) participate in the shift with zeros shifted into the Round bit. The exponent is regarded as if its range were unlimited.

After normalization, or if normalization was not required, the intermediate result may have a nonzero significand and an exponent value that is less than the minimum value that can be represented in the format specified for the result. In this case, the intermediate result is said to be "Tiny" and the stored result is determined by the rules described in Section 4.4.4, "Underflow Exception," on page 160. These rules may require denormalization.

A number is denormalized by shifting its significand right while incrementing its exponent by 1 for each bit shifted, until the exponent is equal to the format's minimum value. If any significant bits are lost in this shifting process then "Loss of Accuracy" has occurred (see Section 4.4.4, "Underflow Exception," on page 160) and Underflow Exception is signaled.

4.3.5 Data Handling and Precision

Instructions are defined to move floating-point data between the FPRs and storage. For double format data, the data are not altered during the move. For single format data, a format conversion from single to double is performed when loading from storage into an FPR and a format conversion from double to single is performed when storing from an FPR to storage. No floating-point exceptions are caused by these instructions.

All computational, *Move*, and *Select* instructions use the floating-point double format.

Floating-point single-precision is obtained with the implementation of four types of instruction.

Programming Note

A single-precision value can be used in double-precision arithmetic operations. The reverse is true only if the double-precision value is representable in single format.

Some implementations may execute single-precision arithmetic instructions faster than double-precision arithmetic instructions. Therefore, if double-precision accuracy is not required, single-precision data and instructions should be used.

Programming Note

The *Floating Round to Single-Precision* instruction is provided to allow value conversion from double-precision to single-precision with appropriate exception checking and rounding. This instruction should be used to convert double-precision floating-point values (produced by double-precision load and arithmetic instructions and by *fcfid*) to single-precision values prior to storing them into single format storage elements or using them as operands for single-precision arithmetic instructions. Values produced by single-precision load and arithmetic instructions are already single-precision values and can be stored directly into single format storage elements, or used directly as operands for single-precision arithmetic instructions, without preceding the store, or the arithmetic instruction, by a *Floating Round to Single-Precision* instruction.

1. Load Floating-Point Single

This form of instruction accesses a single-precision operand in single format in storage, converts it to double format, and loads it into an FPR. No floating-point exceptions are caused by these instructions.

2. Round to Floating-Point Single-Precision

The *Floating Round to Single-Precision* instruction rounds a double-precision operand to single-precision if the operand is not already in single-precision range, checking the exponent for single-precision range and handling any exceptions according to respective enable bits, and places that operand into an FPR as a double-precision operand. For results produced by single-precision arithmetic instructions, single-precision loads, and other instances of the *Floating Round to Single-Precision* instruction, this operation does not alter the value.

3. Single-Precision Arithmetic Instructions

This form of instruction takes operands from the FPRs in double format, performs the operation as if it produced an intermediate result correct to infinite precision and with unbounded range, and then coerces this intermediate result to fit in single format. Status bits, in the FPSCR and optionally in the Condition Register, are set to reflect the single-precision result. The result is then converted to double format and placed into an FPR. The result lies in the range supported by the single format.

All input values must be representable in single format: if they are not, the result placed into the target FPR, and the setting of status bits in the FPSCR and in the Condition Register (if Rc=1), are undefined.

4. Store Floating-Point Single

This form of instruction converts a double-precision operand to single format and stores that operand into storage. No floating-point exceptions are caused by these instructions. (The value being stored is effectively assumed to be the result of an instruction of one of the preceding three types.)

When the result of a *Load Floating-Point Single*, *Floating Round to Single-Precision*, or single-precision arithmetic instruction is stored in an FPR, the low-order 29 FRACTION bits are zero.

4.3.6 Rounding

With the exception of the two optional *Estimate* instructions, *Floating Reciprocal Estimate Single* and *Floating Reciprocal Square Root Estimate,* all arithmetic, rounding, and conversion instructions defined by this architecture produce an intermediate result that can be regarded as being infinitely precise. This result must then be written with a precision of finite length into an FPR. After normalization or denormalization, if the infinitely precise intermediate result is not representable in the precision required by the instruction then it is rounded before being placed into the target FPR.

The instructions that may round their result are the *Arithmetic* and *Rounding and Conversion* instructions. For a given instance of one of these instructions, whether rounding actually occurs depends on the values of the inputs. Each of these instructions sets FPSCR bits FR and FI according to whether rounding occurred (FI) and whether the fraction was incremented (FR). If rounding occurred, FI is set to 1, and FR may be set to either 0 or 1. If rounding did not occur, both FR and FI are set to 0.

The two *Estimate* instructions set FR and FI to undefined values. The remaining floating-point instructions do not alter FR and FI.

Four user-selectable rounding modes are provided through the Floating-Point Rounding Control field in the FPSCR. See Section 4.2.2, "Floating-Point Status and Control Register," on page 137. These are encoded as follows:

RN	Rounding Mode
00	Round to Nearest
01	Round toward Zero
10	Round toward +Infinity
11	Round toward −Infinity

Let Z be the infinitely precise intermediate arithmetic result or the operand of a convert operation. If Z can be represented exactly in the target format, then no rounding occurs, and the result in all rounding modes is equivalent to truncation of Z. If Z cannot be represented exactly in the target format, let $Z1$ and $Z2$ bound Z as the next larger and next smaller numbers representable in the target format. Then $Z1$ or $Z2$ can be used to approximate the result in the target format.

Figure 30 on page 150 shows the relation of Z, $Z1$, and $Z2$ in this case. The following rules specify the rounding in the four modes. "LSB" means "least significant bit."

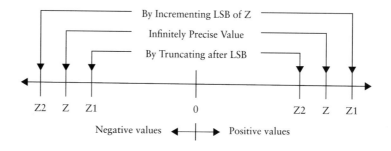

Figure 30. **Selection of Z1 and Z2**

Round to Nearest
   Choose the best approximation (Z1 or Z2). In case of a tie, choose the
   one that is even (least significant bit 0).

Round toward Zero
   Choose the smaller in magnitude (Z1 or Z2).

Round toward +Infinity
   Choose Z1.

Round toward –Infinity
   Choose Z2.

   See Section 4.5.1, "Execution Model for IEEE Operations," on
page 163 for a detailed explanation of rounding.
   An Overflow Exception or an Underflow Exception may occur, as
described in Section 4.4.3, "Overflow Exception," on page 159, and Section 4.4.4, "Underflow Exception," on page 160.

4.4 Floating-Point Exceptions

This architecture defines the following floating-point exceptions:

■ Invalid Operation Exception

   SNaN

   Infinity–Infinity

   Infinity÷Infinity

   Zero÷Zero

> Infinity×Zero
>
> Invalid Compare
>
> Software Request
>
> Invalid Square Root
>
> Invalid Integer Convert

- Zero Divide Exception

- Overflow Exception

- Underflow Exception

- Inexact Exception

These exceptions may occur during execution of computational instructions. In addition, an Invalid Operation Exception occurs when a *Floating-Point Status and Control Register* instruction sets FPSCR$_{VX\text{-}SOFT}$ to 1 (Software Request). An Invalid Square Root exception can occur only if at least one of the *Floating Square Root* instructions defined in Appendix A, "Optional Instructions," on page 197, is implemented.

Each floating-point exception, and each category of Invalid Operation Exception, has an exception bit in the FPSCR. In addition, each floating-point exception has a corresponding enable bit in the FPSCR. The exception bit indicates occurrence of the corresponding exception. If an exception occurs, the corresponding enable bit governs the result produced by the instruction and, in conjunction with the FE0 and FE1 bits (see page 153), whether and how the system floating-point enabled exception error handler is invoked. (In general, the enabling specified by the enable bit is one of invoking the system error handler, not of permitting the exception to occur. The occurrence of an exception depends only on the instruction and its inputs, not on the setting of any control bits. The only deviation from this general rule is that the occurrence of an Underflow Exception may depend on the setting of the enable bit.)

The Floating-Point Exception Summary bit (FX) in the FPSCR is set to 1 by any floating-point instruction, except *mtfsfi* and *mtfsf*, that causes any of the floating-point exception bits in the FPSCR to change from 0 to 1, or by a *mtfsfi*, *mtfsf*, or *mtfsb1* instruction that explicitly sets the bit to 1. The Floating-Point Enabled Exception Summary bit (FEX) in the FPSCR is set when any of the exceptions is set and the exception is enabled (enable bit is 1).

A single instruction, other than *mtfsfi* or *mtfsf*, may set more than one exception only in the following cases:

- Inexact Exception may be set with Overflow Exception.

- Inexact Exception may be set with Underflow Exception.

- Invalid Operation Exception (SNaN) is set with Invalid Operation Exception ($\infty \times 0$) for *Multiply-Add* instructions for which the values being multiplied are infinity and zero and the value being added is an SNaN.

- Invalid Operation Exception (SNaN) may be set with Invalid Operation Exception (Invalid Compare) for *Compare Ordered* instructions.

- Invalid Operation Exception (SNaN) may be set with Invalid Operation Exception (Invalid Integer Convert) for *Convert to Integer* instructions.

When an exception occurs the instruction execution may be suppressed or a result may be delivered, depending on the exception.

Instruction execution is suppressed for the following kinds of exception, so that there is no possibility that one of the operands is lost.

- Enabled Invalid Operation

- Enabled Zero Divide

For the remaining kinds of exception, a result is generated and written to the destination specified by the instruction causing the exception. The result may be a different value for the enabled and disabled conditions for some of these exceptions. The kinds of exception that deliver a result are the following.

- Disabled Invalid Operation

- Disabled Zero Divide

- Disabled Overflow

- Disabled Underflow

- Disabled Inexact

- Enabled Overflow

- Enabled Underflow

- Enabled Inexact

Subsequent sections define each of the floating-point exceptions and specify the action that is taken when they are detected.

The IEEE standard specifies the handling of exceptional conditions in terms of "traps" and "trap handlers." In this architecture, an FPSCR exception enable bit of 1 causes generation of the result value specified in the IEEE standard for the "trap enabled" case: the expectation is that the exception will be detected by software, which will revise the result. An FPSCR exception enable bit of 0 causes generation of the "default result" value specified for the "trap disabled" (or "no trap occurs" or "trap is not implemented") case: the expectation is that the exception will not be detected by software, which will simply use the default result. The result to be delivered in each case for each exception is described in the sections below.

The IEEE default behavior when an exception occurs is to generate a default value and not to notify software. In this architecture, if the IEEE default behavior when an exception occurs is desired for all exceptions, all FPSCR exception enable bits should be set to 0 and Ignore Exceptions Mode (see below) should be used. In this case the system floating-point enabled exception error handler is not invoked, even if floating-point exceptions occur: software can inspect the FPSCR exception bits if necessary, to determine whether exceptions have occurred.

In this architecture, if software is to be notified that a given kind of exception has occurred, the corresponding FPSCR exception enable bit must be set to 1 and a mode other than Ignore Exceptions Mode must be used. In this case the system floating-point enabled exception error handler is invoked if an enabled floating-point exception occurs.

The FE0 and FE1 bits control whether and how the system floating-point enabled exception error handler is invoked if an enabled floating-point exception occurs. The location of these bits and the requirements for altering them are described in Book III, Section 2.2.3, "Machine State Register," on page 374 and Chapter 7, "Synchronization Requirements for Special Registers and for Lookaside Buffers," on page 483. (The system floating-point enabled exception error handler is never invoked because of a disabled floating-point exception.) The effects of the four possible settings of these bits are as follows.

FE0	FE1	Description

0　0　**Ignore Exceptions Mode**
Floating-point exceptions do not cause the system floating-point enabled exception error handler to be invoked.

0　1　**Imprecise Nonrecoverable Mode**
The system floating-point enabled exception error handler is invoked at some point at or beyond the instruction that caused

In any of the three non-Precise modes, a *Floating-Point Status and Control Register* instruction can be used to force any exceptions, due to instructions initiated before the *Floating-Point Status and Control Register* instruction, to be recorded in the FPSCR. (This forcing is superfluous for Precise Mode.)

In either of the Imprecise modes, a *Floating-Point Status and Control Register* instruction can be used to force any invocations of the system floating-point enabled exception error handler, due to instructions initiated before the *Floating-Point Status and Control Register* instruction, to occur. (This forcing has no effect in Ignore Exceptions Mode and is superfluous for Precise Mode.)

A *sync* instruction, or any other execution synchronizing instruction or event (e.g., *isync*: see Book II, "Instruction Synchronize XL-form," on page 346), also has the effects described above. However, in order to obtain the best performance across the widest range of implementations, a *Floating-Point Status and Control Register* instruction should be used to obtain these effects.

the enabled exception. It may not be possible to identify the excepting instruction or the data that caused the exception. Results produced by the excepting instruction may have been used by or may have affected subsequent instructions that are executed before the error handler is invoked.

1   0   **Imprecise Recoverable Mode**
The system floating-point enabled exception error handler is invoked at some point at or beyond the instruction that caused the enabled exception. Sufficient information is provided to the error handler that it can identify the excepting instruction and the operands, and correct the result. No results produced by the excepting instruction have been used by or have affected subsequent instructions that are executed before the error handler is invoked.

1   1   **Precise Mode**
The system floating-point enabled exception error handler is invoked precisely at the instruction that caused the enabled exception.

In all cases, the question of whether a floating-point result is stored, and what value is stored, is governed by the FPSCR exception enable bits, as described in subsequent sections, and is not affected by the value of the FE0 and FE1 bits.

In all cases in which the system floating-point enabled exception error handler is invoked, all instructions before the instruction at which the system floating-point enabled exception error handler is invoked have completed, and no instruction after the instruction at which the system floating-point enabled exception error handler is invoked has been executed. (Recall that, for the two Imprecise modes, the instruction at which the system floating-point enabled exception error handler is invoked need not be the instruction that caused the exception.) The instruction at which the system floating-point enabled exception error handler is invoked has not been executed unless it is the excepting instruction, in which case it has been executed if the exception is not among those listed on page 152 as suppressed.

In order to obtain the best performance across the widest range of implementations, the programmer should obey the following guidelines.

■ If the IEEE default results are acceptable to the application, Ignore Exceptions Mode should be used with all FPSCR exception enable bits set to 0.

■ If the IEEE default results are not acceptable to the application, Imprecise Nonrecoverable Mode should be used, or Imprecise Recoverable Mode if recoverability is needed, with FPSCR exception enable bits set to 1 for those exceptions for which the system floating-point enabled exception error handler is to be invoked.

■ Ignore Exceptions Mode should not, in general, be used when any FPSCR exception enable bits are set to 1.

■ Precise Mode may degrade performance in some implementations, perhaps substantially, and therefore should be used only for debugging and other specialized applications.

4.4.1 Invalid Operation Exception

Definition

An Invalid Operation Exception occurs whenever an operand is invalid for the specified operation. The invalid operations are:

■ Any floating-point operation on a signaling NaN (SNaN).

■ For add or subtract operations, magnitude subtraction of infinities $(\infty - \infty)$

■ Division of infinity by infinity $(\infty \div \infty)$

■ Division of zero by zero $(0 \div 0)$

■ Multiplication of infinity by zero $(\infty \times 0)$

■ Ordered comparison involving a NaN (Invalid Compare)

■ Square root or reciprocal square root of a negative (and nonzero) number (Invalid Square Root)

■ Integer convert involving a large number, an infinity, or a NaN (Invalid Integer Convert)

    In addition, an Invalid Operation Exception occurs if software explicitly requests this by executing an *mtfsfi, mtfsf,* or *mtfsb1* instruction that sets FPSCR$_{VXSOFT}$ to 1 (Software Request). An Invalid Square Root exception can occur only if at least one of the *Floating Square Root* instructions defined in Appendix A, "Optional Instructions," on page 197, is implemented.

Programming Note

The purpose of FPSCR$_{VXSOFT}$ is to allow software to cause an Invalid Operation Exception for a condition that is not necessarily associated with the execution of a floating-point instruction. For example, it might be set by a program that computes a square root, if the source operand is negative.

Action

The action to be taken depends on the setting of the Invalid Operation Exception Enable bit of the FPSCR.

When Invalid Operation Exception is enabled (FPSCR$_{VE}$=1) and Invalid Operation occurs or software explicitly requests the exception, then the following actions are taken:

1. One or two Invalid Operation Exceptions are set

FPSCR$_{VXSNAN}$	(if SNaN)
FPSCR$_{VXISI}$	(if $\infty - \infty$)
FPSCR$_{VXIDI}$	(if $\infty \div \infty$)
FPSCR$_{VXZDZ}$	(if $0 \div 0$)
FPSCR$_{VXIMZ}$	(if $\infty \times 0$)
FPSCR$_{VXVC}$	(if invalid compare)
FPSCR$_{VXSOFT}$	(if software request)
FPSCR$_{VXSQRT}$	(if invalid square root)
FPSCR$_{VXCVI}$	(if invalid integer convert)

2. If the operation is an arithmetic, *Floating Round to Single-Precision,* or convert to integer operation,

the target FPR is unchanged

FPSCR$_{FR\ FI}$ are set to zero

FPSCR$_{FPRF}$ is unchanged

3. If the operation is a compare,

FPSCR$_{FR\ FI\ C}$ are unchanged

FPSCR$_{FPCC}$ is set to reflect unordered

4. If software explicitly requests the exception,

FPSCR$_{FR\ FI\ FPRF}$ are as set by the *mtfsfi, mtfsf,* or *mtfsb1* instruction

When Invalid Operation Exception is disabled (FPSCR$_{VE}$=0) and Invalid Operation occurs or software explicitly requests the exception, then the following actions are taken:

1. One or two Invalid Operation Exceptions are set

FPSCR$_{VXSNAN}$	(if SNaN)
FPSCR$_{VXISI}$	(if $\infty - \infty$)
FPSCR$_{VXIDI}$	(if $\infty \div \infty$)
FPSCR$_{VXZDZ}$	(if $0 \div 0$)
FPSCR$_{VXIMZ}$	(if $\infty \times 0$)
FPSCR$_{VXVC}$	(if invalid compare)
FPSCR$_{VXSOFT}$	(if software request)
FPSCR$_{VXSQRT}$	(if invalid square root)
FPSCR$_{VXCVI}$	(if invalid integer convert)

2. If the operation is an arithmetic or *Floating Round to Single-Precision* operation,

> the target FPR is set to a Quiet NaN
>
> FPSCR$_{FR\ FI}$ are set to zero
>
> FPSCR$_{FPRF}$ is set to indicate the class of the result (Quiet NaN)

3. If the operation is a convert to 64-bit integer operation,

> the target FPR is set as follows:
>
>> FRT is set to the most positive 64-bit integer if the operand in FRB is a positive number or $+\infty$, and to the most negative 64-bit integer if the operand in FRB is a negative number, $-\infty$, or NaN
>
> FPSCR$_{FR\ FI}$ are set to zero
>
> FPSCR$_{FPRF}$ is undefined

4. If the operation is a convert to 32-bit integer operation,

> the target FPR is set as follows:
>
>> FRT$_{0:31}$ ← undefined
>>
>> FRT$_{32:63}$ are set to the most positive 32-bit integer if the operand in FRB is a positive number or $+\infty$, and to the most negative 32-bit integer if the operand in FRB is a negative number, $-\infty$, or NaN
>
> FPSCR$_{FR\ FI}$ are set to zero
>
> FPSCR$_{FPRF}$ is undefined

5. If the operation is a compare,

$\text{FPSCR}_{\text{FR FI C}}$ are unchanged

$\text{FPSCR}_{\text{FPCC}}$ is set to reflect unordered

6. If software explicitly requests the exception,

$\text{FPSCR}_{\text{FR FI FPRF}}$ are as set by the *mtfsfi, mtfsf,* or *mtfsb1* instruction

4.4.2 Zero Divide Exception

Definition

A Zero Divide Exception occurs when a *Divide* instruction is executed with a zero divisor value and a finite nonzero dividend value. It also occurs when a *Reciprocal Estimate* instruction (*fres* or *frsqrte*) is executed with an operand value of zero.

Action

The action to be taken depends on the setting of the Zero Divide Exception Enable bit of the FPSCR.

When Zero Divide Exception is enabled ($\text{FPSCR}_{\text{ZE}}=1$) and Zero Divide occurs, then the following actions are taken:

1. Zero Divide Exception is set

$\text{FPSCR}_{\text{ZX}} \leftarrow 1$

2. The target FPR is unchanged

3. $\text{FPSCR}_{\text{FR FI}}$ are set to zero

4. $\text{FPSCR}_{\text{FPRF}}$ is unchanged

When Zero Divide Exception is disabled ($\text{FPSCR}_{\text{ZE}}=0$) and Zero Divide occurs, then the following actions are taken:

1. Zero Divide Exception is set

$\text{FPSCR}_{\text{ZX}} \leftarrow 1$

2. The target FPR is set to ± Infinity, where the sign is determined by the XOR of the signs of the operands

3. FPSCR$_{FR\ FI}$ are set to zero

4. FPSCR$_{FPRF}$ is set to indicate the class and sign of the result ($\pm$ Infinity)

4.4.3 Overflow Exception

Definition

Overflow occurs when the magnitude of what would have been the rounded result if the exponent range were unbounded exceeds that of the largest finite number of the specified result precision.

Action

The action to be taken depends on the setting of the Overflow Exception Enable bit of the FPSCR.

When Overflow Exception is enabled (FPSCR$_{OE}$=1) and exponent overflow occurs, then the following actions are taken:

1. Overflow Exception is set

   FPSCR$_{OX}$ $\leftarrow$ 1

2. For double-precision arithmetic instructions, the exponent of the normalized intermediate result is adjusted by subtracting 1536

3. For single-precision arithmetic instructions and the *Floating Round to Single-Precision* instruction, the exponent of the normalized intermediate result is adjusted by subtracting 192

4. The adjusted rounded result is placed into the target FPR

5. FPSCR$_{FPRF}$ is set to indicate the class and sign of the result ($\pm$ Normal Number)

When Overflow Exception is disabled (FPSCR$_{OE}$=0) and overflow occurs, then the following actions are taken:

1. Overflow Exception is set

   FPSCR$_{OX}$ $\leftarrow$ 1

2. Inexact Exception is set

   FPSCR$_{XX}$ $\leftarrow$ 1

3. The result is determined by the rounding mode ($FPSCR_{RN}$) and the sign of the intermediate result as follows:

A. Round to Nearest
Store ± Infinity, where the sign is the sign of the intermediate result

B. Round toward Zero
Store the format's largest finite number with the sign of the intermediate result

C. Round toward +Infinity
For negative overflow, store the format's most negative finite number; for positive overflow, store +Infinity

D. Round toward –Infinity
For negative overflow, store –Infinity; for positive overflow, store the format's largest finite number

4. The result is placed into the target FPR

5. $FPSCR_{FR}$ is undefined

6. $FPSCR_{FI}$ is set to 1

7. $FPSCR_{FPRF}$ is set to indicate the class and sign of the result (± Infinity or ± Normal Number)

4.4.4 Underflow Exception

Definition

Underflow Exception is defined separately for the enabled and disabled states:

■ Enabled:
Underflow occurs when the intermediate result is "Tiny."

■ Disabled:
Underflow occurs when the intermediate result is "Tiny" and there is "Loss of Accuracy."

A "Tiny" result is detected before rounding, when a nonzero result value computed as though the exponent range were unbounded would be less in magnitude than the smallest normalized number.

If the intermediate result is "Tiny" and Underflow Exception is disabled (FPSCR$_{UE}$=0) then the intermediate result is denormalized (see Section 4.3.4, "Normalization and Denormalization," on page 147) and rounded (see Section 4.3.6, "Rounding," on page 149) before being placed into the target FPR.

"Loss of Accuracy" is detected when the delivered result value differs from what would have been computed were both the exponent range and precision unbounded.

Action

The action to be taken depends on the setting of the Underflow Exception Enable bit of the FPSCR.

When Underflow Exception is enabled (FPSCR$_{UE}$=1) and exponent underflow occurs, then the following actions are taken:

1. Underflow Exception is set

$$FPSCR_{UX} \leftarrow 1$$

2. For double-precision arithmetic instructions, the exponent of the normalized intermediate result is adjusted by adding 1536

3. For single-precision arithmetic instructions and the *Floating Round to Single-Precision* instruction, the exponent of the normalized intermediate result is adjusted by adding 192

4. The adjusted rounded result is placed into the target FPR

5. FPSCR$_{FPRF}$ is set to indicate the class and sign of the result ($\pm$ Normalized Number)

When Underflow Exception is disabled (FPSCR$_{UE}$=0) and underflow occurs, then the following actions are taken:

1. Underflow Exception is set

$$FPSCR_{UX} \leftarrow 1$$

2. The rounded result is placed into the target FPR

3. FPSCR$_{FPRF}$ is set to indicate the class and sign of the result ($\pm$ Denormalized Number or $\pm$ Zero)

Programming Note

The FR and FI bits are provided to allow the system floating-point enabled exception error handler, when invoked because of an Underflow Exception, to simulate a "trap disabled" environment. That is, the FR and FI bits allow the system floating-point enabled exception error handler to unround the result, thus allowing the result to be denormalized.

Programming Note

In some implementations, enabling Inexact Exceptions may degrade performance more than does enabling other types of floating-point exception.

4.4.5 Inexact Exception

Definition

Inexact Exception occurs when one of two conditions occur during rounding:

1. The rounded result differs from the intermediate result, assuming the intermediate result exponent range and precision to be unbounded.

2. The rounded result overflows and Overflow Exception is disabled.

Action

The action to be taken does not depend on the setting of the Inexact Exception Enable bit of the FPSCR.

When Inexact Exception occurs, then the following actions are taken:

1. Inexact Exception is set

$$FPSCR_{XX} \leftarrow 1$$

2. The rounded or overflowed result is placed into the target FPR

3. $FPSCR_{FPRF}$ is set to indicate the class and sign of the result

4.5 Floating-Point Execution Models

All implementations of this architecture must provide the equivalent of the following execution models to ensure that identical results are obtained.

Special rules are provided in the definition of the computational instructions for the infinities, denormalized numbers, and NaNs.

Although the double format specifies an 11-bit exponent, exponent arithmetic makes use of two additional bit positions to avoid potential transient overflow conditions. One extra bit is required when denormalized double-precision numbers are prenormalized. The second bit is required to permit the computation of the adjusted exponent value in the following cases when the corresponding exception enable bit is 1:

■ Underflow during multiplication using a denormalized operand

■ Overflow during division using a denormalized divisor

The IEEE standard includes 32-bit and 64-bit arithmetic. The standard requires that single-precision arithmetic be provided for single-precision operands. The standard permits double-precision floating-point operations to have either (or both) single-precision or double-precision operands, but it states that single-precision floating-point operations should not accept double-precision operands. The PowerPC Architecture follows these guidelines: double-precision arithmetic instructions can have operands of either or both precisions, while single-precision arithmetic instructions require all operands to be single-precision. Double-precision arithmetic instructions and *fcfid* produce double-precision values, while single-precision arithmetic instructions produce single-precision values.

For arithmetic instructions, conversions from double-precision to single-precision must be done explicitly by software, while conversions from single-precision to double-precision are done implicitly.

4.5.1 Execution Model for IEEE Operations

The following description uses 64-bit arithmetic as an example. 32-bit arithmetic is similar except that the FRACTION is a 23-bit field, and the single-precision Guard, Round, and Sticky bits (described in this section) are logically adjacent to the 23-bit FRACTION field.

IEEE-conforming significand arithmetic is considered to be performed with a floating-point accumulator having the following format:

Figure 31. IEEE 64-bit execution model

The S bit is the sign bit.

The C bit is the carry bit that captures the carry out of the significand.

The L bit is the leading unit bit of the significand that receives the implicit bit from the operand.

The FRACTION is a 52-bit field that accepts the fraction of the operand.

The Guard (G), Round (R), and Sticky (X) bits are extensions to the low-order bits of the accumulator. The G and R bits are required for postnormalization of the result. The G, R, and X bits are required during rounding to determine if the intermediate result is equally near the two nearest representable values. The X bit serves as an extension to the G and R bits by representing the logical OR of all bits that may appear to the low-order side of the R bit, due either to shifting the accumulator right or to other generation of low-order result bits. The G and R bits participate in the left shifts with zeros being shifted into the R bit. Figure 32 shows the significance of the G, R, and X bits with respect to the intermediate result (IR), the representable number next lower in magnitude (NL), and the representable number next higher in magnitude (NH).

G	R	X	Interpretation
0	0	0	IR is exact
0	0	1	
0	1	0	IR closer to NL
0	1	1	
1	0	0	IR midway between NL and NH
1	0	1	
1	1	0	IR closer to NH
1	1	1	

Figure 32.   **Interpretation of G, R, and X bits**

The significand of the intermediate result is made up of the L bit, the FRACTION, and the G,R, and X bits.

The infinitely precise intermediate result of an operation is the result normalized in bits L, FRACTION, G, R, and X of the floating-point accumulator.

Before the result is stored into an FPR, the significand is rounded if necessary, using the rounding mode specified by $FPSCR_{RN}$. If rounding results in a carry into C, the significand is shifted right one position and the exponent incremented by one. This action yields an inexact result and possibly also exponent overflow. Fraction bits to the left of the bit position used for rounding are stored into the FPR and low-order bit positions, if any, are set to zero.

Four user-selectable rounding modes are provided through $FPSCR_{RN}$ as decribed in Section 4.3.6, "Rounding," on page 149. For rounding, the conceptual Guard, Round, and Sticky bits are defined in terms of accumulator bits. Figure 33 on page 165 shows the positions of the Guard, Round, and Sticky bits for double-precision and single-precision floating-point numbers.

Format	Guard	Round	Sticky
Double	G bit	R bit	X bit
Single	24	25	26:52, G,R,X

Figure 33.   **Location of the Guard, Round, and Sticky bits**

Rounding can be treated as though the significand were shifted right, if required, until the least significant bit to be retained is in the low-order bit position of the FRACTION. If any of the Guard, Round, or Sticky bits is nonzero, then the result is inexact.

Z1 and Z2, as defined on page 149, can be used to approximate the result in the target format when one of the following rules is used.

■ *Round to Nearest*

Guard bit = 0
The result is truncated. (Result exact (GRX = 000) or closest to next lower value in magnitude (GRX = 001, 010, or 011))

Guard bit = 1
Depends on Round and Sticky bits:

   Case a
   If the Round or Sticky bit is 1 (inclusive), the result is incremented. (Result closest to next higher value in magitude (GRX = 101, 110, or 111))

   Case b
   If the Round and Sticky bits are 0 (result midway between closest representable values), then if the low-order bit of the result is 1 the result is incremented. Otherwise (the low-order bit of the result is 0) the result is truncated (this is the case of a tie rounded to even).

If during the Round to Nearest process, truncation of the unrounded number would produce the maximum magnitude for the specified precision, then the following action is taken:

Guard bit = 0
Store the truncated (maximum magnitude) value.

Guard bit = 1
Store infinity with the sign of the unrounded result.

- *Round toward Zero*
  Choose the smaller in magnitude of Z1 or Z2. If Guard, Round, or Sticky bit is nonzero, the result is inexact.

- *Round toward +Infinity*
  Choose Z1.

- *Round toward* –Infinity
  Choose Z2.

Where the result is to have fewer than 53 bits of precision because the instruction is a *Floating Round to Single-Precision* or single-precision arithmetic instruction, the intermediate result either is normalized or is placed in correct denormalized form before any rounding is done.

4.5.2 Execution Model for Multiply-Add Type Instructions

The PowerPC Architecture makes use of a special form of instruction that performs up to three operations in one instruction (a multiplication, an addition, and a negation). With this added capability comes the special ability to produce a more exact intermediate result as an input to the rounder. 32-bit arithmetic is similar except that the FRACTION field is smaller.

The multiply-add operations produce intermediate results conforming to the following model:

Figure 34.   Multiply-Add execution model

The first part of the operation is a multiplication. The multiplication has two 53-bit significands as inputs, which are assumed to be prenormalized, and produces a result conforming to the above model. If there is a carry out of the significand (into the C bit), then the significand is shifted right one position, shifting the L bit (leading unit bit) into the most significant bit of the FRACTION and shifting the C bit (carry out) into the L bit. All 106 bits (L bit, the FRACTION) of the product take part in the add operation. If the exponents of the two inputs to the adder are not equal, the significand of the operand with the smaller exponent is aligned (shifted) to the right by an amount that is added to that exponent to make it equal to the other input's exponent. Zeros are shifted into the left of the significand as it is aligned and bits shifted out of bit 105 of the significand are ORed into the X' bit. The add operation also produces a result conforming to the above model with the X' bit taking part in the add operation.

The result of the addition is then normalized, with all bits of the addition result, except the X' bit, participating in the shift. The normalized result provides an intermediate result as input to the rounder that conforms to the model described in Section 4.5.1, "Execution Model for IEEE Operations," on page 163, where:

- The Guard bit is bit 53 of the intermediate result.

- The Round bit is bit 54 of the intermediate result.

- The Sticky bit is the OR of all remaining bits to the right of bit 55, inclusive.

The rules of rounding the intermediate result are the same as those given in Section 4.5.1, "Execution Model for IEEE Operations," on page 163.

If the instruction is *Floating Negative Multiply-Add* or *Floating Negative Multiply-Subtract,* the final result is negated.

Status bits are set as follows:

- Overflow, Underflow, and Inexact Exception bits, the FR and FI bits, and the FPRF field are set based on the final result of the operation, and not on the result of the multiplication.

- Invalid Operation Exception bits are set as if the multiplication and the addition were performed using two separate instructions (*fmul[s]*, followed by *fadd[s]* or *fsub[s]*). That is, multiplication of infinity by 0 or of anything by an SNaN, and/or addition of an SNaN, cause the corresponding exception bits to be set.

4.6 Floating-Point Processor Instructions

4.6.1 Floating-Point Storage Access Instructions

The *Storage Access* instructions compute the effective address (EA) of the storage to be accessed as described in Section 1.11.2, "Effective Address Calculation," on page 29.

Programming Note

The "la" extended
mnemonic permits
computing an effective
address as a *Load* or *Store*
instruction would, but
loads the address itself
into a GPR rather than
loading the value that is
in storage at that
address. This extended
mnemonic is described in
"Load Address," on
page 232.

The order of bytes accessed by floating-point loads and stores is Big-Endian, unless Little-Endian storage ordering is selected as described in Appendix D, "Little-Endian Byte Ordering," on page 233.

Storage Access Exceptions

Storage accesses will cause the system error handler to be invoked if the program is not allowed to modify the target storage (*Store* only), or if the program attempts to access storage that is unavailable.

4.6.2 Floating-Point Load Instructions

There are two basic forms of load instruction: single-precision and double-precision. Because the FPRs support only floating-point double format, single-precision *Load Floating-Point* instructions convert single-precision data to double format prior to loading the operands into the target FPR. The conversion and loading steps are as follows:

Let $WORD_{0:31}$ be the floating-point single-precision operand accessed from storage.

Normalized Operand
if $WORD_{1:8} > 0$ and $WORD_{1:8} < 255$ then
$\quad FRT_{0:1} \leftarrow WORD_{0:1}$
$\quad FRT_2 \leftarrow \neg WORD_1$
$\quad FRT_3 \leftarrow \neg WORD_1$
$\quad FRT_4 \leftarrow \neg WORD_1$
$\quad FRT_{5:63} \leftarrow WORD_{2:31} \parallel {}^{29}0$

Denormalized Operand
if $WORD_{1:8} = 0$ and $WORD_{9:31} \neq 0$ then
$\quad sign \leftarrow WORD_0$
$\quad exp \leftarrow -126$
$\quad frac_{0:52} \leftarrow 0b0 \parallel WORD_{9:31} \parallel {}^{29}0$
$\quad$ normalize the operand
$\quad\quad$ do while $frac_0 = 0$
$\quad\quad\quad frac \leftarrow frac_{1:52} \parallel 0b0$
$\quad\quad\quad exp \leftarrow exp - 1$
$\quad FRT_0 \leftarrow sign$
$\quad FRT_{1:11} \leftarrow exp + 1023$
$\quad FRT_{12:63} \leftarrow frac_{1:52}$

Zero / Infinity / NaN
if $WORD_{1:8} = 255$ or $WORD_{1:31} = 0$ then
    $FRT_{0:1} \leftarrow WORD_{0:1}$
    $FRT_2 \leftarrow WORD_1$
    $FRT_3 \leftarrow WORD_1$
    $FRT_4 \leftarrow WORD_1$
    $FRT_{5:63} \leftarrow WORD_{2:31} \parallel {}^{29}0$

For double-precision *Load Floating-Point* instructions, no conversion is required as the data from storage are copied directly into the FPR.

Many of the *Load Floating-Point* instructions have an "update" form, in which register RA is updated with the effective address. For these forms, if RA≠0, the effective address is placed into register RA and the storage element (word or doubleword) addressed by EA is loaded into FRT.

Note: Recall that RA and RB denote general purpose registers, while FRT denotes a floating-point register.

Byte order of PowerPC is Big-Endian by default; see Appendix D, "Little-Endian Byte Ordering," on page 233 for PowerPC systems operated with Little-Endian byte ordering.

Load Floating-Point Single   D-form

lfs   FRT,D(RA)

48	FRT	RA	D
0	6	11	16 31

```
if RA = 0 then b ← 0
else            b ← (RA)
EA ← b + EXTS(D)
FRT ← DOUBLE(MEM(EA, 4))
```

Let the effective address (EA) be the sum (RA|0)+D.

The word in storage addressed by EA is interpreted as a floating-point single-precision operand. This word is converted to floating-point double format (see page 168) and placed into register FRT.

Special Registers Altered
    None

Load Floating-Point Single Indexed   X-form

lfsx   FRT,RA,RB

31	FRT	RA	RB	535	/
0	6	11	16	21	31

```
if RA = 0 then b ← 0
else           b ← (RA)
EA ← b + (RB)
FRT ← DOUBLE(MEM(EA, 4))
```

Let the effective address (EA) be the sum (RA|0)+(RB).

The word in storage addressed by EA is interpreted as a floating-point single-precision operand. This word is converted to floating-point double format (see page 168) and placed into register FRT.

Special Registers Altered

None

Load Floating-Point Single with Update   D-form

lfsu   FRT,D(RA)

49	FRT	RA	D	
0	6	11	16	31

```
EA ← (RA) + EXTS(D)
FRT ← DOUBLE(MEM(EA, 4))
RA ← EA
```

Let the effective address (EA) be the sum (RA)+D.

The word in storage addressed by EA is interpreted as a floating-point single-precision operand. This word is converted to floating-point double format (see page 168) and placed into register FRT.

EA is placed into register RA.

If RA=0, the instruction form is invalid.

Special Registers Altered

None

Load Floating-Point Single with Update Indexed   X-form

lfsux   FRT,RA,RB

31	FRT	RA	RB	567	/
0	6	11	16	21	31

```
EA ← (RA) + (RB)
FRT ← DOUBLE(MEM(EA, 4))
RA ← EA
```

Let the effective address (EA) be the sum (RA)+(RB).

The word in storage addressed by EA is interpreted as a floating-point single-precision operand. This word is converted to floating-point double format (see page 168) and placed into register FRT.

EA is placed into register RA.

If RA=0, the instruction form is invalid.

Special Registers Altered

None

Load Floating-Point Double   D-form

lfd   FRT,D(RA)

50	FRT	RA	D
0	6	11	16	31

```
if RA = 0 then b ← 0
else           b ← (RA)
EA ← b + EXTS(D)
FRT ← MEM(EA, 8)
```

Let the effective address (EA) be the sum (RA|0)+D.

The doubleword in storage addressed by EA is placed into register FRT.

Special Registers Altered

None

Load Floating-Point Double Indexed   X-form

lfdx   FRT,RA,RB

31	FRT	RA	RB	599	/
0	6	11	16	21	31

```
if RA = 0 then b ← 0
else           b ← (RA)
EA ← b + (RB)
FRT ← MEM(EA, 8)
```

Let the effective address (EA) be the sum (RA|0)+(RB).

The doubleword in storage addressed by EA is placed into register FRT.

Special Registers Altered

   None

Load Floating-Point Double with Update   D-form

lfdu   FRT,D(RA)

51	FRT	RA	D
0	6	11	16 31

```
EA ← (RA) + EXTS(D)
FRT ← MEM(EA, 8)
RA ← EA
```

Let the effective address (EA) be the sum (RA)+D.

The doubleword in storage addressed by EA is placed into register FRT.

EA is placed into register RA.

If RA=0, the instruction form is invalid.

Special Registers Altered

   None

Load Floating-Point Double with Update Indexed   X-form

lfdux   FRT,RA,RB

31	FRT	RA	RB	631	/
0	6	11	16	21	31

```
EA ← (RA) + (RB)
FRT ← MEM(EA, 8)
RA ← EA
```

Let the effective address (EA) be the sum (RA)+(RB).

The doubleword in storage addressed by EA is placed into register FRT.

EA is placed into register RA.

If RA=0, the instruction form is invalid.

Special Registers Altered

```
None
```

4.6.3 Floating-Point Store Instructions

There are three basic forms of store instruction: single-precision, double-precision, and integer. The integer form is provided by the optional *Store Floating-Point as Integer Word* instruction, described on page 198. Because the FPRs support only floating-point double format for floating-point data, single-precision *Store Floating-Point* instructions convert double-precision data to single format prior to storing the operands into storage. The conversion steps are as follows:

Let $WORD_{0:31}$ be the word in storage written to.

No Denormalization Required (includes Zero / Infinity / NaN)
if $FRS_{1:11} > 896$ or $FRS_{1:63} = 0$ then
$\quad WORD_{0:1} \leftarrow FRS_{0:1}$
$\quad WORD_{2:31} \leftarrow FRS_{5:34}$

Denormalization Required
if $874 \leq FRS_{1:11} \leq 896$ then
$\quad sign \leftarrow FRS_0$
$\quad exp \leftarrow FRS_{1:11} - 1023$
$\quad frac \leftarrow 0b1 \parallel FRS_{12:63}$
$\quad$ denormalize the operand
$\quad\quad$ do while $exp < -126$
$\quad\quad\quad frac \leftarrow 0b0 \parallel frac_{0:62}$
$\quad\quad\quad exp \leftarrow exp + 1$
$\quad WORD_0 \leftarrow sign$
$\quad WORD_{1:8} \leftarrow 0x00$
$\quad WORD_{9:31} \leftarrow frac_{1:23}$
else $WORD \leftarrow$ undefined

Notice that if the value to be stored by a single-precision *Store Floating-Point* instruction is larger in magnitude than the maximum number representable in single format, the first case above (No Denormalization Required) applies. The result stored in WORD is then a well-defined value, but it is not numerically equal to the value in the source register (i.e., the result of a single-precision *Load Floating-Point* from WORD will not compare equal to the contents of the original source register).

For double-precision *Store Floating-Point* instructions and for the *Store Floating-Point as Integer Word* instruction, no conversion is required, as the data from the FPR are copied directly into storage.

Many of the *Store Floating-Point* instructions have an "update" form, in which register RA is updated with the effective address. For these forms, if RA≠0, the effective address is placed into register RA.

Note: Recall that RA and RB denote general purpose registers, while FRS denotes a floating-point register.

Byte order of PowerPC is Big-Endian by default; see Appendix D, "Little-Endian Byte Ordering," on page 233 for PowerPC systems operated with Little-Endian byte ordering.

Store Floating-Point Single   D-form

stfs   FRS,D(RA)

52	FRS	RA	D
0	6	11	16 31

```
if RA = 0 then b ← 0
else            b ← (RA)
EA ← b + EXTS(D)
MEM(EA, 4) ← SINGLE(FRS)
```

Let the effective address (EA) be the sum (RA|0)+D.

The contents of register FRS are converted to single format (see page 173) and stored into the word in storage addressed by EA.

Special Registers Altered
```
None
```

Store Floating-Point Single Indexed   X-form

stfsx   FRS,RA,RB

31	FRS	RA	RB	663	/
0	6	11	16	21	31

```
if RA = 0 then b ← 0
else            b ← (RA)
EA ← b + (RB)
MEM(EA, 4) ← SINGLE(FRS)
```

Let the effective address (EA) be the sum (RA|0)+(RB).

The contents of register FRS are converted to single format (see page 173) and stored into the word in storage addressed by EA.

Special Registers Altered

    None

Store Floating-Point Single with Update   D-form

stfsu   FRS,D(RA)

53	FRS	RA	D
0	6	11	16 31

```
EA ← (RA) + EXTS(D)
MEM(EA, 4) ← SINGLE(FRS)
RA ← EA
```

Let the effective address (EA) be the sum (RA)+D.

The contents of register FRS are converted to single format (see page 173) and stored into the word in storage addressed by EA.

EA is placed into register RA.

If RA=0, the instruction form is invalid.

Special Registers Altered

    None

Store Floating-Point Single with Update Indexed   X-form

stfsux   FRS,RA,RB

31	FRS	RA	RB	695	/
0	6	11	16	21	31

```
EA ← (RA) + (RB)
MEM(EA, 4) ← SINGLE(FRS)
RA ← EA
```

Let the effective address (EA) be the sum (RA)+(RB).

The contents of register FRS are converted to single format (see page 173) and stored into the word in storage addressed by EA.

EA is placed into register RA.

If RA=0, the instruction form is invalid.

Special Registers Altered

```
None
```

Store Floating-Point Double   D-form

stfd   FRS,D(RA)

54	FRS	RA	D
0	6	11	16 31

```
if RA = 0 then b ← 0
else            b ← (RA)
EA ← b + EXTS(D)
MEM(EA, 8) ← (FRS)
```

Let the effective address (EA) be the sum (RA|0)+D.

The contents of register FRS are stored into the doubleword in storage addressed by EA.

Special Registers Altered

```
None
```

Store Floating-Point Double Indexed   X-form

stfdx   FRS,RA,RB

31	FRS	RA	RB	727	/
0	6	11	16	21	31

```
if RA = 0 then b ← 0
else            b ← (RA)
EA ← b + (RB)
MEM(EA, 8) ← (FRS)
```

Let the effective address (EA) be the sum (RA|0)+(RB).

The contents of register FRS are stored into the doubleword in storage addressed by EA.

Special Registers Altered

None

Store Floating-Point Double with Update   D-form

stfdu   FRS,D(RA)

55	FRS	RA	D
0	6	11	16 31

```
EA ← (RA) + EXTS(D)
MEM(EA, 8) ← (FRS)
RA ← EA
```

Let the effective address (EA) be the sum (RA)+D.

The contents of register FRS are stored into the doubleword in storage addressed by EA.

EA is placed into register RA.

If RA=0, the instruction form is invalid.

Special Registers Altered

None

Store Floating-Point Double with Update Indexed   X-form

stfdux   FRS,RA,RB

31	FRS	RA	RB	759	/
0	6	11	16	21	31

```
EA ← (RA) + (RB)
MEM(EA, 8) ← (FRS)
RA ← EA
```

Let the effective address (EA) be the sum (RA)+(RB).

The contents of register FRS are stored into the doubleword in storage addressed by EA.

EA is placed into register RA.

If RA=0, the instruction form is invalid.

Special Registers Altered

None

4.6.4 Floating-Point Move Instructions

These instructions copy data from one floating-point register to another, altering the sign bit (bit 0) as described below for *fneg, fabs,* and *fnabs*. These instructions treat NaNs just like any other kind of value (e.g., the sign bit of a NaN may be altered by *fneg, fabs,* and *fnabs*). These instructions do not alter the FPSCR.

Floating Move Register   X-form

| fmr | FRT,FRB | (Rc=0) |
| fmr. | FRT,FRB | (Rc=1) |

63	FRT	///	FRB	72	Rc
0	6	11	16	21	31

The contents of register FRB are placed into register FRT.

Special Registers Altered
    CR1   (if Rc=1)

Floating Negate   X-form

| fneg | FRT,FRB | (Rc=0) |
| fneg. | FRT,FRB | (Rc=1) |

63	FRT	///	FRB	40	Rc
0	6	11	16	21	31

The contents of register FRB with bit 0 inverted are placed into register FRT.

Special Registers Altered
    CR1   (if Rc=1)

Floating Absolute Value   X-form

| fabs | FRT,FRB | (Rc=0) |
| fabs. | FRT,FRB | (Rc=1) |

63	FRT	///	FRB	264	Rc
0	6	11	16	21	31

The contents of register FRB with bit 0 set to zero are placed into register FRT.

Special Registers Altered
```
CR1                                                      (if Rc=1)
```

Floating Negative Absolute Value   X-form

fnabs	FRT,FRB	(Rc=0)
fnabs.	FRT,FRB	(Rc=1)

63	FRT	///	FRB	136	Rc
0	6	11	16	21	31

The contents of register FRB with bit 0 set to one are placed into register FRT.

Special Registers Altered
```
CR1                                                      (if Rc=1)
```

4.6.5 Floating-Point Arithmetic Instructions

Floating-Point Elementary Arithmetic Instructions

Floating Add [Single]   A-form

fadd	FRT,FRA,FRB	(Rc=0)
fadd.	FRT,FRA,FRB	(Rc=1)

[POWER mnemonics: fa, fa.]

63	FRT	FRA	FRB	///	21	Rc
0	6	11	16	21	26	31

fadds	FRT,FRA,FRB	(Rc=0)
fadds.	FRT,FRA,FRB	(Rc=1)

59	FRT	FRA	FRB	///	21	Rc
0	6	11	16	21	26	31

The floating-point operand in register FRA is added to the floating-point operand in register FRB.

If the most significant bit of the resultant significand is not 1, the result is normalized. The result is rounded to the target precision under control of the Floating-Point Rounding Control field RN of the FPSCR and placed into register FRT.

Floating-point addition is based on exponent comparison and addition of the two significands. The exponents of the two operands are compared, and the significand accompanying the smaller exponent is shifted right, with its exponent increased by one for each bit shifted, until the two exponents are equal. The two significands are then added or subtracted as appropriate, depending on the signs of the operands, to form an intermediate sum. All 53 bits in the significand as well as all three guard bits (G, R, and X) enter into the computation.

If a carry occurs, the sum's significand is shifted right one bit position and the exponent is increased by one.

$FPSCR_{FPRF}$ is set to the class and sign of the result, except for Invalid Operation Exceptions when $FPSCR_{VE}=1$.

Special Registers Altered

```
FPRF FR FI
FX OX UX XX
VXSNAN VXISI
CR1                                          (if Rc=1)
```

Floating Subtract [Single]   A-form

fsub   FRT,FRA,FRB   (Rc=0)
fsub.   FRT,FRA,FRB   (Rc=1)

[POWER mnemonics: fs, fs.]

63	FRT	FRA	FRB	///	20	Rc
0	6	11	16	21	26	31

fsubs   FRT,FRA,FRB   (Rc=0)
fsubs.   FRT,FRA,FRB   (Rc=1)

59	FRT	FRA	FRB	///	20	Rc
0	6	11	16	21	26	31

The floating-point operand in register FRB is subtracted from the floating-point operand in register FRA.

If the most significant bit of the resultant significand is not 1, the result is normalized. The result is rounded to the target precision under control of the Floating-Point Rounding Control field RN of the FPSCR and placed into register FRT.

The execution of the *Floating Subtract* instruction is identical to that of *Floating Add*, except that the contents of FRB participate in the operation with the sign bit (bit 0) inverted.

FPSCR$_{FPRF}$ is set to the class and sign of the result, except for Invalid Operation Exceptions when FPSCR$_{VE}$=1.

Special Registers Altered

```
FPRF FR FI
FX OX UX XX
VXSNAN VXISI
CR1                                                 (if Rc=1)
```

Floating Multiply [Single]   A-form

fmul	FRT,FRA,FRC	(Rc=0)
fmul.	FRT,FRA,FRC	(Rc=1)

[POWER mnemonics: fm, fm.]

63	FRT	FRA	///	FRC	25	Rc
0	6	11	16	21	26	31

fmuls	FRT,FRA,FRC	(Rc=0)
fmuls.	FRT,FRA,FRC	(Rc=1)

59	FRT	FRA	///	FRC	25	Rc
0	6	11	16	21	26	31

The floating-point operand in register FRA is multiplied by the floating-point operand in register FRC.

If the most significant bit of the resultant significand is not 1, the result is normalized. The result is rounded to the target precision under control of the Floating-Point Rounding Control field RN of the FPSCR and placed into register FRT.

Floating-point multiplication is based on exponent addition and multiplication of the significands.

FPSCR$_{FPRF}$ is set to the class and sign of the result, except for Invalid Operation Exceptions when FPSCR$_{VE}$=1.

Special Registers Altered

```
FPRF FR FI
FX OX UX XX
VXSNAN VXIMZ
CR1                                                 (if Rc=1)
```

Floating Divide [Single]   A-form

fdiv	FRT,FRA,FRB					(Rc=0)
fdiv.	FRT,FRA,FRB					(Rc=1)

[POWER mnemonics: fd, fd.]

63	FRT	FRA	FRB	///	18	Rc
0	6	11	16	21	26	31

fdivs	FRT,FRA,FRB					(Rc=0)
fdivs.	FRT,FRA,FRB					(Rc=1)

59	FRT	FRA	FRB	///	18	Rc
0	6	11	16	21	26	31

The floating-point operand in register FRA is divided by the floating-point operand in register FRB. The remainder is not supplied as a result.

If the most significant bit of the resultant significand is not 1, the result is normalized. The result is rounded to the target precision under control of the Floating-Point Rounding Control field RN of the FPSCR and placed into register FRT.

Floating-point division is based on exponent subtraction and division of the significands.

$FPSCR_{FPRF}$ is set to the class and sign of the result, except for Invalid Operation Exceptions when $FPSCR_{VE}=1$ and Zero Divide Exceptions when $FPSCR_{ZE}=1$.

Special Registers Altered

```
FPRF FR FI
FX OX UX ZX XX
VXSNAN VXIDI VXZDZ
CR1                                           (if Rc=1)
```

Floating-Point Multiply-Add Instructions

These instructions combine a multiply operation and an add operation without an intermediate rounding operation. The fraction part of the intermediate product is 106 bits wide (L bit, Fraction), and all 106 bits take part in the add/subtract portion of the instruction.

Floating Multiply-Add [Single]   A-form

fmadd   FRT,FRA,FRC,FRB   (Rc=0)
fmadd.   FRT,FRA,FRC,FRB   (Rc=1)

[POWER mnemonics: fma, fma.]

63	FRT	FRA	FRB	FRC	29	Rc
0	6	11	16	21	26	31

fmadds   FRT,FRA,FRC,FRB   (Rc=0)
fmadds.   FRT,FRA,FRC,FRB   (Rc=1)

59	FRT	FRA	FRB	FRC	29	Rc
0	6	11	16	21	26	31

The operation

$$FRT \leftarrow [(FRA) \times (FRC)] + (FRB)$$

is performed.

The floating-point operand in register FRA is multiplied by the floating-point operand in register FRC. The floating-point operand in register FRB is added to this intermediate result.

If the most significant bit of the resultant significand is not 1, the result is normalized. The result is rounded to the target precision under control of the Floating-Point Rounding Control field RN of the FPSCR and placed into register FRT.

$FPSCR_{FPRF}$ is set to the class and sign of the result, except for Invalid Operation Exceptions when $FPSCR_{VE}=1$.

Special Registers Altered

```
FPRF FR FI
FX OX UX XX
VXSNAN VXISI VXIMZ
CR1                                        (if Rc=1)
```

Floating Multiply-Subtract [Single]   A-form

fmsub	FRT,FRA,FRC,FRB	(Rc=0)
fmsub.	FRT,FRA,FRC,FRB	(Rc=1)

[POWER mnemonics: fms, fms.]

63	FRT	FRA	FRB	FRC	28	Rc
0	6	11	16	21	26	31

fmsubs	FRT,FRA,FRC,FRB	(Rc=0)
fmsubs.	FRT,FRA,FRC,FRB	(Rc=1)

59	FRT	FRA	FRB	FRC	28	Rc
0	6	11	16	21	26	31

The operation

$$FRT \leftarrow [(FRA) \times (FRC)] - (FRB)$$

is performed.

The floating-point operand in register FRA is multiplied by the floating-point operand in register FRC. The floating-point operand in register FRB is subtracted from this intermediate result.

If the most significant bit of the resultant significand is not 1, the result is normalized. The result is rounded to the target precision under control of the Floating-Point Rounding Control field RN of the FPSCR and placed into register FRT.

$FPSCR_{FPRF}$ is set to the class and sign of the result, except for Invalid Operation Exceptions when $FPSCR_{VE}=1$.

Special Registers Altered

```
FPRF FR FI
FX OX UX XX
VXSNAN VXISI VXIMZ
CR1                                            (if Rc=1)
```

Floating Negative Multiply-Add [Single]   A-form

fnmadd	FRT,FRA,FRC,FRB	(Rc=0)
fnmadd.	FRT,FRA,FRC,FRB	(Rc=1)

[POWER mnemonics: fnma, fnma.]

63	FRT	FRA	FRB	FRC	31	Rc
0	6	11	16	21	26	31

fnmadds	FRT,FRA,FRC,FRB	(Rc=0)
fnmadds.	FRT,FRA,FRC,FRB	(Rc=1)

59	FRT	FRA	FRB	FRC	31	Rc
0	6	11	16	21	26	31

The operation

$$FRT \leftarrow - ([(FRA) \times (FRC)] + (FRB))$$

is performed.

The floating-point operand in register FRA is multiplied by the floating-point operand in register FRC. The floating-point operand in register FRB is added to this intermediate result.

If the most significant bit of the resultant significand is not 1, the result is normalized. The result is rounded to the target precision under control of the Floating-Point Rounding Control field RN of the FPSCR, then negated and placed into register FRT.

This instruction produces the same result as would be obtained by using the *Floating Multiply-Add* instruction and then negating the result, with the following exceptions:

■ QNaNs propagate with no effect on their "sign" bit.

■ QNaNs that are generated as the result of a disabled Invalid Operation Exception have a "sign" bit of 0.

■ SNaNs that are converted to QNaNs as the result of a disabled Invalid Operation Exception retain the "sign" bit of the SNaN.

$FPSCR_{FPRF}$ is set to the class and sign of the result, except for Invalid Operation Exceptions when $FPSCR_{VE}=1$.

Special Registers Altered
```
FPRF FR FI
FX OX UX XX
VXSNAN VXISI VXIMZ
CR1                                          (if Rc=1)
```

Floating Negative Multiply-Subtract [Single]   A-form

| fnmsub | FRT,FRA,FRC,FRB | (Rc=0) |
| fnmsub. | FRT,FRA,FRC,FRB | (Rc=1) |

[POWER mnemonics: fnms, fnms.]

63	FRT	FRA	FRB	FRC	30	Rc
0	6	11	16	21	26	31

| fnmsubs | FRT,FRA,FRC,FRB | (Rc=0) |
| fnmsubs. | FRT,FRA,FRC,FRB | (Rc=1) |

59	FRT	FRA	FRB	FRC	30	Rc
0	6	11	16	21	26	31

The operation

$$FRT \leftarrow - (\; [(FRA) \times (FRC)] - (FRB)\;)$$

is performed.

The floating-point operand in register FRA is multiplied by the floating-point operand in register FRC. The floating-point operand in register FRB is subtracted from this intermediate result.

If the most significant bit of the resultant significand is not 1, the result is normalized. The result is rounded to the target precision under control of the Floating-Point Rounding Control field RN of the FPSCR, then negated and placed into register FRT.

This instruction produces the same result as would be obtained by using the *Floating Multiply-Subtract* instruction and then negating the result, with the following exceptions:

■ QNaNs propagate with no effect on their "sign" bit.

■ QNaNs that are generated as the result of a disabled Invalid Operation Exception have a "sign" bit of 0.

■ SNaNs that are converted to QNaNs as the result of a disabled Invalid Operation Exception retain the "sign" bit of the SNaN.

$FPSCR_{FPRF}$ is set to the class and sign of the result, except for Invalid Operation Exceptions when $FPSCR_{VE}=1$.

Special Registers Altered

```
FPRF FR FI
FX OX UX XX
VXSNAN VXISI VXIMZ
CR1                                          (if Rc=1)
```

4.6.6 Floating-Point Rounding and Conversion Instructions

Floating Round to Single-Precision   X-form

| frsp | FRT,FRB | (Rc=0) |
| frsp. | FRT,FRB | (Rc=1) |

63	FRT	///	FRB	12	Rc
0	6	11	16	21	31

Programming Note

Examples of uses of the conversion instructions can be found in Appendix E.3 , "Floating-Point Conversions," on page 259.

If it is already in single-precision range, the floating-point operand in register FRB is placed into register FRT. Otherwise, the floating-point operand in register FRB is rounded to single-precision using the rounding mode specified by $FPSCR_{RN}$ and placed into register FRT.

The rounding is described fully in Appendix B.1, "Floating-Point Round to Single-Precision Model," on page 203.

$FPSCR_{FPRF}$ is set to the class and sign of the result, except for Invalid Operation Exceptions when $FPSCR_{VE}=1$.

Special Registers Altered

```
FPRF FR FI
FX OX UX XX
VXSNAN
CR1                                          (if Rc=1)
```

Floating Convert To Integer Doubleword   X-form

| fctid | FRT,FRB | (Rc=0) |
| fctid. | FRT,FRB | (Rc=1) |

63	FRT	///	FRB	814	Rc
0	6	11	16	21	31

The floating-point operand in register FRB is converted to a 64-bit signed fixed-point integer, using the rounding mode specified by FPSCR$_{RN}$, and placed into register FRT.

If the operand in FRB is greater than $2^{63}-1$, then FRT is set to 0x7FFF_FFFF_FFFF_FFFF. If the operand in FRB is less than -2^{63}, then FRT is set to 0x8000_0000_0000_0000.

The conversion is described fully in Appendix B.2, "Floating-Point Convert to Integer Model," on page 209.

Except for enabled Invalid Operation Exceptions, FPSCR$_{FPRF}$ is undefined. FPSCR$_{FR}$ is set if the result is incremented when rounded. FPSCR$_{FI}$ is set if the result is inexact.

This instruction is defined only for 64-bit implementations. Using it on a 32-bit implementation will cause the system illegal instruction error handler to be invoked.

Special Registers Altered

```
FPRF(undefined) FR FI
FX XX
VXSNAN VXCVI
CR1                                          (if Rc=1)
```

Floating Convert To Integer Doubleword with round toward Zero   X-form

| fctidz | FRT,FRB | (Rc=0) |
| fctidz. | FRT,FRB | (Rc=1) |

63	FRT	///	FRB	815	Rc
0	6	11	16	21	31

The floating-point operand in register FRB is converted to a 64-bit signed fixed-point integer, using the rounding mode *Round toward Zero*, and placed into register FRT.

If the operand in FRB is greater than $2^{63}-1$, then FRT is set to 0x7FFF_FFFF_FFFF_FFFF. If the operand in FRB is less than -2^{63}, then FRT is set to 0x8000_0000_0000_0000.

The conversion is described fully in Appendix B.2, "Floating-Point Convert to Integer Model," on page 209.

Except for enabled Invalid Operation Exceptions, FPSCR$_{FPRF}$ is undefined. FPSCR$_{FR}$ is set if the result is incremented when rounded. FPSCR$_{FI}$ is set if the result is inexact.

This instruction is defined only for 64-bit implementations. Using it on a 32-bit implementation will cause the system illegal instruction error handler to be invoked.

Special Registers Altered

```
FPRF(undefined) FR FI
FX XX
VXSNAN VXCVI
CR1                                                    (if Rc=1)
```

Floating Convert To Integer Word   X-form

fctiw	FRT,FRB	(Rc=0)
fctiw.	FRT,FRB	(Rc=1)

[POWER2 mnemonics: fcir, fcir.]

63	FRT	///	FRB	14	Rc
0	6	11	16	21	31

The floating-point operand in register FRB is converted to a 32-bit signed fixed-point integer, using the rounding mode specified by $FPSCR_{RN}$, and placed in bits 32:63 of register FRT. Bits 0:31 of register FRT are undefined.

If the operand in FRB is greater than $2^{31}-1$, then bits 32:63 of FRT are set to 0x7FFF_FFFF. If the operand in FRB is less than -2^{31}, then bits 32:63 of FRT are set to 0x8000_0000.

The conversion is described fully in Appendix B.2, "Floating-Point Convert to Integer Model," on page 209.

Except for enabled Invalid Operation Exceptions, $FPSCR_{FPRF}$ is undefined. $FPSCR_{FR}$ is set if the result is incremented when rounded. $FPSCR_{FI}$ is set if the result is inexact.

Special Registers Altered

```
FPRF(undefined) FR FI
FX XX
VXSNAN VXCVI
CR1                                                    (if Rc=1)
```

Floating Convert To Integer Word with round toward Zero   X-form

fctiwz   FRT,FRB   (Rc=0)
fctiwz.   FRT,FRB   (Rc=1)

[POWER2 mnemonics: fcirz, fcirz.]

63		FRT		///		FRB		15		Rc
0		6		11		16		21		31

The floating-point operand in register FRB is converted to a 32-bit signed fixed-point integer, using the rounding mode *Round toward Zero*, and placed in bits 32:63 of register FRT. Bits 0:31 of register FRT are undefined.

If the operand in FRB is greater than $2^{31}-1$, then bits 32:63 of FRT are set to 0x7FFF_FFFF. If the operand in FRB is less than -2^{31}, then bits 32:63 of FRT are set to 0x8000_0000.

The conversion is described fully in Appendix B.2, "Floating-Point Convert to Integer Model," on page 209.

Except for enabled Invalid Operation Exceptions, FPSCR$_{FPRF}$ is undefined. FPSCR$_{FR}$ is set if the result is incremented when rounded. FPSCR$_{FI}$ is set if the result is inexact.

Special Registers Altered

```
FPRF(undefined) FR FI
FX XX
VXSNAN VXCVI
CR1                                              (if Rc=1)
```

Floating Convert From Integer Doubleword   X-form

fcfid   FRT,FRB   (Rc=0)
fcfid.   FRT,FRB   (Rc=1)

63		FRT		///		FRB		846		Rc
0		6		11		16		21		31

The 64-bit signed fixed-point operand in register FRB is converted to an infinitely precise floating-point integer. If the result of the conversion is already in double-precision range, it is placed into register FRT. Otherwise the result of the conversion is rounded to double-precision, using the rounding mode specified by FPSCR$_{RN}$, and placed into register FRT.

The conversion is described fully in Appendix B.3, "Floating-Point Convert from Integer Model," on page 212.

$FPSCR_{FPRF}$ is set to the class and sign of the result. $FPSCR_{FR}$ is set if the result is incremented when rounded. $FPSCR_{FI}$ is set if the result is inexact.

This instruction is defined only for 64-bit implementations. Using it on a 32-bit implementation will cause the system illegal instruction error handler to be invoked.

Special Registers Altered

```
FPRF FR FI
FX XX
CR1                                              (if Rc=1)
```

4.6.7 Floating-Point Compare Instructions

The floating-point *Compare* instructions compare the contents of two floating-point registers. Comparison ignores the sign of zero (i.e., regards +0 as equal to −0). The comparison can be ordered or unordered.

The comparison sets one bit in the designated CR field to 1 and the other three to 0. The FPCC is set in the same way.

The CR field and the FPCC are interpreted as follows:

Bit	Name	Description
0	FL	(FRA) < (FRB)
1	FG	(FRA) > (FRB)
2	FE	(FRA) = (FRB)
3	FU	(FRA) ? (FRB) (unordered)

Floating Compare Unordered   X-form

fcmpu   BF,FRA,FRB

63	BF	//	FRA	FRB	0	/
0	6	9	11	16	21	31

```
if (FRA) is a NaN or
  (FRB) is a NaN then c ← 0b0001
else if (FRA) < (FRB) then c ← 0b1000
else if (FRA) > (FRB) then c ← 0b0100
else                   c ← 0b0010
FPCC ← c
CR₄ₓ₆F:₄ₓ₆F₊₃ ← c
if (FRA) is an SNaN or
  (FRB) is an SNaN then
     VXSNAN ← 1
```

The floating-point operand in register FRA is compared to the floating-point operand in register FRB. The result of the compare is placed into CR field BF and the FPCC.

If either of the operands is a NaN, either quiet or signaling, then CR field BF and the FPCC are set to reflect unordered. If either of the operands is a Signalling NaN, then VXSNAN is set.

Special Registers Altered

```
CR field BF
FPCC
FX
VXSNAN
```

Floating Compare Ordered   X-form

fcmpo   BF,FRA,FRB

63	BF	//	FRA	FRB	32	/
0	6	9	11	16	21	31

```
if (FRA) is a NaN or
  (FRB) is a NaN then c ← 0b0001
else if (FRA) < (FRB) then c ← 0b1000
else if (FRA) > (FRB) then c ← 0b0100
else                   c ← 0b0010
FPCC ← c
CR₄ₓ₆F:₄ₓ₆F₊₃ ← c
if (FRA) is an SNaN or
  (FRB) is an SNaN then
     VXSNAN ← 1
       if VE = 0 then VXVC ← 1
else if (FRA) is a QNaN or
  (FRB) is a QNaN then VXVC ← 1
```

The floating-point operand in register FRA is compared to the float-ing-point operand in register FRB. The result of the compare is placed into CR field BF and the FPCC.

If either of the operands is a NaN, either quiet or signaling, then CR field BF and the FPCC are set to reflect unordered. If either of the oper-ands is a Signalling NaN, then VXSNAN is set and, if Invalid Operation is disabled (VE=0), VXVC is set. If neither operand is a Signaling NaN but at least one operand is a Quiet NaN, then VXVC is set.

Special Registers Altered

```
CR field BF
FPCC
FX
VXSNAN VXVC
```

4.6.8 Floating-Point Status and Control Register Instructions

Every *Floating-Point Status and Control Register* instruction appears to synchronize the effects of all floating-point instructions executed by a given processor. Executing a *Floating-Point Status and Control Register* instruction ensures that all floating-point instructions previously initiated by the given processor appear to have completed before the *Floating-Point Status and Control Register* instruction is initiated, and that no subsequent floating-point instructions appear to be initiated by the given processor until the *Floating-Point Status and Control Register* instruction has completed. In particular:

■ All exceptions that will be caused by the previously initiated instruc-tions are recorded in the FPSCR before the *Floating-Point Status and Control Register* instruction is initiated.

■ All invocations of the system floating-point enabled exception error handler that will be caused by the previously initiated instructions have occurred before the *Floating-Point Status and Control Register* instruction is initiated.

■ No subsequent floating-point instruction that depends on or alters the settings of any FPSCR bits appears to be initiated until the *Floating-Point Status and Control Register* instruction has completed.

(Floating-point *Storage Access* instructions are not affected.)

Move From FPSCR   X-form

mffs   FRT   (Rc=0)
mffs.   FRT   (Rc=1)

63	FRT	///	///	583	Rc
0	6	11	16	21	31

The contents of the FPSCR are placed into bits 32:63 of register FRT. Bits 0:31 of register FRT are undefined.

Special Registers Altered

```
CR1                                                    (if Rc=1)
```

Move to Condition Register from FPSCR   X-form

mcrfs   BF,BFA

63	BF	//	BFA	//	///	64	/
0	6	9	11	14	16	21	31

The contents of FPSCR field BFA are copied to CR field BF. All exception bits copied (except FEX and VX) are set to 0 in the FPSCR.

Special Registers Altered

```
CR field BF
FX OX                                                  (if BFA=0)
UX ZX XX VXSNAN                                         (if BFA=1)
VXISI VXIDI VXZDZ VXIMZ                                 (if BFA=2)
VXVC                                                   (if BFA=3)
VXSOFT VXSQRT VXCVI                                     (if BFA=5)
```

Move To FPSCR Field Immediate   X-form

mtfsfi   BF,U   (Rc=0)
mtfsfi.   BF,U   (Rc=1)

63	BF	//	///	U	/	134	Rc
0	6	9	11	16	20	21	31

The value of the U field is placed into FPSCR field BF. $FPSCR_{FX}$ is altered only if BF = 0.

Programming Note

When $FPSCR_{0:3}$ is specified for *mtfsfi*, bits 0 (FX) and 3 (OX) are set to the values of U_0 and U_3 (i.e., even if this instruction causes OX to change from 0 to 1, FX is set from U_0 and not by the usual rule that FX is set to 1 when an exception bit changes from 0 to 1). Bits 1 and 2 (FEX and VX) are set according to the usual rule, given on page 137, and not from $U_{1:2}$.

Special Registers Altered

```
FPSCR field BF
CR1                                                      (if Rc=1)
```

Move To FPSCR Fields   XFL-form

mtfsf	FLM,FRB	(Rc=0)
mtfsf.	FLM,FRB	(Rc=1)

63	/	FLM	/	FRB	711	Rc
0	6	7	15	16	21	31

The contents of bits 32:63 of register FRB are placed into the FPSCR under control of the field mask specified by FLM. The field mask identifies the 4-bit fields affected. Let i be an integer in the range 0–7. If FLM_i=1 then FPSCR field i (FPSCR bits 4×i through 4×i+3) is set to the contents of the corresponding field of the low-order 32 bits of register FRB.

$FPSCR_{FX}$ is altered only if FLM_0 = 1.

Special Registers Altered

```
FPSCR fields selected by mask
CR1                                                      (if Rc=1)
```

Move To FPSCR Bit 0   X-form

mtfsb0	BT	(Rc=0)
mtfsb0.	BT	(Rc=1)

63	BT	///	///	70	Rc
0	6	11	16	21	31

Bit BT of the FPSCR is set to 0.

Special Registers Altered

```
FPSCR bit BT
CR1                                                      (if Rc=1)
```

Programming Note

When $FPSCR_{0:3}$ is specified for *mtfsf*, bits 0 (FX) and 3 (OX) are set to the values of $(FRB)_{32}$ and $(FRB)_{35}$ (i.e., even if this instruction causes OX to change from 0 to 1, FX is set from $(FRB)_{32}$ and not by the usual rule that FX is set to 1 when an exception bit changes from 0 to 1). Bits 1 and 2 (FEX and VX) are set according to the usual rule, given on page 137, and not from $(FRB)_{33:34}$.

Programming Note

Updating fewer than all eight fields of the FPSCR may result in substantially poorer performance on some implementations than updating all the fields.

Programming Note

Bits 1 and 2 (FEX and VX) cannot be explicitly reset by *mtfsb0*.

Programming Note

Bits 1 and 2 (FEX and VX) cannot be explicitly set by *mtfsb1*.

Move To FPSCR Bit 1   X-form

| mtfsb1 | BT | (Rc=0) |
| mtfsb1. | BT | (Rc=1) |

63	BT	///	///	38	Rc
0	6	11	16	21	31

Bit BT of the FPSCR is set to 1.

Special Registers Altered
```
FPSCR bits BT and FX
CR1                                         (if Rc=1)
```

Optional Instructions

The instructions described in this appendix are optional. If an instruction is implemented that matches the semantics of an instruction described here, the implementation should be as specified here. The optional instructions are divided into two groups. Additional groups may be defined in the future.

- General Purpose group: *fsqrt* and *fsqrts*.

- Graphics group: *stfiwx, fres, frsqrte,* and *fsel*.

If an implementation claims to support a given group, it must implement all the instructions in the group.

A.1 Floating-Point Processor Instructions

A.1.1 Floating-Point Store Instruction

Byte ordering on PowerPC is Big-Endian by default. See Appendix D, "Little-Endian Byte Ordering," on page 233 for the effects of operating a PowerPC system with Little-Endian byte ordering.

Store Floating-Point as Integer Word Indexed   X-form

stfiwx   FRS,RA,RB

31	FRS	RA	RB	983	/
0	6	11	16	21	31

```
if RA = 0 then b ← 0
else            b ← (RA)
EA ← b + (RB)
MEM(EA, 4) ← (FRS)32:63
```

Let the effective address (EA) be the sum (RA|0)+(RB).

The contents of the low-order 32 bits of register FRS are stored, without conversion, into the word in storage addressed by EA.

If the contents of register FRS were produced, either directly or indirectly, by a *Load Floating-Point Single* instruction, a single-precision arithmetic instruction, or *frsp*, then the value stored is undefined. (The contents of register FRS are produced directly by such an instruction if FRS is the target register for the instruction. The contents of register FRS are produced indirectly by such an instruction if FRS is the final target register of a sequence of one or more *Floating-Point Move* instructions, with the input to the sequence having been produced directly by such an instruction.)

Special Registers Altered
    None

A.1.2 Floating-Point Arithmetic Instructions

Floating-Point Elementary Arithmetic Instructions

Floating Square Root [Single]   A-form

fsqrt   FRT,FRB   (Rc=0)
fsqrt.   FRT,FRB   (Rc=1)

63	FRT	///	FRB	///	22	Rc
0	6	11	16	21	26	31

| fsqrts | FRT,FRB | (Rc=0) |
| fsqrts. | FRT,FRB | (Rc=1) |

59	FRT	///	FRB	///	22	Rc
0	6	11	16	21	26	31

The square root of the floating-point operand in register FRB is placed into register FRT.

If the most significant bit of the resultant significand is not 1, the result is normalized. The result is rounded to the target precision under control of the Floating-Point Rounding Control field RN of the FPSCR and placed into register FRT.

Operation with various special values of the operand is summarized below.

Operand	Result	Exception
$-\infty$	QNaN[1]	VXSQRT
< 0	QNaN[1]	VXSQRT
-0	-0	None
$+\infty$	$+\infty$	None
SNaN	QNaN[1]	VXSNAN
QNaN	QNaN	None

[1]No result if $FPSCR_{VE} = 1$.

$FPSCR_{FPRF}$ is set to the class and sign of the result, except for Invalid Operation Exceptions when $FPSCR_{VE}=1$.

Special Registers Altered

```
FPRF FR FI
FX XX
VXSNAN VXSQRT
CR1                                              (if Rc=1)
```

Floating Reciprocal Estimate Single   A-form

| fres | FRT,FRB | (Rc=0) |
| fres. | FRT,FRB | (Rc=1) |

59	FRT	///	FRB	///	24	Rc
0	6	11	16	21	26	31

A single-precision estimate of the reciprocal of the floating-point operand in register FRB is placed into register FRT. The estimate placed into register FRT is correct to a precision of one part in 256 of the reciprocal of (FRB), i.e.,

$$\text{ABS}\left(\frac{\text{estimate} - 1/x}{1/x}\right) \leq \frac{1}{256}$$

where x is the initial value in FRB. Note that the value placed into register FRT may vary between implementations, and between different executions on the same implementation.

Operation with various special values of the operand is summarized below.

Operand	Result	Exception
$-\infty$	-0	None
-0	$-\infty$[1]	ZX
$+0$	$+\infty$[1]	ZX
$+\infty$	$+0$	None
SNaN	QNaN[2]	VXSNAN
QNaN	QNaN	None

[1]No result if FPSCR_{ZE} = 1.
[2]No result if FPSCR_{VE} = 1.

FPSCR_{FPRF} is set to the class and sign of the result, except for Invalid Operation Exceptions when FPSCR_{VE}=1 and Zero Divide Exceptions when FPSCR_{ZE}=1.

Special Registers Altered

```
FPRF FR(undefined)  FI(undefined)
FX OX UX ZX
VXSNAN
CR1                                      (if Rc=1)
```

Floating Reciprocal Square Root Estimate A-form

frsqrte	FRT,FRB	(Rc=0)
frsqrte.	FRT,FRB	(Rc=1)

63	FRT	///	FRB	///	26	Rc
0	6	11	16	21	26	31

A double-precision estimate of the reciprocal of the square root of the floating-point operand in register FRB is placed into register FRT. The estimate placed into register FRT is correct to a precision of one part in 32 of the reciprocal of the square root of (FRB), i.e.,

$$\text{ABS} \left(\frac{\text{estimate} \ - 1/\sqrt{x}}{1/\sqrt{x}} \right) \le \frac{1}{32}$$

where x is the initial value in FRB. Note that the value placed into register FRT may vary between implementations, and between different executions on the same implementation.

Operation with various special values of the operand is summarized below.

Operand	Result	Exception
$-\infty$	QNaN[2]	VXSQRT
<0	QNaN[2]	VXSQRT
-0	$-\infty$[1]	ZX
$+0$	$+\infty$[1]	ZX
$+\infty$	$+0$	None
SNaN	QNaN[2]	VXSNAN
QNaN	QNaN	None

[1]No result if FPSCR$_{ZE}$ = 1.
[2]No result if FPSCR$_{VE}$ = 1.

$FPSCR_{FPRF}$ is set to the class and sign of the result, except for Invalid Operation Exceptions when $FPSCR_{VE}=1$ and Zero Divide Exceptions when $FPSCR_{ZE}=1$.

Special Registers Altered

```
FPRF FR(undefined) FI(undefined)
FX ZX
VXSNAN VXSQRT
CR1                                          (if Rc=1)
```

A.1.3 Floating-Point Select Instruction

Programming Note

Examples of uses of the *fsel* instruction can be found in Sections E.3, "Floating-Point Conversions," on page 259, and E.4, "Floating-Point Selection," on page 264.

Warning:

Care must be taken in using *fsel* if IEEE compatibility is required, or if the values being tested can be NaNs or infinities; see Section E.4.4, "Notes," on page 266.

Floating Select   A-form

fsel	FRT,FRA,FRC,FRB	(Rc=0)
fsel.	FRT,FRA,FRC,FRB	(Rc=1)

63	FRT	FRA	FRB	FRC	23	Rc
0	6	11	16	21	26	31

```
if (FRA) ≥ 0.0 then FRT ← (FRC)
else FRT ← (FRB)
```

The floating-point operand in register FRA is compared to the value zero. If the operand is greater than or equal to zero, register FRT is set to the contents of register FRC. If the operand is less than zero or is a NaN, register FRT is set to the contents of register FRB. The comparison ignores the sign of zero (i.e., regards +0 as equal to −0).

Special Registers Altered

```
CR1                                          (if Rc=1)
```

Suggested Floating-Point Models

B.1 Floating-Point Round to Single-Precision Model

The following describes algorithmically the operation of the *Floating Round to Single-Precision* instruction.

If $(FRB)_{1:11} < 897$ and $(FRB)_{1:63} > 0$ then
    Do
        If $FPSCR_{UE} = 0$ then goto Disabled Exponent Underflow
        If $FPSCR_{UE} = 1$ then goto Enabled Exponent Underflow
    End
If $(FRB)_{1:11} > 1150$ and $(FRB)_{1:11} < 2047$ then
    Do
        If $FPSCR_{OE} = 0$ then goto Disabled Exponent Overflow
        If $FPSCR_{OE} = 1$ then goto Enabled Exponent Overflow
    End
If $(FRB)_{1:11} > 896$ and $(FRB)_{1:11} < 1151$ then goto Normal Operand
If $(FRB)_{1:63} = 0$ then goto Zero Operand
If $(FRB)_{1:11} = 2047$ then
    Do
        If $(FRB)_{12:63} = 0$ then goto Infinity Operand
        If $(FRB)_{12} = 1$ then goto QNaN Operand
        If $(FRB)_{12} = 0$ and $(FRB)_{13:63} > 0$ then goto SNaN Operand
    End

Disabled Exponent Underflow:

sign $\leftarrow$ $(FRB)_0$

If $(FRB)_{1:11} = 0$ then

    Do

        exp $\leftarrow$ -1022

        $frac_{0:52} \leftarrow$ 0b0 $\parallel$ $(FRB)_{12:63}$

    End

If $(FRB)_{1:11} > 0$ then

    Do

        exp $\leftarrow$ $(FRB)_{1:11} - 1023$

        $frac_{0:52} \leftarrow$ 0b1 $\parallel$ $(FRB)_{12:63}$

    End

Denormalize operand:

    G $\parallel$ R $\parallel$ X $\leftarrow$ 0b000

    Do while exp < -126

        exp $\leftarrow$ exp $+ 1$

        $frac_{0:52}$ $\parallel$ G $\parallel$ R $\parallel$ X $\leftarrow$ 0b0 $\parallel$ $frac_{0:52}$ $\parallel$ G $\parallel$ (R $\mid$ X)

    End

$FPSCR_{UX} \leftarrow frac_{24:52}$ $\parallel$ G $\parallel$ R $\parallel$ X > 0

Round Single(sign,exp,$frac_{0:52}$,G,R,X)

$FPSCR_{XX} \leftarrow FPSCR_{XX}$ $\mid$ $FPSCR_{FI}$

If $frac_{0:52} = 0$ then

    Do

        $FRT_0 \leftarrow$ sign

        $FRT_{1:63} \leftarrow 0$

        If sign = 0 then $FPSCR_{FPRF} \leftarrow$ "+zero"

        If sign = 1 then $FPSCR_{FPRF} \leftarrow$ "$-$zero"

    End

If $frac_{0:52} > 0$ then

    Do

        If $frac_0 = 1$ then

            Do

                If sign = 0 then $FPSCR_{FPRF} \leftarrow$ "+normal number"

                If sign = 1 then $FPSCR_{FPRF} \leftarrow$ "$-$normal number"

            End

        If $frac_0 = 0$ then

            Do

                If sign = 0 then $FPSCR_{FPRF} \leftarrow$ "+denormalized number"

                If sign = 1 then $FPSCR_{FPRF} \leftarrow$ "$-$denormalized number"

            End

Normalize operand:
       Do while $frac_0 = 0$
            $exp \leftarrow exp{-}1$
            $frac_{0:52} \leftarrow frac_{1:52} \parallel 0b0$
       End
    $FRT_0 \leftarrow sign$
    $FRT_{1:11} \leftarrow exp + 1023$
    $FRT_{12:63} \leftarrow frac_{1:52}$
   End
Done

Enabled Exponent Underflow:
   $FPSCR_{UX} \leftarrow 1$
   $sign \leftarrow (FRB)_0$
   If $(FRB)_{1:11} = 0$ then
      Do
           $exp \leftarrow -1022$
           $frac_{0:52} \leftarrow 0b0 \parallel (FRB)_{12:63}$
      End
   If $(FRB)_{1:11} > 0$ then
      Do
           $exp \leftarrow (FRB)_{1:11} - 1023$
           $frac_{0:52} \leftarrow 0b1 \parallel (FRB)_{12:63}$
      End
   Normalize operand:
      Do while $frac_0 = 0$
           $exp \leftarrow exp - 1$
           $frac_{0:52} \leftarrow frac_{1:52} \parallel 0b0$
      End
   Round Single$(sign,exp,frac_{0:52},0,0,0)$
   $FPSCR_{XX} \leftarrow FPSCR_{XX} \mid FPSCR_{FI}$
   $exp \leftarrow exp + 192$
   $FRT_0 \leftarrow sign$
   $FRT_{1:11} \leftarrow exp + 1023$
   $FRT_{12:63} \leftarrow frac_{1:52}$
   If $sign = 0$ then $FPSCR_{FPRF} \leftarrow$ "+normal number"
   If $sign = 1$ then $FPSCR_{FPRF} \leftarrow$ "−normal number"
   Done

Disabled Exponent Overflow:

    $FPSCR_{OX} \leftarrow 1$

    If $FPSCR_{RN}$ = 0b00 then   /* Round to Nearest */

        Do

            If $(FRB)_0$ = 0 then $FRT \leftarrow 0x7FF0\_0000\_0000\_0000$

            If $(FRB)_0$ = 1 then $FRT \leftarrow 0xFFF0\_0000\_0000\_0000$

            If $(FRB)_0$ = 0 then $FPSCR_{FPRF} \leftarrow$ "+infinity"

            If $(FRB)_0$ = 1 then $FPSCR_{FPRF} \leftarrow$ "−infinity"

        End

    If $FPSCR_{RN}$ = 0b01 then   /* Round toward Zero */

        Do

            If $(FRB)_0$ = 0 then $FRT \leftarrow 0x47EF\_FFFF\_E000\_0000$

            If $(FRB)_0$ = 1 then $FRT \leftarrow 0xC7EF\_FFFF\_E000\_0000$

            If $(FRB)_0$ = 0 then $FPSCR_{FPRF} \leftarrow$ "+normal number"

            If $(FRB)_0$ = 1 then $FPSCR_{FPRF} \leftarrow$ "−normal number"

        End

    If $FPSCR_{RN}$ = 0b10 then   /* Round toward +Infinity */

        Do

            If $(FRB)_0$ = 0 then $FRT \leftarrow 0x7FF0\_0000\_0000\_0000$

            If $(FRB)_0$ = 1 then $FRT \leftarrow 0xC7EF\_FFFF\_E000\_0000$

            If $(FRB)_0$ = 0 then $FPSCR_{FPRF} \leftarrow$ "+infinity"

            If $(FRB)_0$ = 1 then $FPSCR_{FPRF} \leftarrow$ "−normal number"

        End

    If $FPSCR_{RN}$ = 0b11 then   /* Round toward −Infinity */

        Do

            If $(FRB)_0$ = 0 then $FRT \leftarrow 0x47EF\_FFFF\_E000\_0000$

            If $(FRB)_0$ = 1 then $FRT \leftarrow 0xFFF0\_0000\_0000\_0000$

            If $(FRB)_0$ = 0 then $FPSCR_{FPRF} \leftarrow$ "+normal number"

            If $(FRB)_0$ = 1 then $FPSCR_{FPRF} \leftarrow$ "−infinity"

        End

    $FPSCR_{FR} \leftarrow$ undefined

    $FPSCR_{FI} \leftarrow 1$

    $FPSCR_{XX} \leftarrow 1$

    Done

Enabled Exponent Overflow:

    $sign \leftarrow (FRB)_0$

    $exp \leftarrow (FRB)_{1:11} - 1023$

    $frac_{0:52} \leftarrow 0b1 \parallel (FRB)_{12:63}$

    Round Single$(sign,exp,frac_{0:52},0,0,0)$

    $FPSCR_{XX} \leftarrow FPSCR_{XX} \mid FPSCR_{FI}$

Enabled Overflow:
   $FPSCR_{OX} \leftarrow 1$
   $exp \leftarrow exp - 192$
   $FRT_0 \leftarrow sign$
   $FRT_{1:11} \leftarrow exp + 1023$
   $FRT_{12:63} \leftarrow frac_{1:52}$
   If sign = 0 then $FPSCR_{FPRF} \leftarrow$ "+normal number"
   If sign = 1 then $FPSCR_{FPRF} \leftarrow$ "−normal number"
   Done

Zero Operand:
   $FRT \leftarrow (FRB)$
   If $(FRB)_0 = 0$ then $FPSCR_{FPRF} \leftarrow$ "+zero"
   If $(FRB)_0 = 1$ then $FPSCR_{FPRF} \leftarrow$ "−zero"
   $FPSCR_{FR\ FI} \leftarrow 0b00$
   Done

Infinity Operand:
   $FRT \leftarrow (FRB)$
   If $(FRB)_0 = 0$ then $FPSCR_{FPRF} \leftarrow$ "+infinity"
   If $(FRB)_0 = 1$ then $FPSCR_{FPRF} \leftarrow$ "−infinity"
   $FPSCR_{FR\ FI} \leftarrow 0b00$
   Done

QNaN Operand:
   $FRT \leftarrow (FRB)_{0:34} \parallel {}^{29}0$
   $FPSCR_{FPRF} \leftarrow$ "QNaN"
   $FPSCR_{FR\ FI} \leftarrow 0b00$
   Done

SNaN Operand:
   $FPSCR_{VXSNAN} \leftarrow 1$
   If $FPSCR_{VE} = 0$ then
      Do
         $FRT_{0:11} \leftarrow (FRB)_{0:11}$
         $FRT_{12} \leftarrow 1$
         $FRT_{13:63} \leftarrow (FRB)_{13:34} \parallel {}^{29}0$
         $FPSCR_{FPRF} \leftarrow$ "QNaN"
      End
   $FPSCR_{FR\ FI} \leftarrow 0b00$
   Done

Normal Operand:
   sign ← $(FRB)_0$
   exp ← $(FRB)_{1:11}$ − 1023
   $frac_{0:52}$ ← 0b1 || $(FRB)_{12:63}$
   Round Single(sign,exp,$frac_{0:52}$,0,0,0)
   $FPSCR_{XX}$ ← $FPSCR_{XX}$ | $FPSCR_{FI}$
   If exp > 127 and $FPSCR_{OE}$ = 0 then go to Disabled Exponent Overflow
   If exp > 127 and $FPSCR_{OE}$ = 1 then go to Enabled Overflow
   FRT_0 ← sign
   $FRT_{1:11}$ ← exp + 1023
   $FRT_{12:63}$ ← $frac_{1:52}$
   If sign = 0 then $FPSCR_{FPRF}$ ← "+normal number"
   If sign = 1 then $FPSCR_{FPRF}$ ← "−normal number"
   Done

Round Single(sign,exp,$frac_{0:52}$,G,R,X):
   /* comparisons ignore u bits */
   inc ← 0
   lsb ← $frac_{23}$
   gbit ← $frac_{24}$
   rbit ← $frac_{25}$
   xbit ← $(frac_{26:52}||G||R||X) \neq 0$
   If $FPSCR_{RN}$ = 0b00 then
      Do
         If sign || lsb || gbit || rbit || xbit = 0bu11uu then inc ← 1
         If sign || lsb || gbit || rbit || xbit = 0bu011u then inc ← 1
         If sign || lsb || gbit || rbit || xbit = 0bu01u1 then inc ← 1
      End
   If $FPSCR_{RN}$ = 0b10 then
      Do
         If sign || lsb || gbit || rbit || xbit = 0b0u1uu then inc ← 1
         If sign || lsb || gbit || rbit || xbit = 0b0uu1u then inc ← 1
         If sign || lsb || gbit || rbit || xbit = 0b0uuu1 then inc ← 1
      End
   If $FPSCR_{RN}$ = 0b11 then
      Do
         If sign || lsb || gbit || rbit || xbit = 0b1u1uu then inc ← 1
         If sign || lsb || gbit || rbit || xbit = 0b1uu1u then inc ← 1
         If sign || lsb || gbit || rbit || xbit = 0b1uuu1 then inc ← 1
      End
   $frac_{0:23}$ ← $frac_{0:23}$ + inc
   If carry_out = 1 then

Do
$\quad$ $frac_{0:23} \leftarrow 0b1 \parallel frac_{0:22}$
$\quad$ $exp \leftarrow exp + 1$
End
$frac_{24:52} \leftarrow {}^{29}0$
$FPSCR_{FR} \leftarrow inc$
$FPSCR_{FI} \leftarrow gbit \mid rbit \mid xbit$
Return

B.2 Floating-Point Convert to Integer Model

The following describes algorithmically the operation of the *Floating Convert To Integer* instructions.

If *Floating Convert To Integer Word* then
$\quad$ Do
$\qquad$ $round\_mode \leftarrow FPSCR_{RN}$
$\qquad$ $tgt\_precision \leftarrow$ "32-bit integer"
$\quad$ End
If *Floating Convert To Integer Word with Round toward Zero* then
$\quad$ Do
$\qquad$ $round\_mode \leftarrow 0b01$
$\qquad$ $tgt\_precision \leftarrow$ "32-bit integer"
$\quad$ End
If *Floating Convert To Integer Doubleword* then
$\quad$ Do
$\qquad$ $round\_mode \leftarrow FPSCR_{RN}$
$\qquad$ $tgt\_precision \leftarrow$ "64-bit integer"
$\quad$ End
If *Floating Convert To Integer Doubleword with Round toward Zero* then
$\quad$ Do
$\qquad$ $round\_mode \leftarrow 0b01$
$\qquad$ $tgt\_precision \leftarrow$ "64-bit integer"
$\quad$ End

$sign \leftarrow (FRB)_0$
If $(FRB)_{1:11} = 2047$ and $(FRB)_{12:63} = 0$ then goto Infinity Operand
If $(FRB)_{1:11} = 2047$ and $(FRB)_{12} = 0$ then goto SNaN Operand
If $(FRB)_{1:11} = 2047$ and $(FRB)_{12} = 1$ then goto QNaN Operand
If $(FRB)_{1:11} > 1086$ then goto Large Operand

If $(FRB)_{1:11} > 0$ then $exp \leftarrow (FRB)_{1:11} - 1023$ /* exp − bias */
If $(FRB)_{1:11} = 0$ then $exp \leftarrow -1022$
If $(FRB)_{1:11} > 0$ then $frac_{0:64} \leftarrow 0b01 \parallel (FRB)_{12:63} \parallel {}^{11}0$ /* normal */
                /* need leading 0 above for later complement */
If $(FRB)_{1:11} = 0$ then $frac_{0:64} \leftarrow 0b00 \parallel (FRB)_{12:63} \parallel {}^{11}0$ /* denormal */

$gbit \parallel rbit \parallel xbit \leftarrow 0b000$
Do i=1,63−exp   /* do the loop 0 times if exp = 63 */
    $frac_{0:64} \parallel gbit \parallel rbit \parallel xbit \leftarrow 0b0 \parallel frac_{0:64} \parallel gbit \parallel (rbit \mid xbit)$
End

Round Integer(sign,$frac_{0:64}$,gbit,rbit,xbit,round_mode)

If sign = 1 then $frac_{0:64} \leftarrow \neg frac_{0:64} + 1$
                /* needed leading 0 for $-2^{64} < (FRB) < -2^{63}$ */

If tgt_precision = "32-bit integer" and $frac_{0:64} > 2^{31}-1$
    then goto Large Operand
If tgt_precision = "64-bit integer" and $frac_{0:64} > 2^{63}-1$
    then goto Large Operand
If tgt_precision = "32-bit integer" and $frac_{0:64} < -2^{31}$
    then goto Large Operand
If tgt_precision = "64-bit integer" and $frac_{0:64} < -2^{63}$
    then goto Large Operand

$FPSCR_{XX} \leftarrow FPSCR_{XX} \mid FPSCR_{FI}$

If tgt_precision = "32-bit integer" then
    $FRT \leftarrow 0xuuuu\_uuuu \parallel frac_{33:64}$ /* u is undefined hex digit */
If tgt_precision = "64-bit integer" then $FRT \leftarrow frac_{1:64}$
$FPSCR_{FPRF} \leftarrow$ undefined
Done

Round Integer(sign,$frac_{0:64}$,gbit,rbit,xbit,round_mode):
    /* comparisons ignore u bits */
    $inc \leftarrow 0$
    If round_mode = 0b00 then
        Do
            If $sign \parallel frac_{64} \parallel gbit \parallel rbit \parallel xbit = 0bu11uu$ then $inc \leftarrow 1$
            If $sign \parallel frac_{64} \parallel gbit \parallel rbit \parallel xbit = 0bu011u$ then $inc \leftarrow 1$
            If $sign \parallel frac_{64} \parallel gbit \parallel rbit \parallel xbit = 0bu01u1$ then $inc \leftarrow 1$
        End

If round_mode = 0b10 then
    Do
        If sign || frac_{64} || gbit || rbit || xbit = 0b0u1uu then inc ← 1
        If sign || frac_{64} || gbit || rbit || xbit = 0b0uu1u then inc ← 1
        If sign || frac_{64} || gbit || rbit || xbit = 0b0uuu1 then inc ← 1
    End
If round_mode = 0b11 then
    Do
        If sign || frac_{64} || gbit || rbit || xbit = 0b1u1uu then inc ← 1
        If sign || frac_{64} || gbit || rbit || xbit = 0b1uu1u then inc ← 1
        If sign || frac_{64} || gbit || rbit || xbit = 0b1uuu1 then inc ← 1
    End
$\text{frac}_{0:64}$ ← $\text{frac}_{0:64}$ + inc
FPSCR_{FR} ← inc
FPSCR_{FI} ← gbit | rbit | xbit
Return

Infinity Operand:
    $\text{FPSCR}_{FR\ FI\ VXCVI}$ ← 0b001
    If FPSCR_{VE} = 0 then Do
        If tgt_precision = "32-bit integer" then
            Do   /* u is undefined hex digit */
                If sign = 0 then FRT ← 0xuuuu_uuuu_7FFF_FFFF
                If sign = 1 then FRT ← 0xuuuu_uuuu_8000_0000
            End
        Else
            Do
                If sign = 0 then FRT ← 0x7FFF_FFFF_FFFF_FFFF
                If sign = 1 then FRT ← 0x8000_0000_0000_0000
            End
        FPSCR_{FPRF} ← undefined
        End
    Done

SNaN Operand:
    $\text{FPSCR}_{FR\ FI\ VXSNAN\ VXCVI}$ ← 0b0011
    If FPSCR_{VE} = 0 then
        Do   /* u is undefined hex digit */
            If tgt_precision = "32-bit integer" then FRT ← 0xuuuu_uuuu_8000_0000
            If tgt_precision = "64-bit integer" then FRT ← 0x8000_0000_0000_0000
            FPSCR_{FPRF} ← undefined
        End
    Done

QNaN Operand:

$\text{FPSCR}_{\text{FR FI VXCVI}} \leftarrow 0b001$

If $\text{FPSCR}_{\text{VE}} = 0$ then

    Do   /* u is undefined hex digit */

        If tgt_precision = "32-bit integer" then FRT $\leftarrow$ 0xuuuu_uuuu_8000_0000

        If tgt_precision = "64-bit integer" then FRT $\leftarrow$ 0x8000_0000_0000_0000

        $\text{FPSCR}_{\text{FPRF}} \leftarrow$ undefined

    End

Done

Large Operand:

$\text{FPSCR}_{\text{FR FI VXCVI}} \leftarrow 0b001$

If $\text{FPSCR}_{\text{VE}} = 0$ then Do

    If tgt_precision = "32-bit integer" then

        Do   /* u is undefined hex digit */

            If sign = 0 then FRT $\leftarrow$ 0xuuuu_uuuu_7FFF_FFFF

            If sign = 1 then FRT $\leftarrow$ 0xuuuu_uuuu_8000_0000

        End

    Else

        Do

            If sign = 0 then FRT $\leftarrow$ 0x7FFF_FFFF_FFFF_FFFF

            If sign = 1 then FRT $\leftarrow$ 0x8000_0000_0000_0000

        End

    $\text{FPSCR}_{\text{FPRF}} \leftarrow$ undefined

    End

Done

B.3 Floating-Point Convert from Integer Model

The following describes algorithmically the operation of the *Floating Convert From Integer Doubleword* instruction.

sign $\leftarrow (\text{FRB})_0$

exp $\leftarrow$ 63

$\text{frac}_{0:63} \leftarrow (\text{FRB})$

If $\text{frac}_{0:63} = 0$ then go to Zero Operand

If sign = 1 then $\text{frac}_{0:63} \leftarrow \neg\text{frac}_{0:63} + 1$

Do while $\text{frac}_0 = 0$
    /* do the loop 0 times if (FRB) = maximum negative integer */
    $\text{frac}_{0:63} \leftarrow \text{frac}_{1:63} \parallel 0\text{b}0$
    $\text{exp} \leftarrow \text{exp} - 1$
End
Round Float(sign,exp,$\text{frac}_{0:63}$,FPSCR_{RN})
If sign = 0 then $\text{FPSCR}_{FPRF} \leftarrow$ "+normal number"
If sign = 1 then $\text{FPSCR}_{FPRF} \leftarrow$ "−normal number"
$\text{FRT}_0 \leftarrow \text{sign}$
$\text{FRT}_{1:11} \leftarrow \text{exp} + 1023$ /* exp + bias */
$\text{FRT}_{12:63} \leftarrow \text{frac}_{1:52}$
Done

Zero Operand:
    $\text{FPSCR}_{FR\ FI} \leftarrow 0\text{b}00$
    $\text{FPSCR}_{FPRF} \leftarrow$ "+zero"
    $\text{FRT} \leftarrow \text{0x0000\_0000\_0000\_0000}$
    Done

Round Float(sign,exp,$\text{frac}_{0:63}$,round_mode):
    /* comparisons ignore u bits */
    $\text{inc} \leftarrow 0$
    $\text{lsb} \leftarrow \text{frac}_{52}$
    $\text{gbit} \leftarrow \text{frac}_{53}$
    $\text{rbit} \leftarrow \text{frac}_{54}$
    $\text{xbit} \leftarrow \text{frac}_{55:63} > 0$
    If round_mode = 0b00 then
        Do
            If sign $\parallel$ lsb $\parallel$ gbit $\parallel$ rbit $\parallel$ xbit = 0bu11uu then inc $\leftarrow 1$
            If sign $\parallel$ lsb $\parallel$ gbit $\parallel$ rbit $\parallel$ xbit = 0bu011u then inc $\leftarrow 1$
            If sign $\parallel$ lsb $\parallel$ gbit $\parallel$ rbit $\parallel$ xbit = 0bu01u1 then inc $\leftarrow 1$
        End
    If round_mode = 0b10 then
        Do
            If sign $\parallel$ lsb $\parallel$ gbit $\parallel$ rbit $\parallel$ xbit = 0b0u1uu then inc $\leftarrow 1$
            If sign $\parallel$ lsb $\parallel$ gbit $\parallel$ rbit $\parallel$ xbit = 0b0uu1u then inc $\leftarrow 1$
            If sign $\parallel$ lsb $\parallel$ gbit $\parallel$ rbit $\parallel$ xbit = 0b0uuu1 then inc $\leftarrow 1$
        End

If round_mode = 0b11 then
    Do
        If sign $\parallel$ lsb $\parallel$ gbit $\parallel$ rbit $\parallel$ xbit = 0b1u1uu then inc $\leftarrow$ 1
        If sign $\parallel$ lsb $\parallel$ gbit $\parallel$ rbit $\parallel$ xbit = 0b1uu1u then inc $\leftarrow$ 1
        If sign $\parallel$ lsb $\parallel$ gbit $\parallel$ rbit $\parallel$ xbit = 0b1uuu1 then inc $\leftarrow$ 1
    End
$frac_{0:52} \leftarrow frac_{0:52} + inc$
If carry_out = 1 then $exp \leftarrow exp + 1$
$FPSCR_{FR} \leftarrow inc$
$FPSCR_{FI} \leftarrow gbit \mid rbit \mid xbit$
$FPSCR_{XX} \leftarrow FPSCR_{XX} \mid FPSCR_{FI}$
Return

Assembler Extended Mnemonics

 In order to make assembler language programs simpler to write and easier to understand, a set of extended mnemonics and symbols is provided that defines simple shorthand for the most frequently used forms of *Branch Conditional, Compare, Trap, Rotate and Shift,* and certain other instructions.

Assemblers should provide the mnemonics and symbols listed here, and may provide others.

C.1 Symbols

The following symbols are defined for use in instructions (basic or extended mnemonics) that specify a Condition Register field or a Condition Register bit. The first five (lt, …, un) identify a bit number within a CR field. The remainder (cr0, …, cr7) identify a CR field. An expression in which a CR field symbol is multiplied by 4 and then added to a bit-number-within-CR-field symbol can be used to identify a CR bit.

Symbol	Value	Meaning
lt	0	Less than
gt	1	Greater than
eq	2	Equal
so	3	Summary overflow
un	3	Unordered (after floating-point comparison)
cr0	0	CR Field 0
cr1	1	CR Field 1
cr2	2	CR Field 2
cr3	3	CR Field 3
cr4	4	CR Field 4
cr5	5	CR Field 5
cr6	6	CR Field 6
cr7	7	CR Field 7

The extended mnemonics in Sections C.2.2 and C.3 require identification of a CR bit: if one of the CR field symbols is used, it must be multiplied by 4 and added to a bit-number-within-CR-field (value in the range 0-3, explicit or symbolic). The extended mnemonics in Sections C.2.3 and C.5 require identification of a CR field: if one of the CR field symbols is used, it must *not* be multiplied by 4. (For the extended mnemonics in Section C.2.3, the bit number within the CR field is part of the extended mnemonic. The programmer identifies the CR field, and the Assembler does the multiplication and addition required to produce a CR bit number for the BI field of the underlying basic mnemonic.)

C.2 Branch Mnemonics

The mnemonics discussed in this section are variations of the *Branch Conditional* instructions.

C.2.1 BO and BI Fields

The 5-bit BO field in *Branch Conditional* instructions encodes the following operations:

- Decrement CTR

- Test CTR equal to 0

- Test CTR not equal to 0

- Test condition true

- Test condition false

- Branch prediction (taken, fall through)

The 5-bit BI field in *Branch Conditional* instructions specifies which of the 32 bits in the CR represents the condition to test.

To provide an extended mnemonic for every possible combination of BO and BI fields would require 2^{10} = 1024 mnemonics. Most of these would be only marginally useful. The following abbreviated set is intended to cover the most useful cases. Unusual cases can be coded using a basic *Branch Conditional* mnemonic (*bc, bclr, bcctr*) with the condition to be tested specified as a numeric operand.

C.2.2 Simple Branch Mnemonics

The mnemonics in Table 2 on page 218 allow all the useful BO encodings to be specified, along with the AA (absolute address) and LK (set Link Register) fields.

Notice that there are no extended mnemonics for relative and absolute unconditional branches. For these, the basic mnemonics *b, ba, bl,* and *bla* should be used.

Instructions using one of the mnemonics in Table 2 that tests a condition specify the corresponding Condition Register bit as the first operand. The symbols defined in Section C.1 can be used in this operand.

Examples

1. Decrement CTR and branch if it is still nonzero (closure of a loop controlled by a count loaded into CTR).

bdnz   target   (equivalent to: bc   16,0,target)

Branch semantics	LR not set				LR set			
	bc Relative	*bca* Absolute	*bclr* To LR	*bcctr* To CTR	*bcl* Relative	*bcla* Absolute	*bclrl* To LR	*bcctrl* To CTR
Branch unconditionally	–	–	blr	bctr	–	–	blrl	bctrl
Branch if condition true	bt	bta	btlr	btctr	btl	btla	btlrl	btctrl
Branch if condition false	bf	bfa	bflr	bfctr	bfl	bfla	bflrl	bfctrl
Decrement CTR, branch if CTR nonzero	bdnz	bdnza	bdnzlr	–	bdnzl	bdnzla	bdnzlrl	–
Decrement CTR, branch if CTR nonzero AND condition true	bdnzt	bdnzta	bdnztlr	–	bdnztl	bdnztla	bdnztlrl	–
Decrement CTR, branch if CTR nonzero AND condition false	bdnzf	bdnzfa	bdnzflr	–	bdnzfl	bdnzfla	bdnzflrl	–
Decrement CTR, branch if CTR zero	bdz	bdza	bdzlr	–	bdzl	bdzla	bdzlrl	–
Decrement CTR, branch if CTR zero AND condition true	bdzt	bdzta	bdztlr	–	bdztl	bdztla	bdztlrl	–
Decrement CTR, branch if CTR zero AND condition false	bdzf	bdzfa	bdzflr	–	bdzfl	bdzfla	bdzflrl	–

Table 2.   **Simple branch mnemonics**

2. Same as (1) but branch only if CTR is nonzero and condition in CR0 is "equal."

     bdnzt   eq,target   (equivalent to: bc   8,2,target)

3. Same as (2), but "equal" condition is in CR5.

     bdnzt   4*cr5+eq,target   (equivalent to: bc   8,22,target)

4. Branch if bit 27 of CR is false.

     bf   27,target   (equivalent to: bc   4,27,target)

5. Same as (4), but set the Link Register. This is a form of conditional "call."

     bfl   27,target   (equivalent to: bcl   4,27,target)

C.2.3 Branch Mnemonics Incorporating Conditions

The mnemonics defined in Table 3 on page 220 are variations of the "branch if condition true" and "branch if condition false" BO encodings, with the most useful values of BI represented in the mnemonic rather than specified as a numeric operand.

A standard set of codes has been adopted for the most common combinations of branch conditions.

Code	Meaning
lt	Less than
le	Less than or equal
eq	Equal
ge	Greater than or equal
gt	Greater than
nl	Not less than
ne	Not equal
ng	Not greater than
so	Summary overflow
ns	Not summary overflow
un	Unordered (after floating-point comparison)
nu	Not unordered (after floating-point comparison)

These codes are reflected in the mnemonics shown in Table 3 on page 220.

Instructions using the mnemonics in Table 3 specify the Condition Register field in an optional first operand. If the CR field being tested is CR0, this operand need not be specified. One of the CR field symbols defined in Section C.1 can be used for this operand.

Examples

1. Branch if CR0 reflects condition "not equal."

```
bne     target              (equivalent to:   bc      4,2,target)
```

Branch semantics	LR not set				LR set			
	bc Relative	*bca* Absolute	*bclr* To LR	*bcctr* To CTR	*bcl* Relative	*bcla* Absolute	*bclrl* To LR	*bcctrl* To CTR
Branch if less than	blt	blta	bltlr	bltctr	bltl	bltla	bltlrl	bltctrl
Branch if less than or equal	ble	blea	blelr	blectr	blel	blela	blelrl	blectrl
Branch if equal	beq	beqa	beqlr	beqctr	beql	beqla	beqlrl	beqctrl
Branch if greater than or equal	bge	bgea	bgelr	bgectr	bgel	bgela	bgelrl	bgectrl
Branch if greater than	bgt	bgta	bgtlr	bgtctr	bgtl	bgtla	bgtlrl	bgtctrl
Branch if not less than	bnl	bnla	bnllr	bnlctr	bnll	bnlla	bnllrl	bnlctrl
Branch if not equal	bne	bnea	bnelr	bnectr	bnel	bnela	bnelrl	bnectrl
Branch if not greater than	bng	bnga	bnglr	bngctr	bngl	bngla	bnglrl	bngctrl
Branch if summary overflow	bso	bsoa	bsolr	bsoctr	bsol	bsola	bsolrl	bsoctrl
Branch if not summary overflow	bns	bnsa	bnslr	bnsctr	bnsl	bnsla	bnslrl	bnsctrl
Branch if unordered	bun	buna	bunlr	bunctr	bunl	bunla	bunlrl	bunctrl
Branch if not unordered	bnu	bnua	bnulr	bnuctr	bnul	bnula	bnulrl	bnuctrl

Table 3. **Branch mnemonics incorporating conditions**

2. Same as (1), but condition is in CR3.

    bne   cr3,target   (equivalent to: bc   4,14,target)

3. Branch to an absolute target if CR4 specifies "greater than," setting the Link Register. This is a form of conditional "call."

    bgtla   cr4,target   (equivalent to: bcla   12,17,target)

4. Same as (3), but target address is in the Count Register.

    bgtctrl   cr4   (equivalent to: bcctrl   12,17)

C.2.4 Branch Prediction

In *Branch Conditional* instructions that are not always taken, the low-order bit ("y" bit) of the BO field provides a hint about whether the branch is likely to be taken: see the discussion of the "y" bit in Section 2.4.1, "Branch Instructions," on page 35.

Assemblers should set this bit to 0 unless otherwise directed. This default action means that:

- A *Branch Conditional* with a negative displacement field is predicted to be taken.

- A *Branch Conditional* with a nonnegative displacement field is predicted *not* to be taken (fall through).

- A *Branch Conditional* to an address in the LR or CTR is predicted *not* to be taken (fall through).

If the likely outcome (branch or fall through) of a given *Branch Conditional* instruction is known, a suffix can be added to the mnemonic that tells the assembler how to set the "y" bit.

+   Predict branch to be taken.

–   Predict branch *not* to be taken.

Such a suffix can be added to any *Branch Conditional* mnemonic, either basic or extended.

For relative and absolute branches (*bc[l][a]*), the setting of the "y" bit depends on whether the displacement field is negative or nonnegative. For negative displacement fields, coding the suffix "+" causes the bit to be set to 0, and coding the suffix "–" causes the bit to be set to 1. For nonnegative displacement fields, coding the suffix "+" causes the bit to be set to 1, and coding the suffix "–" causes the bit to be set to 0.

For branches to an address in the LR or CTR (*bclr[l]* or *bcctr[l]*), coding the suffix "+" causes the "y" bit to be set to 1, and coding the suffix "–" causes the bit to be set to 0.

Examples

1. Branch if CR0 reflects condition "less than," specifying that the branch should be predicted to be taken.

blt+   target

2. Same as (1), but target address is in the Link Register and the branch should be predicted not to be taken.

bltlr–

C.3 Condition Register Logical Mnemonics

The *Condition Register Logical* instructions can be used to set (to 1), clear (to 0), copy, or invert a given Condition Register bit. Extended mnemonics are provided in Table 4 that allow these operations to be coded easily.

Operation	Extended mnemonic	Equivalent to
Condition Register set	crset bx	creqv bx,bx,bx
Condition Register clear	crclr bx	crxor bx,bx,bx
Condition Register move	crmove bx,by	cror bx,by,by
Condition Register not	crnot bx,by	crnor bx,by,by

Table 4.   **Condition Register logical mnemonics**

The symbols defined in Section C.1 can be used to identify the Condition Register bits.

Examples

1. Set CR bit 25.

    crset   25   (equivalent to: creqv   25,25,25)

2. Clear the SO bit of CR0.

    crclr   so   (equivalent to: crxor   3,3,3)

3. Same as (2), but SO bit to be cleared is in CR3.

    crclr   4*cr3+so   (equivalent to: crxor   15,15,15)

4. Invert the EQ bit.

    crnot   eq,eq   (equivalent to: crnor   2,2,2)

5. Same as (4), but EQ bit to be inverted is in CR4, and the result is to be placed into the EQ bit of CR5.

    crnot   4*cr5+eq,4*cr4+eq   (equivalent to: crnor   22,18,18)

C.4 Subtract Mnemonics

C.4.1 Subtract Immediate

Although there is no "Subtract Immediate" instruction, its effect can be achieved by using an *Add Immediate* instruction with the immediate operand negated. Extended mnemonics are provided that include this negation, making the intent of the computation clearer.

subi	Rx,Ry,value	(equivalent to:	addi	Rx,Ry,–value)
subis	Rx,Ry,value	(equivalent to:	addis	Rx,Ry,–value)
subic	Rx,Ry,value	(equivalent to:	addic	Rx,Ry,–value)
subic.	Rx,Ry,value	(equivalent to:	addic.	Rx,Ry,–value)

C.4.2 Subtract

The *Subtract From* instructions subtract the second operand (RA) from the third (RB). Extended mnemonics are provided that use the more "normal" order, in which the third operand is subtracted from the second. Both these mnemonics can be coded with a final "o" and/or "." to cause the OE and/or Rc bit to be set in the underlying instruction.

sub	Rx,Ry,Rz	(equivalent to:	subf	Rx,Rz,Ry)
subc	Rx,Ry,Rz	(equivalent to:	subfc	Rx,Rz,Ry)

C.5 Compare Mnemonics

The L field in the fixed-point *Compare* instructions controls whether the operands are treated as 64-bit quantities (L=1) or as 32-bit quantities (L=0). Extended mnemonics are provided that represent the L value in the mnemonic rather than requiring it to be coded as a numeric operand.

The BF field can be omitted if the result of the comparison is to be placed in CR Field 0. Otherwise the target CR field must be specified as the first operand. One of the CR field symbols defined in Section C.1 can be used for this operand.

Note: The basic *Compare* mnemonics of PowerPC are the same as those of Power, but the Power instructions have three operands while the PowerPC instructions have four. The assembler will recognize a basic *Compare* mnemonic with three operands as the Power form and will generate the instruction with L=0. (Thus the assembler must require that the BF field, which normally can be omitted when CR Field 0 is the target, be specified explicitly if L is.)

C.5.1 Doubleword Comparisons

These operations are available only in 64-bit implementations.

Operation	Extended mnemonic	Equivalent to
Compare doubleword immediate	cmpdi bf,ra,si	cmpi bf,1,ra,si
Compare doubleword	cmpd bf,ra,rb	cmp bf,1,ra,rb
Compare logical doubleword immediate	cmpldi bf,ra,ui	cmpli bf,1,ra,ui
Compare logical doubleword	cmpld bf,ra,rb	cmpl bf,1,ra,rb

Table 5.   **Doubleword compare mnemonics**

Examples

1. Compare register Rx and immediate value 100 as unsigned 64-bit integers and place result in CR0.

cmpldi   Rx,100   (equivalent to: cmpli   0,1,Rx,100)

2. Same as (1), but place result in CR4.

cmpldi   cr4,Rx,100   (equivalent to: cmpli   4,1,Rx,100)

3. Compare registers Rx and Ry as signed 64-bit integers and place result in CR0.

cmpd   Rx,Ry   (equivalent to: cmp   0,1,Rx,Ry)

C.5.2 Word Comparisons

These operations are available in all implementations.

Operation	Extended mnemonic	Equivalent to
Compare word immediate	cmpwi bf,ra,si	cmpi bf,0,ra,si
Compare word	cmpw bf,ra,rb	cmp bf,0,ra,rb
Compare logical word immediate	cmplwi bf,ra,ui	cmpli bf,0,ra,ui
Compare logical word	cmplw bf,ra,rb	cmpl bf,0,ra,rb

Table 6. **Word compare mnemonics**

Examples

1. Compare bits 32:63 of register Rx and immediate value 100 as signed 32-bit integers and place result in CR0.

cmpwi   Rx,100   (equivalent to: cmpi   0,0,Rx,100)

2. Same as (1), but place result in CR4.

cmpwi   cr4,Rx,100   (equivalent to: cmpi   4,0,Rx,100)

3. Compare bits 32:63 of registers Rx and Ry as unsigned 32-bit integers and place result in CR0.

cmplw   Rx,Ry   (equivalent to: cmpl   0,0,Rx,Ry)

C.6 Trap Mnemonics

The mnemonics defined in Table 7 on page 227 are variations of the *Trap* instructions, with the most useful values of TO represented in the mnemonic rather than specified as a numeric operand.

A standard set of codes has been adopted for the most common combinations of trap conditions.

These codes are reflected in the mnemonics shown in Table 7.

Code	Meaning	TO encoding	<	>	=	≮	≯
lt	Less than	16	1	0	0	0	0
le	Less than or equal	20	1	0	1	0	0
eq	Equal	4	0	0	1	0	0
ge	Greater than or equal	12	0	1	1	0	0
gt	Greater than	8	0	1	0	0	0
nl	Not less than	12	0	1	1	0	0
ne	Not equal	24	1	1	0	0	0
ng	Not greater than	20	1	0	1	0	0
llt	Logically less than	2	0	0	0	1	0
lle	Logically less than or equal	6	0	0	1	1	0
lge	Logically greater than or equal	5	0	0	1	0	1
lgt	Logically greater than	1	0	0	0	0	1
lnl	Logically not less than	5	0	0	1	0	1
lng	Logically not greater than	6	0	0	1	1	0
(none)	Unconditional	31	1	1	1	1	1

Examples

1. Trap if register Rx is not 0.

    tdnei   Rx,0   (equivalent to: tdi   24,Rx,0)

2. Same as (1), but comparison is to register Ry.

    tdne   Rx,Ry   (equivalent to: td   24,Rx,Ry)

3. Trap if bits 32:63 of register Rx, considered as a 32-bit quantity, are logically greater than 0x7FF.

    twlgti   Rx,0x7FF   (equivalent to: twi   1,Rx,0x7FF)

4. Trap unconditionally.

    trap   (equivalent to: tw   31,0,0)

Trap semantics	64-bit comparison		32-bit comparison	
	tdi Immediate	*td* Register	*twi* Immediate	*tw* Register
Trap unconditionally	–	–	–	trap
Trap if less than	tdlti	tdlt	twlti	twlt
Trap if less than or equal	tdlei	tdle	twlei	twle
Trap if equal	tdeqi	tdeq	tweqi	tweq
Trap if greater than or equal	tdgei	tdge	twgei	twge
Trap if greater than	tdgti	tdgt	twgti	twgt
Trap if not less than	tdnli	tdnl	twnli	twnl
Trap if not equal	tdnei	tdne	twnei	twne
Trap if not greater than	tdngi	tdng	twngi	twng
Trap if logically less than	tdllti	tdllt	twllti	twllt
Trap if logically less than or equal	tdllei	tdlle	twllei	twlle
Trap if logically greater than or equal	tdlgei	tdlge	twlgei	twlge
Trap if logically greater than	tdlgti	tdlgt	twlgti	twlgt
Trap if logically not less than	tdlnli	tdlnl	twlnli	twlnl
Trap if logically not greater than	tdlngi	tdlng	twlngi	twlng

Table 7.   **Trap mnemonics**

C.7 Rotate and Shift Mnemonics

The *Rotate and Shift* instructions provide powerful and general ways to manipulate register contents, but can be difficult to understand. Extended mnemonics are provided that allow some of the simpler operations to be coded easily.

Mnemonics are provided for the following types of operation:

Extract   Select a field of n bits starting at bit position b in the source register; right or left justify this field in the target register; clear all other bits of the target register to 0.

Insert   Select a left-justified or right-justified field of n bits in the source register; insert this field starting at bit position b of the target register; leave other bits of the target register unchanged. (No extended mnemonic is provided for insertion of a left-justified field when operating on doublewords, because such an insertion requires more than one instruction.)

Rotate   Rotate the contents of a register right or left *n* bits without masking.

Shift   Shift the contents of a register right or left *n* bits, clearing vacated bits to 0 (logical shift).

Clear   Clear the leftmost or rightmost *n* bits of a register to 0.

Clear left and shift left

Clear the leftmost *b* bits of a register, then shift the register left by *n* bits. This operation can be used to scale a (known nonnegative) array index by the width of an element.

C.7.1 Operations on Doublewords

These operations are available only in 64-bit implementations. All these mnemonics can be coded with a final "." to cause the Rc bit to be set in the underlying instruction.

Examples

1. Extract the sign bit (bit 0) of register Ry and place the result right-justified into register Rx.

extrdi   Rx,Ry,1,0   (equivalent to: rldicl   Rx,Ry,1,63)

2. Insert the bit extracted in (1) into the sign bit (bit 0) of register Rz.

insrdi   Rz,Rx,1,0   (equivalent to: rldimi   Rz,Rx,63,0)

3. Shift the contents of register Rx left 8 bits.

sldi   Rx,Rx,8   (equivalent to: rldicr   Rx,Rx,8,55)

4. Clear the high-order 32 bits of register Ry and place the result into register Rx.

clrldi   Rx,Ry,32   (equivalent to: rldicl   Rx,Ry,0,32)

Operation	Extended mnemonic		Equivalent to
Extract and left justify immediate	extldi ra,rs,n,b	$(n > 0)$	rldicr ra,rs,b,n–1
Extract and right justify immediate	extrdi ra,rs,n,b	$(n > 0)$	rldicl ra,rs,b+n,64–n
Insert from right immediate	insrdi ra,rs,n,b	$(n > 0)$	rldimi ra,rs,64–(b+n),b
Rotate left immediate	rotldi ra,rs,n		rldicl ra,rs,n,0
Rotate right immediate	rotrdi ra,rs,n		rldicl ra,rs,64–n,0
Rotate left	rotld ra,rs,rb		rldcl ra,rs,rb,0
Shift left immediate	sldi ra,rs,n	$(n < 64)$	rldicr ra,rs,n,63–n
Shift right immediate	srdi ra,rs,n	$(n < 64)$	rldicl ra,rs,64–n,n
Clear left immediate	clrldi ra,rs,n	$(n < 64)$	rldicl ra,rs,0,n
Clear right immediate	clrrdi ra,rs,n	$(n < 64)$	rldicr ra,rs,0,63–n
Clear left and shift left immediate	clrlsldi ra,rs,b,n $(n \leq b < 64)$		rldic ra,rs,n,b–n

Table 8. **Doubleword rotate and shift mnemonics**

C.7.2 Operations on Words

These operations are available in all implementations. All these mnemonics can be coded with a final "." to cause the Rc bit to be set in the underlying instruction. The operations as described above apply to the low-order 32 bits of the registers, as if the registers were 32-bit registers. The Insert operations either preserve the high-order 32 bits of the target register or place rotated data there; the other operations clear these bits.

Examples

1. Extract the sign bit (bit 32) of register Ry and place the result right-justified into register Rx.

extrwi   Rx,Ry,1,0   (equivalent to: rlwinm Rx,Ry,1,31,31)

2. Insert the bit extracted in (1) into the sign bit (bit 32) of register Rz.

insrwi   Rz,Rx,1,0   (equivalent to: rlwimi Rz,Rx,31,0,0)

Operation	Extended mnemonic		Equivalent to
Extract and left justify immediate	extlwi ra,rs,*n*,*b*	(*n* > 0)	rlwinm ra,rs,*b*,0,*n*–1
Extract and right justify immediate	extrwi ra,rs,*n*,*b*	(*n* > 0)	rlwinm ra,rs,*b*+*n*,32–*n*,31
Insert from left immediate	inslwi ra,rs,*n*,*b*	(*n* > 0)	rlwimi ra,rs,32–*b*,*b*,(*b*+*n*)–1
Insert from right immediate	insrwi ra,rs,*n*,*b*	(*n* > 0)	rlwimi ra,rs,32–(*b*+*n*),*b*,(*b*+*n*)–1
Rotate left immediate	rotlwi ra,rs,*n*		rlwinm ra,rs,*n*,0,31
Rotate right immediate	rotrwi ra,rs,*n*		rlwinm ra,rs,32–*n*,0,31
Rotate left	rotlw ra,rs,rb		rlwnm ra,rs,rb,0,31
Shift left immediate	slwi ra,rs,*n*	(*n* < 32)	rlwinm ra,rs,*n*,0,31–*n*
Shift right immediate	srwi ra,rs,*n*	(*n* < 32)	rlwinm ra,rs,32–*n*,*n*,31
Clear left immediate	clrlwi ra,rs,*n*	(*n* < 32)	rlwinm ra,rs,0,*n*,31
Clear right immediate	clrrwi ra,rs,*n*	(*n* < 32)	rlwinm ra,rs,0,0,31–*n*
Clear left and shift left immediate	clrlslwi ra,rs,*b*,*n*	(*n* ≤ *b* < 32)	rlwinm ra,rs,*n*,*b*–*n*,31–*n*

Table 9.   **Word rotate and shift mnemonics**

3. Shift the contents of register Rx left 8 bits, clearing the high-order 32 bits.

    slwi   Rx,Rx,8   (equivalent to: rlwinm   Rx,Rx,8,0,23)

4. Clear the high-order 16 bits of the low-order 32 bits of register Ry and place the result into register Rx, clearing the high-order 32 bits of register Rx.

    clrlwi   Rx,Ry,16   (equivalent to: rlwinm   Rx,Ry,0,16,31)

C.8 Move To/From Special Purpose Register Mnemonics

The *mtspr* and *mfspr* instructions specify a Special Purpose Register (SPR) as a numeric operand. Extended mnemonics are provided that represent the SPR in the mnemonic rather than requiring it to be coded as an operand.

Special Purpose Register	Move To SPR		Move From SPR	
	Extended	*Equivalent to*	*Extended*	*Equivalent to*
Fixed-Point Exception Register (XER)	mtxer Rx	mtspr 1,Rx	mfxer Rx	mfspr Rx,1
Link Register (LR)	mtlr Rx	mtspr 8,Rx	mflr Rx	mfspr Rx,8
Count Register (CTR)	mtctr Rx	mtspr 9,Rx	mfctr Rx	mfspr Rx,9

Table 10.   Extended mnemonics for moving to/from an SPR

Examples

1. Copy the contents of the low-order 32 bits of register Rx to the XER.

mtxer   Rx   (equivalent to: mtspr   1,Rx)

2. Copy the contents of the LR to register Rx.

mflr   Rx   (equivalent to: mfspr   Rx,8)

3. Copy the contents of register Rx to the CTR.

mtctr   Rx   (equivalent to: mtspr   9,Rx)

C.9 Miscellaneous Mnemonics

No-op
Many PowerPC instructions can be coded in a way such that, effectively, no operation is performed. An extended mnemonic is provided for the "preferred" form of no-op. If an implementation performs any type of runtime optimization related to no-ops, the preferred form is the no-op that will trigger this.

nop   (equivalent to: ori   0,0,0)

Load Immediate
The *addi* and *addis* instructions can be used to load an immediate value into a register. Extended mnemonics are provided to convey the idea that no addition is being performed but merely data movement (from the immediate field of the instruction to a register).

Load a 16-bit signed immediate value into register Rx:

li   Rx,value   (equivalent to: addi   Rx,0,value)

Load a 16-bit signed immediate value, shifted left by 16 bits, into register Rx:

lis   Rx,value   (equivalent to: addis   Rx,0,value)

Load Address

This mnemonic permits computing the value of a base-displacement operand, using the *addi* instruction which normally requires separate register and immediate operands.

la   Rx,D(Ry)   (equivalent to: addi   Rx,Ry,D)

The *la* mnemonic is useful for obtaining the address of a variable specified by name, allowing the assembler to supply the base register number and compute the displacement. If the variable v is located at offset Dv bytes from the address in register Rv, and the assembler has been told to use register Rv as a base for references to the data structure containing v, then the following line causes the address of v to be loaded into register Rx.

la   Rx,v   (equivalent to: addi   Rx,Rv,Dv)

Move Register

Several PowerPC instructions can be coded in a way such that they simply copy the contents of one register to another. An extended mnemonic is provided to convey the idea that no computation is being performed but merely data movement (from one register to another).

The following instruction copies the contents of register Ry into register Rx. This mnemonic can be coded with a final "." to cause the Rc bit to be set in the underlying instruction.

mr   Rx,Ry   (equivalent to: or   Rx,Ry,Ry)

Complement Register

Several PowerPC instructions can be coded in a way such that they complement the contents of one register and place the result into another register. An extended mnemonic is provided that allows this operation to be coded easily.

The following instruction complements the contents of register Ry and places the result into register Rx. This mnemonic can be coded with a final "." to cause the Rc bit to be set in the underlying instruction.

not   Rx,Ry   (equivalent to: nor   Rx,Ry,Ry)

Little-Endian Byte Ordering

It is computed that eleven Thousand Persons have, at several Times, suffered Death, rather than submit to break their Eggs at the smaller End. Many hundred large Volumes have been published upon this Controversy ....

Jonathan Swift, *Gulliver's Travels*

D.1 Byte Ordering

If scalars (individual data items and instructions) were indivisible, then there would be no such concept as "byte ordering". It is meaningless to talk of the "order" of bits or groups of bits within the smallest addressable unit of storage, because nothing can be observed about such order. Only when scalars, which the programmer and processor regard as indivisible quantities, can be made up of more than one addressable unit of storage does the question of "order" arise.

For a machine in which the smallest addressable unit of storage is the 64-bit doubleword, there is no question of the ordering of "bytes" within doublewords. All transfers of individual scalars to and from storage (e.g., between registers and storage) are of doublewords, and the address of the "byte" containing the high-order 8 bits of a scalar is no different from the address of a "byte" containing any other part of the scalar.

For PowerPC, as for most computers currently available, the smallest addressable unit of storage is the 8-bit byte. Many scalars are halfwords, words, or doublewords, which consist of groups of bytes. When a word-length scalar is moved from a register to storage, the scalar occupies four consecutive byte addresses. It thus becomes meaningful to discuss the order of the byte addresses with respect to the value of the scalar: which byte contains the highest-order 8 bits of the scalar, which byte contains the next-highest-order 8 bits, and so on.

Given a scalar that spans multiple bytes, the choice of byte ordering is essentially arbitrary. There are 4! = 24 ways to specify the ordering of four bytes within a word, but only two of these orderings are sensible:

■ The ordering that assigns the lowest address to the highest-order ("leftmost") 8 bits of the scalar, the next sequential address to the next-highest-order 8 bits, and so on. This is called *Big-Endian* because the "big end" of the scalar, considered as a binary number, comes first in storage. IBM RISC System/6000, IBM System/370, and Motorola 680x0 are examples of computers using this byte ordering.

■ The ordering that assigns the lowest address to the lowest-order ("rightmost") 8 bits of the scalar, the next sequential address to the next-lowest-order 8 bits, and so on. This is called *Little-Endian* because the "little end" of the scalar, considered as a binary number, comes first in storage. DEC VAX and Intel x86 are examples of computers using this byte ordering.

D.2 Structure Mapping Examples

Figure 35 on page 235 shows an example of a C language structure **s** containing an assortment of scalars and one character string. The value assumed to be in each structure element is shown in hex in the C comments; these values are used below to show how the bytes making up each structure element are mapped into storage.

C structure mapping rules permit the use of padding (skipped bytes) in order to align the scalars on desirable boundaries. Figures 36 and 37 show each scalar aligned at its natural boundary. This alignment introduces padding of four bytes between **a** and **b**, one byte between **d** and **e**, and two bytes between **e** and **f**. The same amount of padding is present for both Big-Endian and Little-Endian mappings.

```
struct {
    int       a;      /*  0x1112_1314                        word*/
    double    b;      /*  0x2122_2324_2526_2728              doubleword */
    char *    c;      /*  0x3132_3334                        word*/
    char      d[7];   /*  'A','B','C','D','E','F','G'        array of bytes*/
    short     e;      /*  0x5152                             halfword*/
    int       f;      /*  0x6162_6364                        word*/
} s;
```

Figure 35.   **C structure 's', showing values of elements**

D.2.1 Big-Endian Mapping

The Big-Endian mapping of structure **s** is shown in Figure 36. Addresses are shown in hex at the left of each doubleword, and below each byte. The content of each byte, as indicated in the C example in Figure 35, is shown in hex (as characters for the elements of the string).

00	11	12	13	14				
	00	01	02	03	04	05	06	07
08	21	22	23	24	25	26	27	28
	08	09	0A	0B	0C	0D	0E	0F
10	31	32	33	34	'A'	'B'	'C'	'D'
	10	11	12	13	14	15	16	17
18	'E'	'F'	'G'		51	52		
	18	19	1A	1B	1C	1D	1E	1F
20	61	62	63	64				
	20	21	22	23				

Figure 36.   **Big-Endian mapping of structure 's'**

D.2.2 Little-Endian Mapping

The same structure **s** is shown mapped Little-Endian in Figure 37. Doublewords are shown laid out from right to left, which is the common way of showing storage maps for Little-Endian machines.

				11	12	13	14	00
07	06	05	04	03	02	01	00	
21	22	23	24	25	26	27	28	08
0F	0E	0D	0C	0B	0A	09	08	
'D'	'C'	'B'	'A'	31	32	33	34	10
17	16	15	14	13	12	11	10	
		51	52		'G'	'F'	'E'	18
1F	1E	1D	1C	1B	1A	19	18	
				61	62	63	64	20
				23	22	21	20	

Figure 37. **Little-Endian mapping of structure 's'**

D.3 PowerPC Byte Ordering

The body of each of the three PowerPC Architecture books: Book I, *PowerPC User Instruction Set Architecture,* Book II, *PowerPC Virtual Environment Architecture,* and Book III, *PowerPC Operating Environment Architecture,* is written as if a PowerPC system runs only in Big-Endian mode. In fact, a PowerPC system can instead run in Little-Endian mode, in which the instruction set behaves as if the byte ordering were Little-Endian, and can change Endian mode dynamically. The remainder of this appendix describes how the mode is controlled, and how running in Little-Endian mode differs from running in Big-Endian mode.

D.3.1 Controlling PowerPC Byte Ordering

The Endian mode of a PowerPC processor is controlled by two bits: the LE (Little-Endian Mode) bit specifies the current mode of the processor, and the ILE (Interrupt Little-Endian Mode) bit specifies the mode that the processor enters when the system error handler is invoked. For both bits, a value of 0 specifies Big-Endian mode and a value of 1 specifies Little-Endian mode. The location of these bits and the requirements for altering them are described in Book III, Section 2.2.3, "Machine State Register," on page 374 and Chapter 7, "Synchronization Requirements for Special Registers and for Lookaside Buffers," on page 483.

When a PowerPC system comes up after power-on-reset, Big-Endian mode is in effect. Thereafter, methods described in Book III can be used to change the mode, as can both invoking the system error handler and returning from the system error handler.

D.3.2 PowerPC Little-Endian Byte Ordering

One might expect that a PowerPC system running in Little-Endian mode would have to perform a 2-way, 4-way, or 8-way byte swap when transferring a halfword, word, or doubleword to or from storage, e.g., when transferring data between storage and a general purpose register or floating-point register, when fetching instructions, and when transferring data between storage and an Input/Output (I/O) device. PowerPC systems do not do such swapping, but instead achieve the effect of Little-Endian byte ordering by modifying the low-order three bits of the effective address (EA) as described below. Individual scalars actually appear in storage in Big-Endian byte order.

The modification affects only the addresses presented to the storage subsystem (see Book III, *PowerPC Operating Environment Architecture*). All effective addresses in architecturally defined registers, as well as the Current Instruction Address (CIA) and Next Instruction Address (NIA), are independent of Endian mode. For example:

■ The effective address placed into the Link Register by a *Branch* instruction with LK=1 is equal to the CIA of the *Branch* instruction + 4;

■ The effective address placed into RA by a *Load/Store with Update* instruction is the value computed as described in the instruction description; and

■ The effective addresses placed into System Registers when the system error handler is invoked (e.g., SRR0, DAR: see Book III, *PowerPC Operating Environment Architecture*) are those that were computed or would have been computed by the interrupted program.

The modification is independent of the address translation mechanism, and is performed regardless of whether translation is enabled or disabled, whether the accessed storage is in an ordinary segment, a direct-store segment, or a BAT area, etc. (see Book III, *PowerPC Operating Environment Architecture*). The actual transfer of data and instructions to and from storage is unaffected (and thus unencumbered by multiplexors for byte swapping).

The modification of the low-order three bits of the effective address in Little-Endian mode is done as follows, for access to an individual aligned scalar. (Alignment is as determined before this modification.) Access to an individual unaligned scalar or to multiple scalars is described in subsequent sections, as is access to certain architecturally defined data in storage, data in caches (see Book II, *PowerPC Virtual Environment Architecture*, and Book III, *PowerPC Operating Environment Architecture*), etc.

In Little-Endian mode, the effective address is computed in the same way as in Big-Endian mode. Then, in Little-Endian mode only, the low-order three bits of the effective address are Exclusive ORed with a three-bit value that depends on the length of the operand (1, 2, 4, or 8 bytes), as shown in Table 11. This modified effective address is then passed to the storage subsystem, and data of the specified length are transferred to or from the addressed (as modified) storage locations(s).

Data length (bytes)	EA modification:
1	XOR with 0b111
2	XOR with 0b110
4	XOR with 0b100
8	(no change)

Table 11.   **PowerPC Little-Endian, effective address modification for individual aligned scalars**

The effective address modification makes it appear to the processor that individual aligned scalars are stored Little-Endian, while in fact they are stored Big-Endian but in different bytes within doublewords from the order in which they are stored in Big-Endian mode.

For example, in Little-Endian mode structure s would be placed in storage as follows, from the point of view of the storage subsystem (i.e., after the effective address modification described above).

00					11	12	13	14
	00	01	02	03	04	05	06	07
08	21	22	23	24	25	26	27	28
	08	09	0A	0B	0C	0D	0E	0F
10	'D'	'C'	'B'	'A'	31	32	33	34
	10	11	12	13	14	15	16	17
18			51	52		'G'	'F'	'E'
	18	19	1A	1B	1C	1D	1E	1F
20					61	62	63	64
	20	21	22	23	24	25	26	27

Figure 38.   **PowerPC Little-Endian, structure 's' in storage subsystem**

Figure 38 is identical to Figure 37 except that the byte numbers within each doubleword are reversed. (This identity is in some sense an artifact of depicting storage as a sequence of doublewords. If storage is instead depicted as a sequence of words, a single byte stream, etc., then no such identity appears. However, regardless of the unit in which storage is depicted or accessed, the address of a given byte in Figure 38 differs from the address of the same byte in Figure 37 only in the low-order three bits, and the sum of the two 3-bit values that comprise the low-order three bits of the two addresses is equal to 7. Depicting storage as a sequence of doublewords makes this relationship easy to see.)

Because of the modification performed on effective addresses, structure s appears to the processor to be mapped into storage as follows when the processor is in Little-Endian mode.

				11	12	13	14	00
07	06	05	04	03	02	01	00	
21	22	23	24	25	26	27	28	08
0F	0E	0D	0C	0B	0A	09	08	
'D'	'C'	'B'	'A'	31	32	33	34	10
17	16	15	14	13	12	11	10	
		51	52		'G'	'F'	'E'	18
1F	1E	1D	1C	1B	1A	19	18	
				61	62	63	64	20
				23	22	21	20	

Figure 39.   **PowerPC Little-Endian, structure 's' as seen by processor**

Notice that, as seen by the program executing in the processor, the mapping for structure s is identical to the Little-Endian mapping shown in Figure 37. From a point of view outside the processor, however, the addresses of the bytes making up structure s are as shown in Figure 38. These addresses match neither the Big-Endian mapping of Figure 36 nor the Little-Endian mapping of Figure 37; allowance must be made for this in certain circumstances (e.g., when performing I/O: see Section D.7).

The following four sections describe in greater detail the effects of running in Little-Endian mode on accessing data storage, on fetching instructions, on explicitly accessing the caches, the Segment Lookaside Buffer, and the Translation Lookaside Buffer (see Book II, *PowerPC Virtual Environment Architecture*, and Book III, *PowerPC Operating Environment Architecture*), and on doing I/O.

D.4 PowerPC Data Storage Addressing in Little-Endian Mode

D.4.1 Individual Aligned Scalars

When the storage operand is aligned for any instruction in the following classes, the effective address presented to the storage subsystem is computed as described in Section D.3.2: *Fixed-Point Load, Fixed-Point Store, Load and Store with Byte Reversal, Storage Synchronization* (excluding **sync**), *Floating-Point Load,* and *Floating-Point Store* (including **stfiwx**).

The *Load and Store with Byte Reversal* instructions have the effect of loading or storing data in the opposite Endian mode from that in which the processor is running. That is, data are loaded or stored in Little-Endian order if the processor is running in Big-Endian mode, and in Big-Endian order if the processor is running in Little-Endian mode.

D.4.2 Other Scalars

As described below, the system alignment error handler may be (see "Individual Unaligned Scalars") or is (see "Multiple Scalars," on page 241) invoked if attempt is made in Little-Endian mode to execute any of the instructions described in the following two subsections.

Individual Unaligned Scalars

The "trick" of Exclusive ORing the low-order three bits of the effective address of an individual scalar does not work unless the scalar is aligned. In Little-Endian mode, PowerPC processors may cause the system alignment error handler to be invoked whenever any of the *Load* or *Store* instructions listed in Section D.4.1 is issued with an unaligned effective address, regardless of whether such an access could be handled without invoking the system alignment error handler in Big-Endian mode.

PowerPC processors are not *required* to invoke the system alignment error handler when an unaligned access is attempted in Little-Endian mode. The implementation may handle some or all such accesses without invoking the system alignment error handler, just as in Big-Endian mode. The architectural requirement is that halfwords, words, and doublewords be placed in storage such that the Little-Endian effective address of the lowest-order byte is the effective address computed by the *Load* or *Store* instruction, the Little-Endian address of the next-lowest-order byte is one greater, and so on. (*lwarx, ldarx, stwcx.*, and *stdcx.* differ somewhat from the rest of the instructions listed in Section D.4.1, in that neither the implementation nor the system alignment error handler is expected to handle these four instructions "correctly" if their operands are not aligned.)

Figure 40 shows an example of a word w stored at Little-Endian address 5. The word is assumed to contain the binary value 0x1112_1314.

```
 12    13    14                                          00
 07    06    05    04    03    02    01    00
                                             11          08
 0F    0E    0D    0C    0B    0A    09    08
```

Figure 40. **Little-Endian mapping of word 'w' stored at address 5**

In Little-Endian mode word w would be placed in storage as follows, from the point of view of the storage subsystem (i.e., after the effective address modification described in Section D.3.2).

```
 00    12    13    14
       00    01    02    03    04    05    06    07
 08                                            11
       08    09    0A    0B    0C    0D    0E    0F
```

Figure 41. **PowerPC Little-Endian, word 'w' stored at address 5 in storage subsystem**

Notice that the unaligned word w in Figure 41 spans two doublewords. The two parts of the unaligned word are not contiguous as seen by the storage subsystem.

An implementation may choose to support some but not all unaligned Little-Endian accesses. For example, an unaligned Little-Endian access that is contained within a single doubleword may be supported, while one that spans doublewords may cause the system alignment error handler to be invoked.

Multiple Scalars

PowerPC has two classes of instructions that handle multiple scalars, namely the *Load and Store Multiple* instructions and the *Move Assist* instructions. Because both classes of instructions potentially deal with

Programming Note

If the system alignment error handler is invoked because one of the instructions described in Section D.4.2 is executed when the processor is in Little-Endian mode, system software must decide whether to emulate the instruction and then resume the program, or treat the instruction as an illegal instruction and terminate the program.

Little-Endian mode programs on PowerPC are of necessity new (not old POWER binaries). It is probably best for the compiler not to generate these instructions in Little-Endian mode, since emulation would be slower than using a series of aligned *Load* or *Store* instructions, either in-line or in a subroutine. An exception is the case of accessing an individual scalar (see "Individual Unaligned Scalars," on page 240) when the alignment is not known by the compiler but the operand is expected usually to be aligned: in this case it may be better for the compiler to generate the individual *Load* or *Store* instruction, and let the system alignment error handler, if invoked, emulate the instruction if the operand is in fact unaligned.

more than one word-length scalar, neither class is amenable to the effective address modification described in Section D.3.2 (e.g., pairs of aligned words would be accessed in reverse order from what the program would expect). Attempting to execute any of these instructions in Little-Endian mode causes the system alignment error handler to be invoked.

D.4.3 Segment Tables and Page Tables

The layout of Segment Tables and Page Tables in storage (see Book III, Chapter 4, "Storage Control," on page 391) is independent of Endian mode. A given byte in one of these tables must be accessed using an effective address appropriate to the mode of the executing program (e.g., the high-order byte of a Page Table Entry must be accessed with an effective address ending with 0b000 in Big-Endian mode, and with an effective address ending with 0b111 in Little-Endian mode).

D.5 PowerPC Instruction Storage Addressing in Little-Endian Mode

Each PowerPC instruction occupies an aligned word in storage. The processor fetches and executes instructions as if the CIA were advanced by four for each sequentially fetched instruction. When the processor is in Little-Endian mode, the effective address presented to the storage subsystem in order to fetch an instruction is the value from the CIA, modified as described in Section D.3.2 for aligned word-length scalars. A Little-Endian program is thus an array of aligned Little-Endian words, with each word fetched and executed in order (discounting branches and invocations of the system error handler).

Figure 42 shows an example of a small assembly language program **p**.

```
loop:
        cmplwi   r5,0
        beq      done
        lwzux    r4,r5,r6
        add      r7,r7,r4
        subi     r5,r5,4
        b        loop
done:
        stw      r7,total
```

Figure 42.   **Assembly language program 'p'**

The Big-Endian mapping for program **p** is shown in Figure 43 (assuming the program starts at address 0).

00	loop: cmplwi r5,0				beq done			
	00	01	02	03	04	05	06	07
08	lwzux r4,r5,r6				add r7,r7,r4			
	08	09	0A	0B	0C	0D	0E	0F
10	subi r5,r5,4				b loop			
	10	11	12	13	14	15	16	17
18	done: stw r7,total							
	18	19	1A	1B	1C	1D	1E	1F

Figure 43.   **Big-Endian mapping of program 'p'**

The same program **p** is shown mapped Little-Endian in Figure 44.

beq done				loop: cmplwi r5,0				
07	06	05	04	03	02	01	00	00
add r7,r7,r4				lwzux r4,r5,r6				
0F	0E	0D	0C	0B	0A	09	08	08
b loop				subi r5,r5,4				
17	16	15	14	13	12	11	10	10
				done: stw r7,total				
1F	1E	1D	1C	1B	1A	19	18	18

Figure 44.   **Little-Endian mapping of program 'p'**

In Little-Endian mode program **p** would be placed in storage as follows, from the point of view of the storage subsystem (i.e., after the effective address modification described in Section D.3.2).

00	beq done				loop: cmplwi r5,0			
	00	01	02	03	04	05	06	07
08	add r7,r7,r4				lwzux r4,r5,r6			
	08	09	0A	0B	0C	0D	0E	0F
10	b loop				subi r5,r5,4			
	10	11	12	13	14	15	16	17
18					done: stw r7,total			
	18	19	1A	1B	1C	1D	1E	1F

Figure 45.   **PowerPC Little-Endian, program 'p' in storage subsystem**

Figure 45 is identical to Figure 44 except that the byte numbers within each doubleword are reversed. (This identity is in some sense an artifact of depicting storage as a sequence of doublewords. If storage is instead depicted as a sequence of words, a single byte stream, etc., then no such identity appears. However, regardless of the unit in which storage is depicted or accessed, the address of a given byte in Figure 45 differs from the address of the same byte in Figure 44 only in the low-order three bits, and the sum of the two 3-bit values that comprise the low-order three bits of the two addresses is equal to 7. Depicting storage as a sequence of doublewords makes this relationship easy to see.)

Each individual machine instruction appears in storage as a 32-bit integer containing the value described in the instruction description, regardless of the Endian mode. This is a consequence of the fact that individual aligned scalars are mapped in storage in Big-Endian byte order.

Notice that, as seen by the processor when executing program **p**, the mapping for program **p** is identical to the Little-Endian mapping shown in Figure 44. From a point of view outside the processor, however, the addresses of the bytes making up program **p** are as shown in Figure 45. These addresses match neither the Big-Endian mapping of Figure 43 nor the Little-Endian mapping of Figure 44.

All instruction effective addresses visible to an executing program are the effective addresses that are computed by that program or, in the case of the system error handler, effective addresses that were or could have been computed by the interrupted program. These effective addresses are independent of Endian mode. Examples for Little-Endian mode include the following:

Programming Note

In general, a given subroutine in storage cannot be shared between programs running in different Endian modes. This affects the sharing of subroutine libraries.

- An instruction address placed in the Link Register by a *Branch* instruction with LK=1, or an instruction address saved in a System Register when the system error handler is invoked, is the effective address that a program executing in Little-Endian mode would use to access the instruction as a data word using a *Load* instruction.

- An offset in a relative *Branch* instruction (*Branch* or *Branch Conditional* with AA=0) reflects the difference between the addresses of the branch and target instructions, using the addresses that a program executing in Little-Endian mode would use to access the instructions as data words using *Load* instructions.

- A target address in an absolute *Branch* instruction (*Branch* or *Branch Conditional* with AA=1) is the address that a program executing in Little-Endian mode would use to access the target instruction as a data word using a *Load* instruction.

- The storage locations that contain the first set of instructions executed by each kind of system error handler must be set in a manner consistent with the Endian mode in which the system error handler will be invoked. (These sets of instructions occupy architecturally defined locations: see Book III, Chapter 5, "Interrupts," on page 453.) Thus if the system error handler is to be invoked in Little-Endian mode, the first set of instructions for each kind of system error handler must appear in storage, from the point of view of the storage subsystem (i.e., after the effective address modification described in Section D.3.2), with the pairs of instructions within each doubleword reversed from the order in which they are to be executed. (If the instructions are placed into storage by a program running in the same Endian mode as that in which the system error handler will be invoked, the appropriate order will be achieved naturally.)

D.6 PowerPC Cache Management and Lookaside Buffer Management Instructions in Little-Endian Mode

The instructions for explicitly accessing the caches, Segment Lookaside Buffer, and Translation Lookaside Buffer (see Book II, *PowerPC Virtual Environment Architecture*, and Book III, *PowerPC Operating Environment Architecture*) are unaffected by Endian mode. (Identification of the block, Segment Table Entry, or Page Table Entry to be accessed is not affected by the low-order three bits of the effective address.)

D.7 PowerPC I/O in Little-Endian Mode

Input/output (I/O), such as writing the contents of a large area of storage to disk, transfers a byte stream on both Big-Endian and Little-Endian systems. For the disk transfer, the first byte of the area is written to the first byte of the disk record and so on.

For a PowerPC system running in Big-Endian mode, I/O transfers happen "naturally" because the byte that the processor sees as byte 0 is the same one that the storage subsystem sees as byte 0.

For a PowerPC system running in Little-Endian mode this is not the case, because of the modification of the low-order three bits of the effective address when the processor accesses storage. In order for I/O transfers to transfer byte streams properly, in Little-Endian mode I/O transfers must be performed as if the bytes transferred were accessed one byte at a time, using the address modification described in Section D.3.2 for single-byte scalars. This does not mean that I/O on Little-Endian PowerPC systems must use only 1-byte-wide transfers; data transfers can be as wide as desired, but the order of the bytes transferred within double-words must appear as if the bytes were fetched or stored one byte at a time. See the System Architecture documentation for a given PowerPC system for details on the transfer width and byte ordering on that system.

However, not all I/O done on PowerPC systems is for large areas of storage as described above. I/O can be performed with certain devices merely by storing to or loading from addresses that are associated with the devices (the terms "memory-mapped I/O" and "programmed I/O" or "PIO" are used for this). For such PIO transfers, care must be taken when defining the addresses to be used, for these addresses are subject to the effective address modification shown in Table 11 on page 238. A *Load* or *Store* instruction that maps to a control register on a device may require that the value loaded or stored have its bytes reversed; if this is required, the *Load and Store with Byte Reversal* instructions can be used. Any requirement for such byte reversal for a particular I/O device register is independent of whether the PowerPC system is running in Big-Endian or Little-Endian mode.

Similarly, the address sent to an I/O device by an *eciwx* or *ecowx* instruction (see Book III, Section A.1, "External Control," on page 489) is subject to the effective address modification shown in Table 11.

D.8 Origin of Endian

The terms *Big-Endian* and *Little-Endian* come from Part I, Chapter 4, of Jonathan Swift's *Gulliver's Travels*. Here is the complete passage, from the edition printed in 1734 by George Faulkner in Dublin.

> ... our Histories of six Thousand Moons make no Mention of any other Regions, than the two great Empires of *Lilliput* and *Blefuscu*. Which two mighty Powers have, as I was going to tell you, been engaged in a most obstinate War for six and thirty Moons past. It began upon the following Occasion. It is allowed on all Hands, that the primitive Way of breaking Eggs before we eat them, was upon the larger End: But his present Majesty's Grand-father, while he was a Boy, going to eat an Egg, and breaking it according to the ancient Practice, happened to cut one of his Fingers. Whereupon the Emperor his Father, published an Edict, commanding all his Subjects, upon great Penalties, to break the smaller End of their Eggs. The People so highly resented this Law, that our Histories tell us, there have been six Rebellions raised on that Account; wherein

one Emperor lost his Life, and another his Crown. These civil Commotions were constantly fomented by the Monarchs of *Blefuscu*; and when they were quelled, the Exiles always fled for Refuge to that Empire. It is computed that eleven Thousand Persons have, at several Times, suffered Death, rather than submit to break their Eggs at the smaller End. Many hundred large Volumes have been published upon this Controversy: But the Books of the *Big-Endians* have been long forbidden, and the whole Party rendered incapable by Law of holding Employments. During the Course of these Troubles, the Emperors of *Blefuscu* did frequently expostulate by their Ambassadors, accusing us of making a Schism in Religion, by offending against a fundamental Doctrine of our great Prophet *Lustrog*, in the fifty-fourth Chapter of the *Brundrecal*, (which is their *Alcoran*.) This, however, is thought to be a mere Strain upon the text: For the Words are these; *That all true Believers shall break their Eggs at the convenient End:* and which is the convenient End, seems, in my humble Opinion, to be left to every Man's Conscience, or at least in the Power of the chief Magistrate to determine. Now the *Big-Endian* Exiles have found so much Credit in the Emperor of *Blefuscu's* Court; and so much private Assistance and Encouragement from their Party here at home, that a bloody War has been carried on between the two Empires for six and thirty Moons with various Success; during which Time we have lost Forty Capital Ships, and a much greater Number of smaller Vessels, together with thirty thousand of our best Seamen and Soldiers; and the Damage received by the Enemy is reckoned to be somewhat greater than ours. However, they have now equipped a numerous Fleet, and are just preparing to make a Descent upon us: and his Imperial Majesty, placing great Confidence in your Valour and Strength, hath commanded me to lay this Account of his Affairs before you.

Programming Examples

E.1 Synchronization

This section gives examples of how the *Storage Synchronization* instructions can be used to emulate various synchronization primitives and to provide more complex forms of synchronization.

These examples have a common form. After possible initialization, there is a "conditional sequence" that begins with a *Load And Reserve* instruction, which may be followed by memory accesses and/or computation that include neither a *Load And Reserve* nor a *Store Conditional*, and ends with a *Store Conditional* instruction with the same target address as the initial *Load And Reserve*. In most of the examples, failure of the *Store Conditional* causes a branch back to the *Load And Reserve* for a repeated attempt. On the assumption that contention is low, the conditional branch in the examples is optimized for the case in which the *Store Conditional* succeeds, by setting the branch-prediction bit appropriately. This is done by appending a minus sign to the instruction mnemonic, as described in Section C.2.4, "Branch Prediction," on page 220. These examples focus on techniques for the correct modification of shared storage locations: see Note 4 in Section E.1.4 for a discussion of how the retry strategy can affect performance.

The *Load And Reserve* and *Store Conditional* instructions depend on the coherence mechanism of the system. Stores to a given location are *coherent* if they are serialized in some order, and no processor is able to observe a subset of those stores as occurring in a conflicting order. See Book II, Section 1.5, "Memory Coherence," on page 323 for additional details.

Programming Note

Because the *Storage Synchronization* instructions have implementation dependencies (e.g., the granularity at which reservations are managed), they must be used with care. The operating system should provide system library programs that use these instructions to implement the high-level synchronization functions (Test and Set, Compare and Swap, etc.) needed by application programs. Application programs should use these library programs, rather than use the *Storage Synchronization* instructions directly.

Each load operation, whether ordinary or *Load And Reserve*, returns a value that has a well-defined *source*. The source can be the *Store* or *Store Conditional* instruction that wrote the value, an operation by some other mechanism that accesses storage (e.g., an I/O device), or the initial state of storage.

The function of an *atomic read/modify/write operation* is to read a location and write its next value, possibly as a function of its current value, all as a single atomic operation. We assume that locations accessed by read/modify/write operations are accessed coherently, so the concept of a value being the next in the sequence of values for a location is well defined. The conditional sequence, as defined above, provides the effect of an atomic read/modify/write operation, but not with a single atomic instruction. Let *addr* be the location that is the common target of the *Load And Reserve* and *Store Conditional* instructions. Then the guarantee the architecture makes for the successful execution of the conditional sequence is that no store into *addr* by another processor or mechanism has intervened between the source of the *Load And Reserve* and the *Store Conditional*.

For each of these examples, it is assumed that a similar sequence of instructions is used by all processes requiring synchronization on the accessed data.

The examples deal with words: they can be used for doublewords by changing all *lwarx* instructions to *ldarx*, all *stwcx.* instructions to *stdcx.*, all *stw* instructions to *std*, and all *cmpw[i]* extended mnemonics to *cmpd[i]*.

E.1.1 Synchronization Primitives

The following examples show how the *lwarx* and *stwcx.* instructions can be used to emulate various synchronization primitives.

The sequences used to emulate the various primitives consist primarily of a loop using *lwarx* and *stwcx.*. No additional synchronization is necessary, because the *stwcx.* will fail, setting the EQ bit to 0, if the word loaded by *lwarx* has changed before the *stwcx.* is executed: see Book II, Section 1.8.2, "Atomic Update Primitives," on page 336 for more detail.

Fetch and No-op

The "Fetch and No-op" primitive atomically loads the current value in a word in storage.

In this example it is assumed that the address of the word to be loaded is in GPR 3 and the data loaded are returned in GPR 4.

```
loop: lwarx   r4,0,r3      #load and reserve
      stwcx.  r4,0,r3      #store old value if still reserved
      bne-    loop         #loop if lost reservation
```

Note:

1. The *stwcx.*, if it succeeds, stores to the target location the same value
that was loaded by the preceding *lwarx*. While the store is redundant
with respect to the value in the location, its success ensures that the
value loaded by the *lwarx* was the current value, i.e., that the source of
the value loaded by the *lwarx* was the last store to the location that
preceded the *stwcx.* in the coherence order for the location.

Fetch and Store

The "Fetch and Store" primitive atomically loads and replaces a word in
storage.

In this example it is assumed that the address of the word to be loaded
and replaced is in GPR 3, the new value is in GPR 4, and the old value is
returned in GPR 5.

```
loop: lwarx   r5,0,r3      #load and reserve
      stwcx.  r4,0,r3      #store new value if still reserved
      bne-    loop         #loop if lost reservation
```

Fetch and Add

The "Fetch and Add" primitive atomically increments a word in storage.

In this example it is assumed that the address of the word to be incremented is in GPR 3, the increment is in GPR 4, and the old value is
returned in GPR 5.

```
loop: lwarx   r5,0,r3      #load and reserve
      add     r0,r4,r5     #increment word
      stwcx.  r0,0,r3      #store new value if still reserved
      bne-    loop         #loop if lost reservation
```

Fetch and AND

The "Fetch and AND" primitive atomically ANDs a value into a word in
storage.

In this example it is assumed that the address of the word to be
ANDed is in GPR 3, the value to AND into it is in GPR 4, and the old
value is returned in GPR 5.

```
loop: lwarx   r5,0,r3      #load and reserve
      and     r0,r4,r5     #AND word
      stwcx.  r0,0,r3      #store new value if still reserved
      bne-    loop         #loop if lost reservation
```

Note:

1. The sequence given above can be changed to perform another Boolean operation atomically on a word in storage, simply by changing the *and* instruction to the desired Boolean instruction (*or, xor,* etc.).

Test and Set

This version of the "Test and Set" primitive atomically loads a word from storage, sets the word in storage to a nonzero value if the value loaded is zero, and sets the EQ bit of CR Field 0 to indicate whether the value loaded is zero.

In this example it is assumed that the address of the word to be tested is in GPR 3, the new value (nonzero) is in GPR 4, and the old value is returned in GPR 5.

```
loop: lwarx   r5,0,r3      #load and reserve
       cmpwi   r5,0         #done if word
       bne-    $+12         #  not equal to 0
       stwcx.  r4,0,r3      #try to store non-0
       bne-    loop         #loop if lost reservation
```

Compare and Swap

The "Compare and Swap" primitive atomically compares a value in a register with a word in storage, if they are equal stores the value from a second register into the word in storage, if they are unequal loads the word from storage into the first register, and sets the EQ bit of CR Field 0 to indicate the result of the comparison.

In this example it is assumed that the address of the word to be tested is in GPR 3, the comparand is in GPR 4 and the old value is returned there, and the new value is in GPR 5.

```
loop: lwarx   r6,0,r3      #load and reserve
       cmpw    r4,r6        #1st 2 operands equal?
       bne-    exit         #skip if not
       stwcx.  r5,0,r3      #store new value if still reserved
       bne-    loop         #loop if lost reservation
exit: mr       r4,r6        #return value from storage
```

Notes:

1. The semantics given for "Compare and Swap" above are based on those of the IBM System/370 Compare and Swap instruction. Other architectures may define a Compare and Swap instruction differently.

2. *Compare and Swap* is shown primarily for pedagogical reasons. It is useful on machines that lack the better synchronization facilities provided by *lwarx* and *stwcx.*. A major weakness of a System/370-style Compare and Swap instruction is that, although the instruction itself is atomic, it checks only that the old and current values of the word being tested are equal, with the result that programs that use such a Compare and Swap to control a shared resource can err if the word has been modified and the old value subsequently restored. The sequence shown above has the same weakness.

3. In some applications the second *bne-* instruction and/or the *mr* instruction can be omitted. The *bne-* is needed only if the application requires that if the EQ bit of CR Field 0 on exit indicates "not equal" then (r4) and (r6) are in fact not equal. The *mr* is needed only if the application requires that if the comparands are not equal then the word from storage is loaded into the register with which it was compared (rather than into a third register). If either or both of these instructions is omitted, the resulting Compare and Swap does not obey System/370 semantics.

E.1.2 Lock Acquisition and Release

This example gives an algorithm for locking that demonstrates the use of synchronization with an atomic read/modify/write operation. A shared storage location, the address of which is an argument of the "lock" and "unlock" procedures, given by GPR 3, is used as a lock, to control access to some shared resource such as a shared data structure. The lock is open when its value is 0 and closed (locked) when its value is 1. Before accessing the shared resource, a processor sets the lock by changing its value from 0 to 1. To do this, the "lock" procedure calls *test_and_set*, which executes the code sequence shown in the "Test and Set" example of Section E.1.1, thereby atomically loading the old value of the lock, writing to the lock the new value (1) given in GPR 4, returning the old value in GPR 5 (not used below), and setting the EQ bit of CR Field 0 according to whether the value loaded is 0. The "lock" procedure repeats the *test_and_set* until it succeeds in changing the value of the lock from 0 to 1.

   The processor must not access the shared resource until it sets the lock. After the *bne-* that checks for the success of *test_and_set*, the processor executes an *isync* instruction (see Book II, "Instruction Synchronize XL-form," on page 346). This delays all subsequent instructions until all previous instructions have completed to the extent required by context synchronization (see Book III, Section 1.7.1, "Context Synchronization," on page 371). *sync* could be used, but performance would be degraded unnecessarily because *sync* waits for all prior storage accesses to complete with respect to all other processors, which is not necessary here.

```
lock: li    r4,1        #obtain lock:
loop: bl    test_and_set #  test-and-set
      bne-  loop        #  retry til old = 0
# Delay subsequent inst'ns til prior inst'ns finish
      isync
      blr               #return
```

The "unlock" procedure writes a 0 to the lock location. Most applications that use locking require, for correctness, that if the access to the shared resource included write operations, the processor must execute a *sync* instruction to make its modifications visible to all processors before releasing the lock. In this example, the "unlock" procedure begins with a *sync* for this purpose.

```
unlock: sync          #delay til prior stores finish
        li   r1,0     #store 0 to lock location
        stw  r1,0(r3)
        blr           #return
```

E.1.3 List Insertion

This example shows how the *lwarx* and *stwcx.* instructions can be used to implement simple insertion into a singly linked list. (Complicated list insertion, in which multiple values must be changed atomically, or in which the correct order of insertion depends on the contents of the elements, cannot be implemented in the manner shown below and requires a more complicated strategy such as using locks.)

The "next element pointer" from the list element after which the new element is to be inserted, here called the "parent element," is stored into the new element, so that the new element points to the next element in the list: this store is performed unconditionally. Then the address of the new element is conditionally stored into the parent element, thereby adding the new element to the list.

In this example it is assumed that the address of the parent element is in GPR 3, the address of the new element is in GPR 4, and the next element pointer is at offset 0 from the start of the element. It is also assumed that the next element pointer of each list element is in a "reservation granule" separate from that of the next element pointer of all other list elements: see Book II, Section 1.8.2, "Atomic Update Primitives," on page 336.

```
loop: lwarx  r2,0,r3     #get next pointer
      stw    r2,0(r4)    #store in new element
      sync               #let store settle (can omit if not MP)
      stwcx. r4,0,r3     #add new element to list
      bne-   loop        #loop if stwcx. failed
```

In the preceding example, if two list elements have next element pointers in the same reservation granule then, in a multiprocessor, "livelock" can occur. (Livelock is a state in which processors interact in a way such that no processor makes progress.)

If it is not possible to allocate list elements such that each element's next element pointer is in a different reservation granule, then livelock can be avoided by using the following, more complicated, sequence.

```
        lwz    r2,0(r3)    #get next pointer
loop1:  mr     r5,r2       #keep a copy
        stw    r2,0(r4)    #store in new element
        sync               #let store settle
loop2:  lwarx  r2,0,r3     #get it again
        cmpw   r2,r5       #loop if changed (someone
        bne-   loop1       # else progressed)
        stwcx. r4,0,r3     #add new element to list
        bne-   loop2       #loop if stwcx. failed
```

E.1.4 Notes

1. In general, *lwarx* and *stwcx.* instructions should be paired, with the same effective address used for both. The exception is an isolated *stwcx.* instruction that is used to clear any existing reservation on the processor, for which there is no paired *lwarx* and for which any (scratch) effective address can be used.

2. It is acceptable to execute a *lwarx* instruction for which no *stwcx.* instruction is executed. For example, this occurs in the "Test and Set" sequence shown above if the value loaded is not zero.

3. To increase the likelihood that forward progress is made, it is important that looping on *lwarx/stwcx.* pairs be minimized. For example, in the sequence shown above for "Test and Set," this is achieved by testing the old value before attempting the store: were the order reversed, more *stwcx.* instructions might be executed, and reservations might more often be lost between the *lwarx* and the *stwcx.*.

4. The manner in which *lwarx* and *stwcx.* are communicated to other processors and mechanisms, and between levels of the storage subsystem within a given processor (see Book II, *PowerPC Virtual Environment Architecture*), is implementation-dependent. In some implementations, performance may be improved by minimizing looping on a *lwarx* instruction that fails to return a desired value. For example, in the "Test and Set" example shown above, if the programmer wishes to stay in the loop until the word loaded is zero, he could change the "bne- $+12" to "bne- loop". However, in some implementations better performance may be obtained by using an ordinary *Load* instruction to do the initial checking of the value, as follows.

```
loop: lwz     r5,0(r3)    #load the word
      cmpwi   r5,0        #loop back if word
      bne-    loop        #  not equal to 0
      lwarx   r5,0,r3     #try again, reserving
      cmpwi   r5,0        #  (likely to succeed)
      bne-    loop
      stwcx.  r4,0,r3     #try to store non-0
      bne-    loop        #loop if lost reservation
```

5. In a multiprocessor, livelock is possible if a loop containing a *lwarx/stwcx.* pair also contains an ordinary *Store* instruction for which any byte of the affected storage area is in the reservation granule: see Book II, Section 1.8.2, "Atomic Update Primitives," on page 336. For example, the first code sequence shown in Section E.1.3 can cause livelock if two list elements have next element pointers in the same reservation granule.

E.2 Multiple-Precision Shifts

This section gives examples of how multiple-precision shifts can be programmed.

A multiple-precision shift is initially defined to be a shift of an N-doubleword quantity (64-bit mode) or an N-word quantity (32-bit mode), where N>1. The quantity to be shifted is contained in N registers (in the low-order 32 bits in 32-bit mode). The shift amount is specified either by an immediate value in the instruction, or by bits 57:63 (64-bit mode) or 58:63 (32-bit mode) of a register.

The examples shown below distinguish between the cases N=2 and N>2. If N=2, the shift amount may be in the range 0 through 127 (64-bit mode) or 0 through 63 (32-bit mode), which are the maximum ranges supported by the *Shift* instructions used. However, if N>2, the shift amount must be in the range 0 through 63 (64-bit mode) or 0 through 31 (32-bit mode), in order for the examples to yield the desired result. The specific instance shown for N>2 is N=3: extending those code sequences to larger N is straightforward, as is reducing them to the case N=2 when the more stringent restriction on shift amount is met. For shifts with immediate shift amounts only the case N=3 is shown, because the more stringent restriction on shift amount is always met.

In the examples it is assumed that GPRs 2 and 3 (and 4) contain the quantity to be shifted, and that the result is to be placed into the same registers, except for the immediate left shifts in 64-bit mode for which the result is placed into GPRs 3, 4, and 5. In all cases, for both input and result, the lowest-numbered register contains the highest-order part of the data and highest-numbered register contains the lowest-order part. In 32-bit mode, the high-order 32 bits of these registers are assumed not to be part of the quantity to be shifted or of the result. For non-immediate shifts, the shift amount is assumed to be in bits 57:63 (64-bit mode) or 58:63 (32-bit mode) of GPR 6. For immediate shifts, the shift amount is assumed to be greater than 0. GPRs 0 and 31 are used as scratch registers.

For N>2, the number of instructions required is 2N−1 (immediate shifts) or 3N−1 (non-immediate shifts).

Multiple-precision shifts in 64-bit mode		Multiple-precision shifts in 32-bit mode	
Shift Left Immediate, N = 3 (shift amnt < 64)		**Shift Left Immediate, N = 3 (shift amnt < 32)**	
rldicr	r5,r4,sh,63-sh	rlwinm	r2,r2,sh,0,31-sh
rldimi	r4,r3,0,sh	rlwimi	r2,r3,sh,32-sh,31
rldicl	r4,r4,sh,0	rlwinm	r3,r3,sh,0,31-sh
rldimi	r3,r2,0,sh	rlwimi	r3,r4,sh,32-sh,31
rldicl	r3,r3,sh,0	rlwinm	r4,r4,sh,0,31-sh
Shift Left, N = 2 (shift amnt < 128)		**Shift Left, N = 2 (shift amnt < 64)**	
subfic	r31,r6,64	subfic	r31,r6,32
sld	r2,r2,r6	slw	r2,r2,r6
srd	r0,r3,r31	srw	r0,r3,r31
or	r2,r2,r0	or	r2,r2,r0
addi	r31,r6,-64	addi	r31,r6,-32
sld	r0,r3,r31	slw	r0,r3,r31
or	r2,r2,r0	or	r2,r2,r0
sld	r3,r3,r6	slw	r3,r3,r6

Multiple-precision shifts in 64-bit mode		Multiple-precision shifts in 32-bit mode	
Shift Left, N = 3 (shift amnt < 64)		Shift Left, N = 3 (shift amnt < 32)	
subfic	r31,r6,64	subfic	r31,r6,32
sld	r2,r2,r6	slw	r2,r2,r6
srd	r0,r3,r31	srw	r0,r3,r31
or	r2,r2,r0	or	r2,r2,r0
sld	r3,r3,r6	slw	r3,r3,r6
srd	r0,r4,r31	srw	r0,r4,r31
or	r3,r3,r0	or	r3,r3,r0
sld	r4,r4,r6	slw	r4,r4,r6
Shift Right Immediate, N = 3 (shift amnt < 64)		Shift Right Immediate, N = 3 (shift amnt < 32)	
rldimi	r4,r3,0,64-sh	rlwinm	r4,r4,32-sh,sh,31
rldicl	r4,r4,64-sh,0	rlwimi	r4,r3,32-sh,0,sh-1
rldimi	r3,r2,0,64-sh	rlwinm	r3,r3,32-sh,sh,31
rldicl	r3,r3,64-sh,0	rlwimi	r3,r2,32-sh,0,sh-1
rldicl	r2,r2,64-sh,sh	rlwinm	r2,r2,32-sh,sh,31
Shift Right, N = 2 (shift amnt < 128)		Shift Right, N = 2 (shift amnt < 64)	
subfic	r31,r6,64	subfic	r31,r6,32
srd	r3,r3,r6	srw	r3,r3,r6
sld	r0,r2,r31	slw	r0,r2,r31
or	r3,r3,r0	or	r3,r3,r0
addi	r31,r6,-64	addi	r31,r6,-32
srd	r0,r2,r31	srw	r0,r2,r31
or	r3,r3,r0	or	r3,r3,r0
srd	r2,r2,r6	srw	r2,r2,r6
Shift Right, N = 3 (shift amnt < 64)		Shift Right, N = 3 (shift amnt < 32)	
subfic	r31,r6,64	subfic	r31,r6,32
srd	r4,r4,r6	srw	r4,r4,r6
sld	r0,r3,r31	slw	r0,r3,r31
or	r4,r4,r0	or	r4,r4,r0
srd	r3,r3,r6	srw	r3,r3,r6
sld	r0,r2,r31	slw	r0,r2,r31
or	r3,r3,r0	or	r3,r3,r0
srd	r2,r2,r6	srw	r2,r2,r6
Shift Right Algebraic Immediate, N = 3 (shift amnt < 64)		Shift Right Algebraic Immediate, N = 3 (shift amnt < 32)	
rldimi	r4,r3,0,64-sh	rlwinm	r4,r4,32-sh,sh,31
rldicl	r4,r4,64-sh,0	rlwimi	r4,r3,32-sh,0,sh-1
rldimi	r3,r2,0,64-sh	rlwinm	r3,r3,32-sh,sh,31
rldicl	r3,r3,64-sh,0	rlwimi	r3,r2,32-sh,0,sh-1
sradi	r2,r2,sh	srawi	r2,r2,sh
Shift Right Algebraic, N = 2 (shift amnt < 128)		Shift Right Algebraic, N = 2 (shift amnt < 64)	
subfic	r31,r6,64	subfic	r31,r6,32
srd	r3,r3,r6	srw	r3,r3,r6

Multiple-precision shifts in 64-bit mode		Multiple-precision shifts in 32-bit mode	
sld	r0,r2,r31	slw	r0,r2,r31
or	r3,r3,r0	or	r3,r3,r0
addic.	r31,r6,-64	addic.	r31,r6,-32
srad	r0,r2,r31	sraw	r0,r2,r31
ble	$+8	ble	$+8
ori	r3,r0,0	ori	r3,r0,0
srad	r2,r2,r6	sraw	r2,r2,r6
Shift Right Algebraic, N = 3 (shift amnt < 64)		Shift Right Algebraic, N = 3 (shift amnt < 32)	
subfic	r31,r6,64	subfic	r31,r6,32
srd	r4,r4,r6	srw	r4,r4,r6
sld	r0,r3,r31	slw	r0,r3,r31
or	r4,r4,r0	or	r4,r4,r0
srd	r3,r3,r6	srw	r3,r3,r6
sld	r0,r2,r31	slw	r0,r2,r31
or	r3,r3,r0	or	r3,r3,r0
srad	r2,r2,r6	sraw	r2,r2,r6

E.3 Floating-Point Conversions

This section gives examples of how the *Floating-Point Conversion* instructions can be used to perform various conversions.

Warning: Some of the examples use the *fsel* instruction. Care must be taken in using *fsel* if IEEE compatibility is required or if the values being tested can be NaNs or infinities: see Section E.4.4, "Notes," on page 266.

E.3.1 Conversion from Floating-Point Number to Floating-Point Integer

In a 64-bit implementation
The full *convert to floating-point integer* function can be implemented with the sequence shown below, assuming the floating-point value to be converted is in FPR 1, and the result is returned in FPR 3.

```
mtfsb0    23          #clear VXCVI
fctid[z]  f3,f1       #convert to fx int
fcfid     f3,f3       #convert back again
mcrfs     7,5         #VXCVI to CR
bf        31,$+8      #skip if VXCVI was 0
fmr       f3,f1       #input was fp int
```

In a 32-bit implementation

This example will be provided in a subsequent edition.

E.3.2 Conversion from Floating-Point Number to Signed Fixed-Point Integer Doubleword

This example applies to 64-bit implementations only.

The full *convert to signed fixed-point integer doubleword* function can be implemented with the sequence shown below, assuming the floating-point value to be converted is in FPR 1, the result is returned in GPR 3, and a doubleword at displacement "disp" from the address in GPR 1 can be used as scratch space.

```
fctid[z]  f2,f1          #convert to dword int
stfd      f2,disp(r1)    #store float
ld        r3,disp(r1)    #load dword
```

E.3.3 Conversion from Floating-Point Number to Unsigned Fixed-Point Integer Doubleword

This example applies to 64-bit implementations only.

The full *convert to unsigned fixed-point integer doubleword* function can be implemented with the sequence shown below, assuming the floating-point value to be converted is in FPR 1, the value 0 is in FPR 0, the value $2^{64}-2048$ is in FPR 3, the value 2^{63} is in FPR 4 and GPR 4, the result is returned in GPR 3, and a doubleword at displacement "disp" from the address in GPR 1 can be used as scratch space.

```
fsel      f2,f1,f1,f0    #use 0 if < 0
fsub      f5,f3,f1       #use max if > max
fsel      f2,f5,f2,f3
fsub      f5,f2,f4       #subtract 2**63
fcmpu     cr2,f2,f4      #use diff if ≥ 2**63
fsel      f2,f5,f5,f2
fctid[z]  f2,f2          #convert to fx int
stfd      f2,disp(r1)    #store float
ld        r3,disp(r1)    #load dword
blt       cr2,$+8        #add 2**63 if input
add       r3,r3,r4       #  was ≥ 2**63
```

E.3.4 Conversion from Floating-Point Number to Signed Fixed-Point Integer Word

The full *convert to signed fixed-point integer word* function can be implemented with the sequence shown below, assuming the floating-point value to be converted is in FPR 1, the result is returned in GPR 3, and a doubleword at displacement "disp" from the address in GPR 1 can be used as scratch space. The last instruction is needed only if a 64-bit result is required, and applies to 64-bit implementations only.

```
fctiw[z] f2,f1          #convert to fx int
stfd     f2,disp(r1)    #store float
lwz      r3,disp+4(r1)  #load word and zero
extsw    r3,r3          #(for 64-bit result)
```

E.3.5 Conversion from Floating-Point Number to Unsigned Fixed-Point Integer Word

In a 64-bit implementation
The full *convert to unsigned fixed-point integer word* function can be implemented with the sequence shown below, assuming the floating-point value to be converted is in FPR 1, the value 0 is in FPR 0, the value $2^{32}-1$ is in FPR 3, the result is returned in GPR 3, and a doubleword at displacement "disp" from the address in GPR 1 can be used as scratch space.

```
fsel     f2,f1,f1,f0    #use 0 if < 0
fsub     f4,f3,f1       #use max if > max
fsel     f2,f4,f2,f3
fctid[z] f2,f2          #convert to fx int
stfd     f2,disp(r1)    #store float
lwz      r3,disp+4(r1)  #load word and zero
```

In a 32-bit implementation
The full *convert to unsigned fixed-point integer word* function can be implemented with the sequence shown below, assuming the floating-point value to be converted is in FPR 1, the value 0 is in FPR 0, the value 2^{32} is in FPR 3, the value 2^{31} is in FPR 4, the result is returned in GPR 3, and a doubleword at displacement "disp" from the address in GPR 1 can be used as scratch space.

```
fsel       f2,f1,f1,f0      #use 0 if < 0
fsub       f5,f3,f1         #use max if > max
fsel       f2,f5,f2,f3
fsub       f5,f2,f4         #subtract 2**31
fcmpu      cr2,f2,f4        #use diff if ≥ 2**31
fsel       f2,f5,f5,f2
fctiw[z]   f2,f2            #convert to fx int
stfd       f2,disp(r1)      #store float
lwz        r3,disp+4(r1)    #load word
blt        cr2,$+8          #add 2**31 if input
xoris      r3,r3,0x8000     #   was ≥ 2**31
```

E.3.6 Conversion from Signed Fixed-Point Integer Doubleword to Floating-Point Number

This example applies to 64-bit implementations only.

The full *convert from signed fixed-point integer doubleword* function, using the rounding mode specified by FPSCR$_{RN}$, can be implemented with the sequence shown below, assuming the fixed-point value to be converted is in GPR 3, the result is returned in FPR 1, and a doubleword at displacement "disp" from the address in GPR 1 can be used as scratch space.

```
std        r3,disp(r1)      #store dword
lfd        f1,disp(r1)      #load float
fcfid      f1,f1            #convert to fp int
```

E.3.7 Conversion from Unsigned Fixed-Point Integer Doubleword to Floating-Point Number

This example applies to 64-bit implementations only.

The full *convert from unsigned fixed-point integer doubleword* function, using the rounding mode specified by FPSCR$_{RN}$, can be implemented with the sequence shown below, assuming the fixed-point value to be converted is in GPR 3, the value 2^{32} is in FPR 4, the result is returned in FPR 1, and two doublewords at displacement "disp" from the address in GPR 1 can be used as scratch space.

```
rldicl    r2,r3,32,32      #isolate high half
rldicl    r0,r3,0,32       #isolate low half
std       r2,disp(r1)      #store dword both
std       r0,disp+8(r1)
lfd       f2,disp(r1)      #load float both
lfd       f1,disp+8(r1)
fcfid     f2,f2            #convert each half to
fcfid     f1,f1            #  fp int (no round)
fmadd     f1,f4,f2,f1      #(2**32)*high + low
                           #  (only add can round)
```

An alternative, shorter, sequence can be used if rounding according to FSCPR$_{RN}$ is desired and FPSCR$_{RN}$ specifies *Round toward +Infinity* or *Round toward* –Infinity, or if it is acceptable for a rounded answer to be either of the two representable floating-point integers nearest to the given fixed-point integer. In this case the full *convert from unsigned fixed-point integer doubleword* function can be implemented with the sequence shown below, assuming the value 2^{64} is in FPR 2.

```
std       r3,disp(r1)      #store dword
lfd       f1,disp(r1)      #load float
fcfid     f1,f1            #convert to fp int
fadd      f4,f1,f2         #add 2**64
fsel      f1,f1,f1,f4      #  if r3 < 0
```

E.3.8 Conversion from Signed Fixed-Point Integer Word to Floating-Point Number

In a 64-bit implementation

The full *convert from signed fixed-point integer word* function can be implemented with the sequence shown below, assuming the fixed-point value to be converted is in GPR 3, the result is returned in FPR 1, and a doubleword at displacement "disp" from the address in GPR 1 can be used as scratch space. (Rounding cannot occur.)

```
extsw     r3,r3            #extend sign
std       r3,disp(r1)      #store dword
lfd       f1,disp(r1)      #load float
fcfid     f1,f1            #convert to fp int
```

In a 32-bit implementation

This example will be provided in a subsequent edition.

E.3.9 Conversion from Unsigned Fixed-Point Integer Word to Floating-Point Number

In a 64-bit implementation

The full *convert from unsigned fixed-point integer word* function can be implemented with the sequence shown below, assuming the fixed-point value to be converted is in GPR 3, the result is returned in FPR 1, and a doubleword at displacement "disp" from the address in GPR 1 can be used as scratch space. (Rounding cannot occur.)

```
rldicl   r0,r3,0,32     #zero-extend
std      r0,disp(r1)    #store dword
lfd      f1,disp(r1)    #load float
fcfid    f1,f1          #convert to fp int
```

In a 32-bit implementation

This example will be provided in a subsequent edition.

E.4 Floating-Point Selection

This section gives examples of how the *Floating Select* instruction can be used to implement floating-point minimum and maximum functions, and certain simple forms of if-then-else constructions, without branching.

The examples show program fragments in an imaginary, C-like, high-level programming language, and the corresponding program fragment using *fsel* and other PowerPC instructions. In the examples, *a, b, x, y,* and *z* are floating-point variables, which are assumed to be in FPRs *fa, fb, fx, fy,* and *fz*. FPR *fs* is assumed to be available for scratch space.

Additional examples can be found in Section E.3, "Floating-Point Conversions," on page 259.

Warning: Care must be taken in using *fsel* if IEEE compatibility is required or if the values being tested can be NaNs or infinities: see Section E.4.4, "Notes," on page 266.

E.4.1 Comparison to Zero

High-level language:	PowerPC:	Notes
if a ≥ 0.0 then x ← y else x ← z	fsel fx,fa,fy,fz	(1)
if a > 0.0 then x ← y else x ← z	fneg fs,fa fsel fx,fs,fz,fy	(1,2)
if a = 0.0 then x ← y else x ← z	fsel fx,fa,fy,fz fneg fs,fa fsel fx,fs,fx,fz	(1)

E.4.2 Minimum and Maximum

High-level language:	PowerPC:	Notes
x ← min(a,b)	fsub fs,fa,fb fsel fx,fs,fb,fa	(3,4,5)
x ← max(a,b)	fsub fs,fa,fb fsel fx,fs,fa,fb	(3,4,5)

E.4.3 Simple if-then-else Constructions

High-level language:	PowerPC:	Notes
if a ≥ b then x ← y else x ← z	fsub fs,fa,fb fsel fx,fs,fy,fz	(4,5)
if a > b then x ← y else x ← z	fsub fs,fb,fa fsel fx,fs,fz,fy	(3,4,5)
if a = b then x ← y else x ← z	fsub fs,fa,fb fsel fx,fs,fy,fz fneg fs,fs fsel fx,fs,fx,fz	(4,5)

E.4.4 Notes

The following Notes apply to the preceding examples and to the corresponding cases using the other three arithmetic relations ($<$, $\leq$, and $\neq$). They should also be considered when any other use of *fsel* is contemplated.

In these Notes, the "optimized program" is the PowerPC program shown, and the "unoptimized program" (not shown) is the corresponding PowerPC program that uses *fcmpu* and *Branch Conditional* instructions instead of *fsel*.

1. The unoptimized program affects the VXSNAN bit of the FPSCR, and therefore may cause the system error handler to be invoked if the corresponding exception is enabled, while the optimized program does not affect this bit. This property of the optimized program is incompatible with the IEEE standard.

2. The optimized program gives the incorrect result if a is a NaN.

3. The optimized program gives the incorrect result if a and/or b is a NaN (except that it may give the correct result in some cases for the minimum and maximum functions, depending on how those functions are defined to operate on NaNs).

4. The optimized program gives the incorrect result if a and b are infinities of the same sign. (Here it is assumed that Invalid Operation Exceptions are disabled, in which case the result of the subtraction is a NaN. The analysis is more complicated if Invalid Operation Exceptions are enabled, because in that case the target register of the subtraction is unchanged.)

5. The optimized program affects the OX, UX, XX, and VXISI bits of the FPSCR, and therefore may cause the system error handler to be invoked if the corresponding exceptions are enabled, while the unoptimized program does not affect these bits. This property of the optimized program is incompatible with the IEEE standard.

Cross-Reference for Changed POWER Mnemonics

F

The following table lists the POWER instruction mnemonics that have been changed in the PowerPC Architecture, sorted by POWER mnemonic.

To determine the PowerPC mnemonic for one of these POWER mnemonics, find the POWER mnemonic in the second column of the table: the remainder of the line gives the PowerPC mnemonic and the page on which the instruction is described, as well as the instruction names. The Book number is shown in the "Page" column for instructions that are not defined in Book I.

POWER mnemonics that have not changed are not listed. POWER instruction names that are the same in PowerPC are not repeated: i.e., for these, the last column of the table is blank.

| Page | POWER | | PowerPC | |
	Mnemonic	Instruction	Mnemonic	Instruction
85	a[o][.]	Add	addc[o][.]	Add Carrying
86	ae[o][.]	Add Extended	adde[o][.]	
84	ai	Add Immediate	addic	Add Immediate Carrying
84	ai.	Add Immediate and Record	addic.	Add Immediate Carrying and Record
87	ame[o][.]	Add To Minus One Extended	addme[o][.]	Add to Minus One Extended

Page	POWER		PowerPC	
	Mnemonic	Instruction	Mnemonic	Instruction
106	andil.	AND Immediate Lower	andi.	AND Immediate
106	andiu.	AND Immediate Upper	andis.	AND Immediate Shifted
88	aze[o][.]	Add To Zero Extended	addze[o][.]	Add to Zero Extended
40	bcc[l]	Branch Conditional to Count Register	bcctr[l]	
39	bcr[l]	Branch Conditional to Link Register	bclr[l]	
82	cal	Compute Address Lower	addi	Add Immediate
82	cau	Compute Address Upper	addis	Add Immediate Shifted
83	cax[o][.]	Compute Address	add[o][.]	Add
114	cntlz[.]	Count Leading Zeros	cntlzw[.]	Count Leading Zeros Word
347 (II)	dclz	Data Cache Line Set to Zero	dcbz	Data Cache Block set to Zero
80	dcs	Data Cache Synchronize	sync	Synchronize
113	exts[.]	Extend Sign	extsh[.]	Extend Sign Halfword
179	fa[.]	Floating Add	fadd[.]	
182	fd[.]	Floating Divide	fdiv[.]	
181	fm[.]	Floating Multiply	fmul[.]	
183	fma[.]	Floating Multiply-Add	fmadd[.]	
184	fms[.]	Floating Multiply-Subtract	fmsub[.]	
185	fnma[.]	Floating Negative Multiply-Add	fnmadd[.]	
186	fnms[.]	Floating Negative Multiply-Subtract	fnmsub[.]	
180	fs[.]	Floating Subtract	fsub[.]	
346 (II)	ics	Instruction Cache Synchronize	isync	Instruction Synchronize
55	l	Load	lwz	Load Word and Zero
69	lbrx	Load Byte-Reverse Indexed	lwbrx	Load Word Byte-Reverse Indexed
71	lm	Load Multiple	lmw	Load Multiple Word

Page	POWER		PowerPC	
	Mnemonic	Instruction	Mnemonic	Instruction
73	lsi	Load String Immediate	lswi	Load String Word Immediate
74	lsx	Load String Indexed	lswx	Load String Word Indexed
56	lu	Load with Update	lwzu	Load Word and Zero with Update
57	lux	Load with Update Indexed	lwzux	Load Word and Zero with Update Indexed
56	lx	Load Indexed	lwzx	Load Word and Zero Indexed
441 (III)	mtsri	Move To Segment Register Indirect	mtsrin	
90	muli	Multiply Immediate	mulli	Multiply Low Immediate
91	muls[o][.]	Multiply Short	mullw[o][.]	Multiply Low Word
107	oril	OR Immediate Lower	ori	OR Immediate
107	oriu	OR Immediate Upper	oris	OR Immediate Shifted
122	rlimi[.]	Rotate Left Immediate Then Mask Insert	rlwimi[.]	Rotate Left Word Immediate then Mask Insert
119	rlinm[.]	Rotate Left Immediate Then AND With Mask	rlwinm[.]	Rotate Left Word Immediate then AND with Mask
121	rlnm[.]	Rotate Left Then AND With Mask	rlwnm[.]	Rotate Left Word then AND with Mask
86	sf[o][.]	Subtract From	subfc[o][.]	Subtract From Carrying
87	sfe[o][.]	Subtract From Extended	subfe[o][.]	
85	sfi	Subtract From Immediate	subfic	Subtract From Immediate Carrying
88	sfme[o][.]	Subtract From Minus One Extended	subfme[o][.]	
89	sfze[o][.]	Subtract From Zero Extended	subfze[o][.]	
124	sl[.]	Shift Left	slw[.]	Shift Left Word
125	sr[.]	Shift Right	srw[.]	Shift Right Word
128	sra[.]	Shift Right Algebraic	sraw[.]	Shift Right Algebraic Word
126	srai[.]	Shift Right Algebraic Immediate	srawi[.]	Shift Right Algebraic Word Immediate

Page	POWER		PowerPC	
	Mnemonic	Instruction	Mnemonic	Instruction
64	st	Store	stw	Store Word
70	stbrx	Store Byte-Reverse Indexed	stwbrx	Store Word Byte-Reverse Indexed
72	stm	Store Multiple	stmw	Store Multiple Word
75	stsi	Store String Immediate	stswi	Store String Word Immediate
76	stsx	Store String Indexed	stswx	Store String Word Indexed
65	stu	Store with Update	stwu	Store Word with Update
66	stux	Store with Update Indexed	stwux	Store Word with Update Indexed
65	stx	Store Indexed	stwx	Store Word Indexed
41	svca	Supervisor Call	sc	System Call (see also Book III, page 378)
105	t	Trap	tw	Trap Word
103	ti	Trap Immediate	twi	Trap Word Immediate
444 (III)	tlbi	TLB Invalidate Entry	tlbie	
108	xoril	XOR Immediate Lower	xori	XOR Immediate
108	xoriu	XOR Immediate Upper	xoris	XOR Immediate Shifted

Incompatibilities with the POWER Architecture

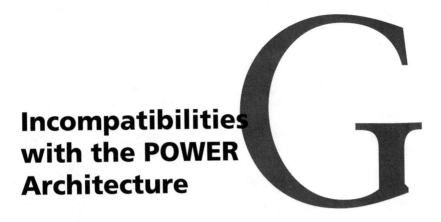

This appendix identifies the known incompatibilities that must be managed in the migration from the POWER Architecture to the PowerPC Architecture. Some of the incompatibilities can, at least in principle, be detected by the processor, which could trap and let software simulate the POWER operation. Others cannot be detected by the processor even in principle. In general, the incompatibilities identified here are those that affect a POWER application program: incompatiblities for instructions that can be used only by POWER system programs are not necessarily discussed.

G.1 New Instructions, Formerly Privileged Instructions

Instructions new to PowerPC typically use opcode values (including extended opcode) that are illegal in POWER. A few instructions that are privileged in POWER (e.g., *dclz*, called *dcbz* in PowerPC) have been made nonprivileged in PowerPC. Any POWER program that executes one of these now-valid or now-nonprivileged instructions, expecting to cause the system illegal instruction error handler or the system privileged instruction error handler to be invoked, will not execute correctly on PowerPC.

G.2 Newly Privileged Instructions

The following instructions are nonprivileged in POWER but privileged in PowerPC.

mfmsr

mfsr

G.3 Reserved Bits in Instructions

These are shown with '/'s in the instruction layouts. In POWER such bits are ignored by the processor. In PowerPC they must be 0 or the instruction form is invalid.

In several cases, the PowerPC Architecture assumes that such bits in POWER instructions are indeed 0. The cases include the following:

■ *cmpi, cmp, cmpli,* and *cmpl* assume that bit 10 in the POWER instructions is 0.

■ *mtspr* and *mfspr* assume that bits 16:20 in the POWER instructions are 0.

G.4 Reserved Bits in Registers

POWER defines these bits to be 0 on read, and either 0 or 1 on write. In PowerPC it is implementation-dependent, for each bit, whether the bit is:

■ 0 on read and ignored on write; or

■ copied from source to target on both read and write.

G.5 Alignment Check

The POWER MSR AL bit (bit 24) is no longer supported: the bit is reserved in PowerPC. The low-order bits of the EA are always used. (Notice that the value 0—the normal value for a reserved SPR bit—means "ignore the low-order EA bits" in POWER, and the value 1 means "use the low-order EA bits.") However, MSR bit 24 will not be assigned new meaning in the near future (see Book III, Section 2.2.3, "Machine State Register," on page 374), and software is permitted to write the value 1 to the bit.

G.6 Condition Register

The following instructions specify a field in the CR explicitly (via the BF field) and also, in POWER, use bit 31 as the Record bit. In PowerPC, if bit 31=1 for these instructions the instruction form is invalid. In POWER, if Rc=1 the instructions execute normally except as follows:

cmp   CR0 is undefined if Rc=1 and BF≠0

cmpl   CR0 is undefined if Rc=1 and BF≠0

mcrxr   CR0 is undefined if Rc=1 and BF≠0

fcmpu   CR1 is undefined if Rc=1

fcmpo   CR1 is undefined if Rc=1

mcrfs   CR1 is undefined if Rc=1 and BF≠1

G.7 Inappropriate use of LK and Rc Bits

For the instructions listed below, if bit 31 (LK or Rc bit in POWER) is set to 1, POWER executes the instruction normally with the exception of setting the Link Register (if LK=1) or Condition Register Field 0 or 1 (if Rc=1) to an undefined value. In PowerPC such instruction forms are invalid.

PowerPC instructions that are invalid form if bit 31=1 (LK bit in POWER):

sc (*svc* in POWER)

the *Condition Register Logical* instructions

mcrf

isync (*ics* in POWER)

PowerPC instructions that are invalid form if bit 31=1 (Rc bit in POWER):

fixed-point X-form *Load* and *Store* instructions

fixed-point X-form *Compare* instructions

the X-form *Trap* instruction

mtspr, mfspr, mtcrf, mcrxr, mfcr

floating-point X-form *Load* and *Store* instructions

floating-point *Compare* instructions

mcrfs

dcbz (*dclz* in POWER)

G.8 BO Field

POWER shows certain bits in the BO field—used by *Branch Conditional* instructions—as "x." Although the POWER Architecture does not say how these bits are to be interpreted, they are in fact ignored by the processor.

PowerPC shows these bits as either "z" or "y." The "z" bits are ignored, as in POWER. However, the "y" bit need not be ignored, but rather can be used to give a hint about whether the branch is likely to be taken. If a POWER program has the "wrong" value for this bit, the program will run correctly but performance may suffer.

G.9 Branch Conditional to Count Register

For the case in which the Count Register is decremented and tested (i.e., the case in which $BO_2=0$), POWER specifies only that the branch target address is undefined, with the implication that the Count Register, and the Link Register if LK=1, are updated in the normal way. PowerPC considers this instruction form invalid.

G.10 System Call

There are several respects in which PowerPC is incompatible with POWER for *System Call* instructions—which in POWER are called *Supervisor Call* instructions.

■ POWER provides a version of the *Supervisor Call* instruction (bit 30=0) that allows instruction fetching to continue at any one of 128 locations. It is used for "fast SVCs." PowerPC provides no such version: if bit 30 of the instruction is 0 the instruction form is invalid.

■ POWER provides a version of the *Supervisor Call* instruction (bits 30:31=0b11) that resumes instruction fetching at one location and sets the Link Register to the address of the next instruction. PowerPC provides no such version: if bit 31 of the instruction is 1 the instruction form is invalid.

■ For POWER, information from the MSR is saved in the Count Register. For PowerPC, this information is saved in SRR1.

■ POWER permits bits 16:29 of the instruction to be nonzero, while in PowerPC such an instruction form is invalid.

■ POWER saves the low-order 16 bits of the instruction, in the Count Register. PowerPC does not save them.

■ The settings of MSR bits by the associated interrupt differ between POWER and PowerPC: see *POWER Processor Architecture* and Book III, Figure 80, "MSR setting due to interrupt," on page 458.

G.11 Fixed-Point Exception Register (XER)

Bits 16:23 of the XER are reserved in PowerPC, while in POWER they are defined and contain the comparison byte for the *lscbx* instruction (which PowerPC lacks).

G.12 Update Forms of Storage Access

PowerPC requires that RA not be equal to either RT (fixed-point *Load* only) or 0. If the restriction is violated the instruction form is invalid. POWER permits these cases and simply avoids saving the EA.

G.13 Multiple Register Loads

PowerPC requires that RA, and RB if present in the instruction format, not be in the range of registers to be loaded, while POWER permits this and does not alter RA or RB in this case. (The PowerPC restriction applies even if RA=0, although there is no obvious benefit to the restriction in this case since RA is not used to compute the effective address if RA=0.) If the PowerPC restriction is violated, either the system illegal instruction error handler is invoked or the results are boundedly defined. The instructions affected are:

lmw (*lm* in POWER)

lswi (*lsi* in POWER)

lswx (*lsx* in POWER)

For example, an *lmw* instruction that loads all 32 registers is valid in POWER but is an invalid form in PowerPC.

G.14 Alignment for Load/Store Multiple

PowerPC requires the EA to be word-aligned, and yields an Alignment interrupt or boundedly undefined results if it is not. POWER specifies that an Alignment interrupt occurs (if $MSR_{AL}=1$).

G.15 Move Assist Instructions

There are several respects in which PowerPC is incompatible with POWER for *Move Assist* instructions.

- In PowerPC an *lswx* instruction with zero length leaves the content of RT undefined, while in POWER the corresponding instruction (*lsx*) does not alter RT in this case.

- In PowerPC an *lswx* instruction with zero length may alter the Reference bit, and an *stswx* instruction with zero length may alter the Reference and Change bits, while in POWER the corresponding instructions (*lsx* and *stsx*) do not alter the Reference and Change bits in this case.

G.16 Synchronization

The *sync* instruction (called *dcs* in POWER) and the *isync* instruction (called *ics* in POWER) cause much more pervasive synchronization in PowerPC than in POWER.

G.17 Move To/From SPR

There are several respects in which PowerPC is incompatible with POWER for *Move To/From Special Purpose Register* instructions.

■ The SPR field is ten bits long in PowerPC, but only five in POWER (see also Section G.3, "Reserved Bits in Instructions," on page 272).

■ *mfspr* can be used to read the Decrementer in problem state in POWER, but only in privileged state in PowerPC.

■ If the SPR value specified in the instruction is not one of the defined values, POWER behaves as follows.

— If the instruction is executed in problem state and $SPR_0=1$, a Privileged Instruction type Program interrupt occurs. No architected registers are altered except those set by the interrupt.

— Otherwise (the instruction is executed in privileged state or $SPR_0=0$), no architected registers are altered.

In this same case, PowerPC behaves as follows.

— If the instruction is executed in problem state and $spr_0=1$, either an Illegal Instruction type Program interrupt or a Privileged Instruction type Program interrupt occurs. No architected registers are altered except those set by the interrupt.

— Otherwise (the instruction is executed in privileged state or $spr_0=0$), either an Illegal Instruction type Program interrupt occurs (in which case no architected registers are altered except those set by the interrupt) or the results are boundedly undefined.

G.18 Effects of Exceptions on FPSCR Bits FR and FI

For the following cases, POWER does not say how FR and FI are set, while PowerPC preserves them for Invalid Operation Exception caused by a *Compare* instruction, sets FI to 1 and FR to an undefined value for disabled Overflow Exception, and clears them otherwise.

■ Invalid Operation Exception (enabled or disabled)

■ Zero Divide Exception (enabled or disabled)

■ Disabled Overflow Exception

G.19 Floating-Point Store Instructions

POWER uses FPSCR$_{UE}$ to help determine whether denormalization should be done, while PowerPC does not. Use of FPSCR$_{UE}$ is in fact incorrect: if FPSCR$_{UE}$=1 and a denormalized single-precision number is copied from one storage location to another by means of *lfs* followed by *stfs*, the two "copies" may not be the same.

G.20 Move From FPSCR

POWER defines the high-order 32 bits of the result of *mffs* to be 0xFFFF_FFFF, while PowerPC says they are undefined.

G.21 Zeroing Bytes in the Data Cache

The *dclz* instruction of POWER and the *dcbz* instruction of PowerPC have the same opcode. However, the functions differ in the following respects:

- *dclz* clears a line while *dcbz* clears a block.
- *dclz* saves the EA in RA (if RA≠0) while *dcbz* does not.
- *dclz* is privileged while *dcbz* is not.

G.22 Floating-Point Load/Store to Direct-Store Segment

In POWER a floating-point *Load* or *Store* instruction to a direct-store segment causes a Data Storage interrupt, while in PowerPC the instruction either executes correctly or causes an Alignment interrupt.

G.23 Segment Register Instructions

The definitions of the four Segment Register instructions (*mtsr, mtsrin, mfsr,* and *mfsrin*) differ in two respects between POWER and PowerPC. Instructions similar to *mtsrin* and *mfsrin* are called *mtsri* and *mfsri* in POWER.

privilege: *mfsr* and *mfsri* are problem state instructions in POWER, while *mfsr* and *mfsrin* are privileged in PowerPC.

function: the "indirect" instructions (*mtsri* and *mfsri*) in POWER use an RA register in computing the Segment Register number, and the computed EA is stored into RA (if RA≠0 and RA≠RT), while in PowerPC *mtsrin* and *mfsrin* have no RA field and the EA is not stored.

mtsr, mtsrin (mtsri), and *mfsr* have the same opcodes in PowerPC as in POWER. *mfsri* (POWER) and *mfsrin* (PowerPC) have different opcodes.

G.24 TLB Entry Invalidation

The *tlbi* instruction of POWER and the *tlbie* instruction of PowerPC have the same opcode. However, the functions differ in the following respects:

- *tlbi* computes the EA as (RA|0) + (RB), while *tlbie* lacks an RA field and computes the EA as (RB).

- *tlbi* saves the EA in RA (if RA≠0), while *tlbie* lacks an RA field and does not save the EA.

G.25 Floating-Point Interrupts

Both architectures use MSR bit 20 to control the generation of interrupts for floating-point enabled exceptions. However, in PowerPC this bit is part of a two-bit value that controls the occurrence, precision, and recoverability of the interrupt, while in POWER this bit is used independently to control the occurrence of the interrupt (in POWER all floating-point interrupts are precise).

G.26 Timing Facilities

G.26.1 Real-Time Clock

The POWER Real-Time Clock is not supported in PowerPC. Instead, PowerPC provides a Time Base. Both the RTC and the TB are 64-bit Special Purpose Registers, but they differ in the following respects:

- The RTC counts seconds and nanoseconds, while the TB counts "ticks." The ticking rate of the TB is implementation-dependent.

- The RTC increments discontinuously: 1 is added to RTCU when the value in RTCL passes 999_999_999. The TB increments continuously: 1 is added to TBU when the value in TBL passes 0xFFFF_FFFF.

- The RTC is written and read by the *mtspr* and *mfspr* instructions, using SPR numbers that denote the RTCU and RTCL. The TB is written by the *mtspr* instruction (using new SPR numbers), and read by the new *mftb* instruction.

- The SPR numbers that denote POWER's RTCL and RTCU are invalid in PowerPC.

- The RTC is guaranteed to increment at least once in the time required to execute ten *Add Immediate* instructions. No analogous guarantee is made for the TB.

- Not all bits of RTCL need be implemented, while all bits of the TB must be implemented.

G.26.2 Decrementer

The PowerPC Decrementer differs from the POWER Decrementer in the following respects:

- The PowerPC DEC decrements at the same rate that the TB increments, while the POWER Decrementer decrements every nanosecond (which is the same rate that the RTC increments).

- Not all bits of the POWER DEC need be implemented, while all bits of the PowerPC DEC must be implemented.

- The interrupt caused by the DEC has its own interrupt vector location in PowerPC, but is considered an External interrupt in POWER.

G.27 Deleted Instructions

The following instructions are part of the POWER Architecture but have been dropped from the PowerPC Architecture.

abs   Absolute

clcs   Cache Line Compute Size

clf	Cache Line Flush
cli(*)	Cache Line Invalidate
dclst	Data Cache Line Store
div	Divide
divs	Divide Short
doz	Difference Or Zero
dozi	Difference Or Zero Immediate
lscbx	Load String And Compare Byte Indexed
maskg	Mask Generate
maskir	Mask Insert From Register
mfsri	Move From Segment Register Indirect
mul	Multiply
nabs	Negative Absolute
rac(*)	Real Address Compute
rfsvc(*)	Return From SVC
rlmi	Rotate Left Then Mask Insert
rrib	Rotate Right And Insert Bit
sle	Shift Left Extended
sleq	Shift Left Extended With MQ
sliq	Shift Left Immediate With MQ
slliq	Shift Left Long Immediate With MQ
sllq	Shift Left Long With MQ
slq	Shift Left With MQ
sraiq	Shift Right Algebraic Immediate With MQ
sraq	Shift Right Algebraic With MQ
sre	Shift Right Extended
srea	Shift Right Extended Algebraic
sreq	Shift Right Extended With MQ

sriq	Shift Right Immediate With MQ
srliq	Shift Right Long Immediate With MQ
srlq	Shift Right Long With MQ
srq	Shift Right With MQ

(*) This instruction is privileged.

Note: Many of these instructions use the MQ register. The MQ is not defined in the PowerPC Architecture.

G.28 Discontinued Opcodes

Assembler Note

It might be helpful to current software writers for the Assembler to flag the discontinued POWER instructions.

The opcodes listed below are defined in the POWER Architecture but have been dropped from the PowerPC Architecture. The list contains the POWER mnemonic (MNEM), the primary opcode (PRI), and the extended opcode (XOP) if appropriate. The corresponding instructions are reserved in PowerPC.

MNEM	PRI	XOP
abs	31	360
clcs	31	531
clf	31	118
cli(*)	31	502
dclst	31	630
div	31	331
divs	31	363
doz	31	264
dozi	09	–
lscbx	31	277
maskg	31	29
maskir	31	541
mfsri	31	627
mul	31	107
nabs	31	488
rac(*)	31	818

rfsvc(*)	19	82
rlmi	22	–
rrib	31	537
sle	31	153
sleq	31	217
sliq	31	184
slliq	31	248
sllq	31	216
slq	31	152
sraiq	31	952
sraq	31	920
sre	31	665
srea	31	921
sreq	31	729
sriq	31	696
srliq	31	760
srlq	31	728
srq	31	664

(*) This instruction is privileged.

G.29 POWER2 Compatibility

The POWER2 instruction set is a superset of the POWER instruction set. Some of the instructions added for POWER2 are included in the PowerPC Architecture. Those that have been renamed in the PowerPC Architecture are listed in this section, as are the new POWER2 instructions that are not included in the PowerPC Architecture.

Other incompatibilities are also listed.

G.29.1 Cross-Reference for Changed POWER2 Mnemonics

The following table lists the new POWER2 instruction mnemonics that have been changed in the PowerPC User Instruction Set Architecture, sorted by POWER2 mnemonic.

To determine the PowerPC mnemonic for one of these POWER2 mnemonics, find the POWER2 mnemonic in the second column of the table: the remainder of the line gives the PowerPC mnemonic and the page on which the instruction is described, as well as the instruction names. POWER2 mnemonics that have not changed are not listed.

Page	POWER2		PowerPC	
	Mnemonic	Instruction	Mnemonic	Instruction
189	fcir[.]	Floating Convert Double to Integer with Round	fctiw[.]	Floating Convert To Integer Word
190	fcirz[.]	Floating Convert Double to Integer with Round to Zero	fctiwz[.]	Floating Convert To Integer Word with round toward Zero

G.29.2 Floating-Point Conversion to Integer

The *fcir* and *fcirz* instructions of POWER2 have the same opcodes as do the *fctiw* and *fctiwz* instructions, respectively, of PowerPC. However, the functions differ in the following respects.

■ *fcir* and *fcirz* set the high-order 32 bits of the target FPR to 0xFFFF_FFFF, while *fctiw* and *fctiwz* set them to an undefined value.

■ Except for enabled Invalid Operation Exceptions, *fcir* and *fcirz* set the FPRF field of the FPSCR based on the result, while *fctiw* and *fctiwz* set it to an undefined value.

■ *fcir* and *fcirz* do not affect the VXSNAN bit of the FPSCR, while *fctiw* and *fctiwz* do.

■ *fcir* and *fcirz* set $FPSCR_{XX}$ to 1 for certain cases of "Large Operands" (i.e., operands that are too large to be represented as a 32-bit signed fixed-point integer), while *fctiw* and *fctiwz* do not alter it for any case of "Large Operand." (The IEEE standard requires not altering it for "Large Operands.")

G.29.3 Storage Ordering

POWER2 uses MSR bit 28 to control storage ordering. This bit is reserved in PowerPC, and no corresponding control is provided.

G.29.4 Floating-Point Interrupts

Both architectures use MSR bits 20 and 23 to control the generation of interrupts for floating-point enabled exceptions. However, in PowerPC these bits comprise a two-bit value which controls the occurrence, precision, and recoverability of the interrupt, while in POWER2 these bits are used independently to control the occurrence (bit 20) and the precision (bit 23) of the interrupt. Moreover, in PowerPC all floating-point interrupts are considered Program interrupts, while in POWER2 imprecise floating-point interrupts have their own interrupt vector location.

G.29.5 Trace Interrupts

The interrupt vector location differs between the two architectures. Also, the trace facility is optional in PowerPC but required in POWER2.

G.29.6 Deleted Instructions

The following instructions are new in the POWER2 Architecture but have been dropped from the PowerPC Architecture.

lfq	Load Floating-Point Quad
lfqu	Load Floating-Point Quad with Update
lfqux	Load Floating-Point Quad with Update Indexed
lfqx	Load Floating-Point Quad Indexed
stfq	Store Floating-Point Quad
stfqu	Store Floating-Point Quad with Update
stfqux	Store Floating-Point Quad with Update Indexed
stfqx	Store Floating-Point Quad Indexed

G.29.7 Discontinued Opcodes

The opcodes listed below are new in the POWER2 Architecture but have been dropped from the PowerPC Architecture. The list contains the POWER2 mnemonic (MNEM), the primary opcode (PRI), and the extended opcode (XOP) if appropriate. The corresponding instructions are reserved in PowerPC.

MNEM	PRI	XOP
lfq	56	–
lfqu	57	–
lfqux	31	823
lfqx	31	791
stfq	60	–
stfqu	61	–
stfqux	31	951
stfqx	31	919

New Instructions

The following instructions in the PowerPC Architecture are new: they are not in the POWER Architecture.

They are listed in three groups, according to whether they exist in all PowerPC implementations, only in 64-bit implementations, or only in 32-bit implementations.

The following instructions are optional: *eciwx, ecowx, fres, frsqrte, fsel, fsqrt[s], slbia, slbie, stfiwx, tlbia, tlbsync.*

H.1 New Instructions for All Implementations

dcbf   Data Cache Block Flush

dcbi   Data Cache Block Invalidate

dcbst   Data Cache Block Store

dcbt   Data Cache Block Touch

dcbtst   Data Cache Block Touch for Store

divw   Divide Word

divwu   Divide Word Unsigned

eciwx   External Control In Word Indexed

ecowx   External Control Out Word Indexed

eieio   Enforce In-order Execution of I/O

extsb	Extend Sign Byte
fadds	Floating Add Single
fctiw	Floating Convert To Integer Word
fctiwz	Floating Convert To Integer Word with round toward Zero
fdivs	Floating Divide Single
fmadds	Floating Multiply-Add Single
fmsubs	Floating Multiply-Subtract Single
fmuls	Floating Multiply Single
fnmadds	Floating Negative Multiply-Add Single
fnmsubs	Floating Negative Multiply-Subtract Single
fres	Floating Reciprocal Estimate Single
frsqrte	Floating Reciprocal Square Root Estimate
fsel	Floating Select
fsqrt[s]	Floating Square Root [Single]
fsubs	Floating Subtract Single
icbi	Instruction Cache Block Invalidate
lwarx	Load Word And Reserve Indexed
mftb	Move From Time Base
mulhw	Multiply High Word
mulhwu	Multiply High Word Unsigned
stfiwx	Store Floating-Point as Integer Word Indexed
stwcx.	Store Word Conditional Indexed
subf	Subtract From
tlbia	TLB Invalidate All
tlbsync	TLB Synchronize

H.2 New Instructions for 64-Bit Implementations Only

cntlzd	Count Leading Zeros Doubleword
divd	Divide Doubleword
divdu	Divide Doubleword Unsigned
extsw	Extend Sign Word
fcfid	Floating Convert From Integer Doubleword
fctid	Floating Convert To Integer Doubleword
fctidz	Floating Convert To Integer Doubleword with round toward Zero
lwa	Load Word Algebraic
lwaux	Load Word Algebraic with Update Indexed
lwax	Load Word Algebraic Indexed
ld	Load Doubleword
ldarx	Load Doubleword And Reserve Indexed
ldu	Load Doubleword with Update
ldux	Load Doubleword with Update Indexed
ldx	Load Doubleword Indexed
mulhd	Multiply High Doubleword
mulhdu	Multiply High Doubleword Unsigned
mulld	Multiply Low Doubleword
rldcl	Rotate Left Doubleword then Clear Left
rldcr	Rotate Left Doubleword then Clear Right
rldic	Rotate Left Doubleword Immediate then Clear
rldicl	Rotate Left Doubleword Immediate then Clear Left
rldicr	Rotate Left Doubleword Immediate then Clear Right
rldimi	Rotate Left Doubleword Immediate then Mask Insert
slbia	SLB Invalidate All

slbie	SLB Invalidate Entry
sld	Shift Left Doubleword
srad	Shift Right Algebraic Doubleword
sradi	Shift Right Algebraic Doubleword Immediate
srd	Shift Right Doubleword
std	Store Doubleword
stdcx.	Store Doubleword Conditional Indexed
stdu	Store Doubleword with Update
stdux	Store Doubleword with Update Indexed
stdx	Store Doubleword Indexed
td	Trap Doubleword
tdi	Trap Doubleword Immediate

H.3 New Instructions for 32-Bit Implementations Only

mfsrin   Move From Segment Register Indirect

Illegal Instructions

With the exception of the instruction consisting entirely of binary 0s, the instructions in this class are available for future extensions of the PowerPC Architecture: that is, some future version of the PowerPC Architecture may define any of these instructions to perform new functions.

The following primary opcodes are illegal:

1, 4, 5, 6, 56, 57, 60, 61

In addition, the following primary opcodes are illegal for 32-bit implementations (they are defined only for 64-bit implementations):

2, 30, 58, 62

The following primary opcodes have unused extended opcodes. Extended opcodes for instructions that are defined only for 64-bit implementations are illegal in 32-bit implementations, and extended opcodes for instructions that are defined only for 32-bit implementations are illegal in 64-bit implementations. All unused extended opcodes are illegal.

19, 30[1], 31, 59, 62[1], 63

An instruction consisting entirely of binary 0s is illegal, and is guaranteed to be illegal in all future versions of this architecture.

---

[1] Applies only for 64-bit implementations (illegal primary opcode for 32-bit implementations)

Reserved Instructions

J

The instructions in this class are allocated to specific purposes that are outside the scope of the PowerPC User Instruction Set Architecture, PowerPC Virtual Environment Architecture, and PowerPC Operating Environment Architecture.

The following types of instruction are included in this class:

1. The instruction having primary opcode 0, except the instruction consisting entirely of binary 0s (which is an illegal instruction: see Section Section 1.8.2, "Illegal Instruction Class," on page 24).

2. Instructions for the POWER Architecture that have not been included in the PowerPC Architecture. These are listed in Section G.28, "Discontinued Opcodes," on page 282 and Section G.29.7, "Discontinued Opcodes," on page 285.

3. Implementation-specific instructions used to conform to the PowerPC Architecture specifications.

4. Any other instructions contained in the Book IV, *PowerPC Implementation Features Document* for any implementation, that are not defined in the PowerPC User Instruction Set Architecture, PowerPC Virtual Environment Architecture, or PowerPC Operating Environment Architecture.

K

PowerPC Instruction Set Sorted by Opcode

This appendix lists all the instructions in the PowerPC Architecture, in order by opcode. The Book number is shown in the "Page" column for instructions that are not defined in Book I.

Form	Opcode		Mode Dep.[1]	Page	Mnemonic	Instruction
	Primary	Extended				
D	2		()	102	tdi	Trap Doubleword Immediate
D	3			103	twi	Trap Word Immediate
D	7			90	mulli	Multiply Low Immediate
D	8		SR	85	subfic	Subtract From Immediate Carrying
D	10			100	cmpli	Compare Logical Immediate
D	11			99	cmpi	Compare Immediate
D	12		SR	84	addic	Add Immediate Carrying
D	13		SR	84	addic.	Add Immediate Carrying and Record
D	14			82	addi	Add Immediate
D	15			82	addis	Add Immediate Shifted
B	16		CT	38	bc[l][a]	Branch Conditional

Form	Opcode Primary	Opcode Extended	Mode Dep.[1]	Page	Mnemonic	Instruction
SC	17			41	sc	System Call (see also Book III, page 378)
I	18			38	b[l][a]	Branch
XL	19	0		46	mcrf	Move Condition Register Field
XL	19	16	CT	39	bclr[l]	Branch Conditional to Link Register
XL	19	33		44	crnor	Condition Register NOR
XL	19	50		379 (III)	rfi	Return From Interrupt
XL	19	129		45	crandc	Condition Register AND with Complement
XL	19	150		346 (II)	isync	Instruction Synchronize
XL	19	193		43	crxor	Condition Register XOR
XL	19	225		43	crnand	Condition Register NAND
XL	19	257		42	crand	Condition Register AND
XL	19	289		44	creqv	Condition Register Equivalent
XL	19	417		45	crorc	Condition Register OR with Complement
XL	19	449		42	cror	Condition Register OR
XL	19	528	CT	40	bcctr[l]	Branch Conditional to Count Register
M	20		SR	122	rlwimi[.]	Rotate Left Word Immediate then Mask Insert
M	21		SR	119	rlwinm[.]	Rotate Left Word Immediate then AND with Mask
M	23		SR	121	rlwnm[.]	Rotate Left Word then AND with Mask
D	24			107	ori	OR Immediate
D	25			107	oris	OR Immediate Shifted
D	26			108	xori	XOR Immediate
D	27			108	xoris	XOR Immediate Shifted
D	28		SR	106	andi.	AND Immediate
D	29		SR	106	andis.	AND Immediate Shifted

Form	Opcode Primary	Opcode Extended	Mode Dep.[1]	Page	Mnemonic	Instruction
MD	30	0	(SR)	116	rldicl[.]	Rotate Left Doubleword Immediate then Clear Left
MD	30	1	(SR)	117	rldicr[.]	Rotate Left Doubleword Immediate then Clear Right
MD	30	2	(SR)	118	rldic[.]	Rotate Left Doubleword Immediate then Clear
MD	30	3	(SR)	121	rldimi[.]	Rotate Left Doubleword Immediate then Mask Insert
MDS	30	8	(SR)	119	rldcl[.]	Rotate Left Doubleword then Clear Left
MDS	30	9	(SR)	120	rldcr[.]	Rotate Left Doubleword then Clear Right
X	31	0		99	cmp	Compare
X	31	4		105	tw	Trap Word
XO	31	8	SR	86	subfc[o][.]	Subtract From Carrying
XO	31	9	(SR)	92	mulhdu[.]	Multiply High Doubleword Unsigned
XO	31	10	SR	85	addc[o][.]	Add Carrying
XO	31	11	SR	93	mulhwu[.]	Multiply High Word Unsigned
X	31	19		132	mfcr	Move From Condition Register
X	31	20		77	lwarx	Load Word And Reserve Indexed
X	31	21	()	59	ldx	Load Doubleword Indexed
X	31	23		56	lwzx	Load Word and Zero Indexed
X	31	24	SR	124	slw[.]	Shift Left Word
X	31	26	SR	114	cntlzw[.]	Count Leading Zeros Word
X	31	27	(SR)	123	sld[.]	Shift Left Doubleword
X	31	28	SR	109	and[.]	AND
X	31	32		101	cmpl	Compare Logical
XO	31	40	SR	83	subf[o][.]	Subtract From
X	31	53	()	60	ldux	Load Doubleword with Update Indexed
X	31	54		348 (II)	dcbst	Data Cache Block Store

Form	Opcode		Mode Dep.[1]	Page	Mnemonic	Instruction
	Primary	Extended				
X	31	55		57	lwzux	Load Word and Zero with Update Indexed
X	31	58	(SR)	114	cntlzd[.]	Count Leading Zeros Doubleword
X	31	60	SR	111	andc[.]	AND with Complement
X	31	68	()	104	td	Trap Doubleword
XO	31	73	(SR)	91	mulhd[.]	Multiply High Doubleword
XO	31	75	SR	92	mulhw[.]	Multiply High Word
X	31	83		389 (III)	mfmsr	Move From Machine State Register
X	31	84	()	77	ldarx	Load Doubleword And Reserve Indexed
X	31	86		349 (II)	dcbf	Data Cache Block Flush
X	31	87		50	lbzx	Load Byte and Zero Indexed
XO	31	104	SR	89	neg[o][.]	Negate
X	31	119		51	lbzux	Load Byte and Zero with Update Indexed
X	31	124	SR	110	nor[.]	NOR
XO	31	136	SR	87	subfe[o][.]	Subtract From Extended
XO	31	138	SR	86	adde[o][.]	Add Extended
XFX	31	144		131	mtcrf	Move To Condition Register Fields
X	31	146		389 (III)	mtmsr	Move To Machine State Register
X	31	149	()	67	stdx	Store Doubleword Indexed
X	31	150		78	stwcx.	Store Word Conditional Indexed
X	31	151		65	stwx	Store Word Indexed
X	31	181	()	68	stdux	Store Doubleword with Update Indexed
X	31	183		66	stwux	Store Word with Update Indexed
XO	31	200	SR	89	subfze[o][.]	Subtract From Zero Extended
XO	31	202	SR	88	addze[o][.]	Add to Zero Extended

Form	Opcode		Mode Dep.[1]	Page	Mnemonic	Instruction
	Primary	Extended				
X	31	210	{}	440 (III)	mtsr	Move To Segment Register
X	31	214	()	79	stdcx.	Store Doubleword Conditional Indexed
X	31	215		61	stbx	Store Byte Indexed
XO	31	232	SR	88	subfme[o][.]	Subtract From Minus One Extended
XO	31	233	(SR)	90	mulld[o][.]	Multiply Low Doubleword
XO	31	234	SR	87	addme[o][.]	Add to Minus One Extended
XO	31	235	SR	91	mullw[o][.]	Multiply Low Word
X	31	242	{}	441 (III)	mtsrin	Move To Segment Register Indirect
X	31	246		347 (II)	dcbtst	Data Cache Block Touch for Store
X	31	247		62	stbux	Store Byte with Update Indexed
XO	31	266	SR	83	add[o][.]	Add
X	31	278		346 (II)	dcbt	Data Cache Block Touch
X	31	279		52	lhzx	Load Halfword and Zero Indexed
X	31	284	SR	111	eqv[.]	Equivalent
X	31	306		444 (III)	tlbie	TLB Invalidate Entry
X	31	310		491 (III)	eciwx	External Control In Word Indexed
X	31	311		53	lhzux	Load Halfword and Zero with Update Indexed
X	31	316	SR	110	xor[.]	XOR
XFX	31	339		130	mfspr	Move From Special Purpose Register (see also Book III, page 387)
X	31	341	()	58	lwax	Load Word Algebraic Indexed
X	31	343		54	lhax	Load Halfword Algebraic Indexed
X	31	370		445 (III)	tlbia	TLB Invalidate All
XFX	31	371		352 (II)	mftb	Move From Time Base
X	31	373	()	58	lwaux	Load Word Algebraic with Update Indexed

Form	Opcode		Mode Dep.[1]	Page	Mnemonic	Instruction
	Primary	Extended				
X	31	375		55	lhaux	Load Halfword Algebraic with Update Indexed
X	31	407		63	sthx	Store Halfword Indexed
X	31	412	SR	112	orc[.]	OR with Complement
XS	31	413	(SR)	126	sradi[.]	Shift Right Algebraic Doubleword Immediate
X	31	434	()	443 (III)	slbie	SLB Invalidate Entry
X	31	438		492 (III)	ecowx	External Control Out Word Indexed
X	31	439		64	sthux	Store Halfword with Update Indexed
X	31	444	SR	109	or[.]	OR
XO	31	457	(SR)	96	divdu[o][.]	Divide Doubleword Unsigned
XO	31	459	SR	97	divwu[o][.]	Divide Word Unsigned
XFX	31	467		129	mtspr	Move To Special Purpose Register (see also Book III, page 384)
X	31	470		439 (III)	dcbi	Data Cache Block Invalidate
X	31	476	SR	110	nand[.]	NAND
XO	31	489	(SR)	94	divd[o][.]	Divide Doubleword
XO	31	491	SR	95	divw[o][.]	Divide Word
X	31	498	()	444 (III)	slbia	SLB Invalidate All
X	31	512		132	mcrxr	Move to Condition Register from XER
X	31	533		74	lswx	Load String Word Indexed
X	31	534		69	lwbrx	Load Word Byte-Reverse Indexed
X	31	535		170	lfsx	Load Floating-Point Single Indexed
X	31	536	SR	125	srw[.]	Shift Right Word
X	31	539	(SR)	124	srd[.]	Shift Right Doubleword
X	31	566		445 (III)	tlbsync	TLB Synchronize
X	31	567		171	lfsux	Load Floating-Point Single with Update Indexed

Form	Opcode		Mode Dep.[1]	Page	Mnemonic	Instruction
	Primary	Extended				
X	31	595	{}	441 (III)	mfsr	Move From Segment Register
X	31	597		73	lswi	Load String Word Immediate
X	31	598		80	sync	Synchronize
X	31	599		172	lfdx	Load Floating-Point Double Indexed
X	31	631		172	lfdux	Load Floating-Point Double with Update Indexed
X	31	659	{}	442 (III)	mfsrin	Move From Segment Register Indirect
X	31	661		76	stswx	Store String Word Indexed
X	31	662		70	stwbrx	Store Word Byte-Reverse Indexed
X	31	663		175	stfsx	Store Floating-Point Single Indexed
X	31	695		175	stfsux	Store Floating-Point Single with Update Indexed
X	31	725		75	stswi	Store String Word Immediate
X	31	727		176	stfdx	Store Floating-Point Double Indexed
X	31	759		177	stfdux	Store Floating-Point Double with Update Indexed
X	31	790		68	lhbrx	Load Halfword Byte-Reverse Indexed
X	31	792	SR	128	sraw[.]	Shift Right Algebraic Word
X	31	794	(SR)	127	srad[.]	Shift Right Algebraic Doubleword
X	31	824	SR	126	srawi[.]	Shift Right Algebraic Word Immediate
X	31	854		350 (II)	eieio	Enforce In-order Execution of I/O
X	31	918		69	sthbrx	Store Halfword Byte-Reverse Indexed
X	31	922	SR	113	extsh[.]	Extend Sign Halfword
X	31	954	SR	112	extsb[.]	Extend Sign Byte
X	31	982		345 (II)	icbi	Instruction Cache Block Invalidate
X	31	983		198	stfiwx	Store Floating-Point as Integer Word Indexed
X	31	986	(SR)	113	extsw[.]	Extend Sign Word

Form	Opcode		Mode Dep.[1]	Page	Mnemonic	Instruction
	Primary	Extended				
X	31	1014		347 (II)	dcbz	Data Cache Block set to Zero
D	32			55	lwz	Load Word and Zero
D	33			56	lwzu	Load Word and Zero with Update
D	34			50	lbz	Load Byte and Zero
D	35			51	lbzu	Load Byte and Zero with Update
D	36			64	stw	Store Word
D	37			65	stwu	Store Word with Update
D	38			61	stb	Store Byte
D	39			62	stbu	Store Byte with Update
D	40			52	lhz	Load Halfword and Zero
D	41			53	lhzu	Load Halfword and Zero with Update
D	42			54	lha	Load Halfword Algebraic
D	43			54	lhau	Load Halfword Algebraic with Update
D	44			63	sth	Store Halfword
D	45			63	sthu	Store Halfword with Update
D	46			71	lmw	Load Multiple Word
D	47			72	stmw	Store Multiple Word
D	48			169	lfs	Load Floating-Point Single
D	49			170	lfsu	Load Floating-Point Single with Update
D	50			171	lfd	Load Floating-Point Double
D	51			172	lfdu	Load Floating-Point Double with Update
D	52			174	stfs	Store Floating-Point Single
D	53			175	stfsu	Store Floating-Point Single with Update
D	54			176	stfd	Store Floating-Point Double

Form	Opcode		Mode Dep.[1]	Page	Mnemonic	Instruction
	Primary	Extended				
D	55			177	stfdu	Store Floating-Point Double with Update
DS	58	0	()	59	ld	Load Doubleword
DS	58	1	()	60	ldu	Load Doubleword with Update
DS	58	2	()	57	lwa	Load Word Algebraic
A	59	18		182	fdivs[.]	Floating Divide Single
A	59	20		180	fsubs[.]	Floating Subtract Single
A	59	21		179	fadds[.]	Floating Add Single
A	59	22		198	fsqrts[.]	Floating Square Root Single
A	59	24		200	fres[.]	Floating Reciprocal Estimate Single
A	59	25		181	fmuls[.]	Floating Multiply Single
A	59	28		184	fmsubs[.]	Floating Multiply-Subtract Single
A	59	29		183	fmadds[.]	Floating Multiply-Add Single
A	59	30		186	fnmsubs[.]	Floating Negative Multiply-Subtract Single
A	59	31		185	fnmadds[.]	Floating Negative Multiply-Add Single
DS	62	0	()	66	std	Store Doubleword
DS	62	1	()	67	stdu	Store Doubleword with Update
X	63	0		191	fcmpu	Floating Compare Unordered
X	63	12		187	frsp[.]	Floating Round to Single-Precision
X	63	14		189	fctiw[.]	Floating Convert To Integer Word
X	63	15		190	fctiwz[.]	Floating Convert To Integer Word with round toward Zero
A	63	18		182	fdiv[.]	Floating Divide
A	63	20		180	fsub[.]	Floating Subtract
A	63	21		179	fadd[.]	Floating Add
A	63	22		198	fsqrt[.]	Floating Square Root

Form	Opcode		Mode Dep.[1]	Page	Mnemonic	Instruction
	Primary	Extended				
A	63	23		202	fsel[.]	Floating Select
A	63	25		181	fmul[.]	Floating Multiply
A	63	26		201	frsqrte[.]	Floating Reciprocal Square Root Estimate
A	63	28		184	fmsub[.]	Floating Multiply-Subtract
A	63	29		183	fmadd[.]	Floating Multiply-Add
A	63	30		186	fnmsub[.]	Floating Negative Multiply-Subtract
A	63	31		185	fnmadd[.]	Floating Negative Multiply-Add
X	63	32		192	fcmpo	Floating Compare Ordered
X	63	38		196	mtfsb1[.]	Move To FPSCR Bit 1
X	63	40		178	fneg[.]	Floating Negate
X	63	64		194	mcrfs	Move to Condition Register from FPSCR
X	63	70		195	mtfsb0[.]	Move To FPSCR Bit 0
X	63	72		178	fmr[.]	Floating Move Register
X	63	134		194	mtfsfi[.]	Move To FPSCR Field Immediate
X	63	136		179	fnabs[.]	Floating Negative Absolute Value
X	63	264		178	fabs[.]	Floating Absolute Value
X	63	583		194	mffs[.]	Move From FPSCR
XFL	63	711		195	mtfsf[.]	Move To FPSCR Fields
X	63	814	()	187	fctid[.]	Floating Convert To Integer Doubleword
X	63	815	()	188	fctidz[.]	Floating Convert To Integer Doubleword with round toward Zero
X	63	846	()	190	fcfid[.]	Floating Convert From Integer Doubleword

[1]See key to mode dependency column, on page 315.

PowerPC Instruction Set Sorted by Mnemonic

This appendix lists all the instructions in the PowerPC Architecture, in order by mnemonic. The Book number is shown in the "Page" column for instructions that are not defined in Book I.

Form	Opcode		Mode Dep.[1]	Page	Mnemonic	Instruction
	Primary	Extended				
XO	31	266	SR	83	add[o][.]	Add
XO	31	10	SR	85	addc[o][.]	Add Carrying
XO	31	138	SR	86	adde[o][.]	Add Extended
D	14			82	addi	Add Immediate
D	12		SR	84	addic	Add Immediate Carrying
D	13		SR	84	addic.	Add Immediate Carrying and Record
D	15			82	addis	Add Immediate Shifted
XO	31	234	SR	87	addme[o][.]	Add to Minus One Extended
XO	31	202	SR	88	addze[o][.]	Add to Zero Extended
X	31	28	SR	109	and[.]	AND
X	31	60	SR	111	andc[.]	AND with Complement

Form	Opcode		Mode Dep.[1]	Page	Mnemonic	Instruction
	Primary	Extended				
D	28		SR	106	andi.	AND Immediate
D	29		SR	106	andis.	AND Immediate Shifted
I	18			38	b[l][a]	Branch
B	16		CT	38	bc[l][a]	Branch Conditional
XL	19	528	CT	40	bcctr[l]	Branch Conditional to Count Register
XL	19	16	CT	39	bclr[l]	Branch Conditional to Link Register
X	31	0		99	cmp	Compare
D	11			99	cmpi	Compare Immediate
X	31	32		101	cmpl	Compare Logical
D	10			100	cmpli	Compare Logical Immediate
X	31	58	(SR)	114	cntlzd[.]	Count Leading Zeros Doubleword
X	31	26	SR	114	cntlzw[.]	Count Leading Zeros Word
XL	19	257		42	crand	Condition Register AND
XL	19	129		45	crandc	Condition Register AND with Complement
XL	19	289		44	creqv	Condition Register Equivalent
XL	19	225		43	crnand	Condition Register NAND
XL	19	33		44	crnor	Condition Register NOR
XL	19	449		42	cror	Condition Register OR
XL	19	417		45	crorc	Condition Register OR with Complement
XL	19	193		43	crxor	Condition Register XOR
X	31	86		349 (II)	dcbf	Data Cache Block Flush
X	31	470		439 (III)	dcbi	Data Cache Block Invalidate
X	31	54		348 (II)	dcbst	Data Cache Block Store

Form	Opcode Primary	Opcode Extended	Mode Dep.[1]	Page	Mnemonic	Instruction
X	31	278		346 (II)	dcbt	Data Cache Block Touch
X	31	246		347 (II)	dcbtst	Data Cache Block Touch for Store
X	31	1014		347 (II)	dcbz	Data Cache Block set to Zero
XO	31	489	(SR)	94	divd[o][.]	Divide Doubleword
XO	31	457	(SR)	96	divdu[o][.]	Divide Doubleword Unsigned
XO	31	491	SR	95	divw[o][.]	Divide Word
XO	31	459	SR	97	divwu[o][.]	Divide Word Unsigned
X	31	310		491 (III)	eciwx	External Control In Word Indexed
X	31	438		492 (III)	ecowx	External Control Out Word Indexed
X	31	854		350 (II)	eieio	Enforce In-order Execution of I/O
X	31	284	SR	111	eqv[.]	Equivalent
X	31	954	SR	112	extsb[.]	Extend Sign Byte
X	31	922	SR	113	extsh[.]	Extend Sign Halfword
X	31	986	(SR)	113	extsw[.]	Extend Sign Word
X	63	264		178	fabs[.]	Floating Absolute Value
A	63	21		179	fadd[.]	Floating Add
A	59	21		179	fadds[.]	Floating Add Single
X	63	846	()	190	fcfid[.]	Floating Convert From Integer Doubleword
X	63	32		192	fcmpo	Floating Compare Ordered
X	63	0		191	fcmpu	Floating Compare Unordered
X	63	814	()	187	fctid[.]	Floating Convert To Integer Doubleword
X	63	815	()	188	fctidz[.]	Floating Convert To Integer Doubleword with round toward Zero
X	63	14		189	fctiw[.]	Floating Convert To Integer Word

Form	Opcode		Mode Dep.[1]	Page	Mnemonic	Instruction
	Primary	Extended				
X	63	15		190	fctiwz[.]	Floating Convert To Integer Word with round toward Zero
A	63	18		182	fdiv[.]	Floating Divide
A	59	18		182	fdivs[.]	Floating Divide Single
A	63	29		183	fmadd[.]	Floating Multiply-Add
A	59	29		183	fmadds[.]	Floating Multiply-Add Single
X	63	72		178	fmr[.]	Floating Move Register
A	63	28		184	fmsub[.]	Floating Multiply-Subtract
A	59	28		184	fmsubs[.]	Floating Multiply-Subtract Single
A	63	25		181	fmul[.]	Floating Multiply
A	59	25		181	fmuls[.]	Floating Multiply Single
X	63	136		179	fnabs[.]	Floating Negative Absolute Value
X	63	40		178	fneg[.]	Floating Negate
A	63	31		185	fnmadd[.]	Floating Negative Multiply-Add
A	59	31		185	fnmadds[.]	Floating Negative Multiply-Add Single
A	63	30		186	fnmsub[.]	Floating Negative Multiply-Subtract
A	59	30		186	fnmsubs[.]	Floating Negative Multiply-Subtract Single
A	59	24		200	fres[.]	Floating Reciprocal Estimate Single
X	63	12		187	frsp[.]	Floating Round to Single-Precision
A	63	26		201	frsqrte[.]	Floating Reciprocal Square Root Estimate
A	63	23		202	fsel[.]	Floating Select
A	63	22		198	fsqrt[.]	Floating Square Root
A	59	22		198	fsqrts[.]	Floating Square Root Single
A	63	20		180	fsub[.]	Floating Subtract

Form	Opcode		Mode Dep.[1]	Page	Mnemonic	Instruction
	Primary	Extended				
A	59	20		180	fsubs[.]	Floating Subtract Single
X	31	982		345 (II)	icbi	Instruction Cache Block Invalidate
XL	19	150		346 (II)	isync	Instruction Synchronize
D	34			50	lbz	Load Byte and Zero
D	35			51	lbzu	Load Byte and Zero with Update
X	31	119		51	lbzux	Load Byte and Zero with Update Indexed
X	31	87		50	lbzx	Load Byte and Zero Indexed
DS	58	0	()	59	ld	Load Doubleword
X	31	84	()	77	ldarx	Load Doubleword And Reserve Indexed
DS	58	1	()	60	ldu	Load Doubleword with Update
X	31	53	()	60	ldux	Load Doubleword with Update Indexed
X	31	21	()	59	ldx	Load Doubleword Indexed
D	50			171	lfd	Load Floating-Point Double
D	51			172	lfdu	Load Floating-Point Double with Update
X	31	631		172	lfdux	Load Floating-Point Double with Update Indexed
X	31	599		172	lfdx	Load Floating-Point Double Indexed
D	48			169	lfs	Load Floating-Point Single
D	49			170	lfsu	Load Floating-Point Single with Update
X	31	567		171	lfsux	Load Floating-Point Single with Update Indexed
X	31	535		170	lfsx	Load Floating-Point Single Indexed
D	42			54	lha	Load Halfword Algebraic
D	43			54	lhau	Load Halfword Algebraic with Update
X	31	375		55	lhaux	Load Halfword Algebraic with Update Indexed

Form	Opcode		Mode Dep.[1]	Page	Mnemonic	Instruction
	Primary	Extended				
X	31	343		54	lhax	Load Halfword Algebraic Indexed
X	31	790		68	lhbrx	Load Halfword Byte-Reverse Indexed
D	40			52	lhz	Load Halfword and Zero
D	41			53	lhzu	Load Halfword and Zero with Update
X	31	311		53	lhzux	Load Halfword and Zero with Update Indexed
X	31	279		52	lhzx	Load Halfword and Zero Indexed
D	46			71	lmw	Load Multiple Word
X	31	597		73	lswi	Load String Word Immediate
X	31	533		74	lswx	Load String Word Indexed
DS	58	2	()	57	lwa	Load Word Algebraic
X	31	20		77	lwarx	Load Word And Reserve Indexed
X	31	373	()	58	lwaux	Load Word Algebraic with Update Indexed
X	31	341	()	58	lwax	Load Word Algebraic Indexed
X	31	534		69	lwbrx	Load Word Byte-Reverse Indexed
D	32			55	lwz	Load Word and Zero
D	33			56	lwzu	Load Word and Zero with Update
X	31	55		57	lwzux	Load Word and Zero with Update Indexed
X	31	23		56	lwzx	Load Word and Zero Indexed
XL	19	0		46	mcrf	Move Condition Register Field
X	63	64		194	mcrfs	Move to Condition Register from FPSCR
X	31	512		132	mcrxr	Move to Condition Register from XER
X	31	19		132	mfcr	Move From Condition Register
X	63	583		194	mffs[.]	Move From FPSCR

Form	Opcode Primary	Opcode Extended	Mode Dep.[1]	Page	Mnemonic	Instruction
X	31	83		389 (III)	mfmsr	Move From Machine State Register
XFX	31	339		130	mfspr	Move From Special Purpose Register (see also Book III, page 387)
X	31	595	{}	441 (III)	mfsr	Move From Segment Register
X	31	659	{}	442 (III)	mfsrin	Move From Segment Register Indirect
XFX	31	371		352 (II)	mftb	Move From Time Base
XFX	31	144		131	mtcrf	Move To Condition Register Fields
X	63	70		195	mtfsb0[.]	Move To FPSCR Bit 0
X	63	38		196	mtfsb1[.]	Move To FPSCR Bit 1
XFL	63	711		195	mtfsf[.]	Move To FPSCR Fields
X	63	134		194	mtfsfi[.]	Move To FPSCR Field Immediate
X	31	146		389 (III)	mtmsr	Move To Machine State Register
XFX	31	467		129	mtspr	Move To Special Purpose Register (see also Book III, page 384)
X	31	210	{}	440 (III)	mtsr	Move To Segment Register
X	31	242	{}	441 (III)	mtsrin	Move To Segment Register Indirect
XO	31	73	(SR)	91	mulhd[.]	Multiply High Doubleword
XO	31	9	(SR)	92	mulhdu[.]	Multiply High Doubleword Unsigned
XO	31	75	SR	92	mulhw[.]	Multiply High Word
XO	31	11	SR	93	mulhwu[.]	Multiply High Word Unsigned
XO	31	233	(SR)	90	mulld[o][.]	Multiply Low Doubleword
D	7			90	mulli	Multiply Low Immediate
XO	31	235	SR	91	mullw[o][.]	Multiply Low Word
X	31	476	SR	110	nand[.]	NAND
XO	31	104	SR	89	neg[o][.]	Negate

Form	Opcode		Mode Dep.[1]	Page	Mnemonic	Instruction
	Primary	Extended				
X	31	124	SR	110	nor[.]	NOR
X	31	444	SR	109	or[.]	OR
X	31	412	SR	112	orc[.]	OR with Complement
D	24			107	ori	OR Immediate
D	25			107	oris	OR Immediate Shifted
XL	19	50		379 (III)	rfi	Return From Interrupt
MDS	30	8	(SR)	119	rldcl[.]	Rotate Left Doubleword then Clear Left
MDS	30	9	(SR)	120	rldcr[.]	Rotate Left Doubleword then Clear Right
MD	30	2	(SR)	118	rldic[.]	Rotate Left Doubleword Immediate then Clear
MD	30	0	(SR)	116	rldicl[.]	Rotate Left Doubleword Immediate then Clear Left
MD	30	1	(SR)	117	rldicr[.]	Rotate Left Doubleword Immediate then Clear Right
MD	30	3	(SR)	121	rldimi[.]	Rotate Left Doubleword Immediate then Mask Insert
M	20		SR	122	rlwimi[.]	Rotate Left Word Immediate then Mask Insert
M	21		SR	119	rlwinm[.]	Rotate Left Word Immediate then AND with Mask
M	23		SR	121	rlwnm[.]	Rotate Left Word then AND with Mask
SC	17			41	sc	System Call (see also Book III, page 378)
X	31	498	()	444 (III)	slbia	SLB Invalidate All
X	31	434	()	443 (III)	slbie	SLB Invalidate Entry
X	31	27	(SR)	123	sld[.]	Shift Left Doubleword
X	31	24	SR	124	slw[.]	Shift Left Word
X	31	794	(SR)	127	srad[.]	Shift Right Algebraic Doubleword
XS	31	413	(SR)	126	sradi[.]	Shift Right Algebraic Doubleword Immediate
X	31	792	SR	128	sraw[.]	Shift Right Algebraic Word
X	31	824	SR	126	srawi[.]	Shift Right Algebraic Word Immediate

Form	Opcode		Mode Dep.[1]	Page	Mnemonic	Instruction
	Primary	Extended				
X	31	539	(SR)	124	srd[.]	Shift Right Doubleword
X	31	536	SR	125	srw[.]	Shift Right Word
D	38			61	stb	Store Byte
D	39			62	stbu	Store Byte with Update
X	31	247		62	stbux	Store Byte with Update Indexed
X	31	215		61	stbx	Store Byte Indexed
DS	62	0	()	66	std	Store Doubleword
X	31	214	()	79	stdcx.	Store Doubleword Conditional Indexed
DS	62	1	()	67	stdu	Store Doubleword with Update
X	31	181	()	68	stdux	Store Doubleword with Update Indexed
X	31	149	()	67	stdx	Store Doubleword Indexed
D	54			176	stfd	Store Floating-Point Double
D	55			177	stfdu	Store Floating-Point Double with Update
X	31	759		177	stfdux	Store Floating-Point Double with Update Indexed
X	31	727		176	stfdx	Store Floating-Point Double Indexed
X	31	983		198	stfiwx	Store Floating-Point as Integer Word Indexed
D	52			174	stfs	Store Floating-Point Single
D	53			175	stfsu	Store Floating-Point Single with Update
X	31	695		175	stfsux	Store Floating-Point Single with Update Indexed
X	31	663		175	stfsx	Store Floating-Point Single Indexed
D	44			63	sth	Store Halfword
X	31	918		69	sthbrx	Store Halfword Byte-Reverse Indexed
D	45			63	sthu	Store Halfword with Update
X	31	439		64	sthux	Store Halfword with Update Indexed

Form	Opcode		Mode Dep.[1]	Page	Mnemonic	Instruction
	Primary	Extended				
X	31	407		63	sthx	Store Halfword Indexed
D	47			72	stmw	Store Multiple Word
X	31	725		75	stswi	Store String Word Immediate
X	31	661		76	stswx	Store String Word Indexed
D	36			64	stw	Store Word
X	31	662		70	stwbrx	Store Word Byte-Reverse Indexed
X	31	150		78	stwcx.	Store Word Conditional Indexed
D	37			65	stwu	Store Word with Update
X	31	183		66	stwux	Store Word with Update Indexed
X	31	151		65	stwx	Store Word Indexed
XO	31	40	SR	83	subf[o][.]	Subtract From
XO	31	8	SR	86	subfc[o][.]	Subtract From Carrying
XO	31	136	SR	87	subfe[o][.]	Subtract From Extended
D	8		SR	85	subfic	Subtract From Immediate Carrying
XO	31	232	SR	88	subfme[o][.]	Subtract From Minus One Extended
XO	31	200	SR	89	subfze[o][.]	Subtract From Zero Extended
X	31	598		80	sync	Synchronize
X	31	68	()	104	td	Trap Doubleword
D	2		()	102	tdi	Trap Doubleword Immediate
X	31	370	445 (III)		tlbia	TLB Invalidate All
X	31	306	444 (III)		tlbie	TLB Invalidate Entry
X	31	566	445 (III)		tlbsync	TLB Synchronize
X	31	4		105	tw	Trap Word
D	3			103	twi	Trap Word Immediate

Form	Opcode		Mode Dep.[1]	Page	Mnemonic	Instruction
	Primary	Extended				
X	31	316	SR	110	xor[.]	XOR
D	26			108	xori	XOR Immediate
D	27			108	xoris	XOR Immediate Shifted

[1]Key to Mode Dependency Column

The entry is shown in parentheses () if the instruction is defined only for 64-bit implementations.

The entry is shown in braces {} if the instruction is defined only for 32-bit implementations.

blank   The instruction has no mode dependence, except that if the instruction refers to storage when in 32-bit mode, only the low-order 32 bits of the 64-bit effective address are used to address storage. Storage reference instructions include loads, stores, branch instructions, etc.

CT   If the instruction tests the Count Register, it tests the low-order 32 bits when in 32-bit mode and all 64 bits when in 64-bit mode.

SR   The instruction's primary function is mode-independent, but the setting of status registers (such as XER and CR0) is mode-dependent.

Book

II

This book describes additional instructions and facilities beyond those of the PowerPC User Instruction Set Architecture and PowerPC Virtual Environment Architecture. It covers the storage model and related instructions and facilities available to the application programmer, and the Time Base as seen by the application programmer.

PowerPC
Virtual
Environment
Architecture

Storage Model

1.1 Definitions and Notation

The following definitions, in addition to those specified in Book I, are used in this Book.

- **processor**
  A hardware component that executes the PowerPC instructions specified in a program.

- **system**
  A combination of processors, storage, and associated mechanisms that is capable of executing programs. Sometimes the reference to system includes services provided by the operating system.

- **main storage**
  The level of the storage hierarchy in which all storage state is visible to all processors and mechanisms in the system.

- **sequential execution**
  A model for the execution of a sequence of instructions (program) in which one instruction is executed and completed before the next instruction is begun. Instructions are executed in the order in which they appear in the program, except following the execution of a branch instruction, which causes sequential execution to continue at the location specified by the branch instruction.

- **program order**
  The execution of instructions in the strict order in which they occur in the program. See **sequential execution** above.

- storage location
  One or more sequential bytes of storage beginning at the address computed by a *Storage Access* instruction or by the instruction fetching mechanism. The number of bytes comprising the location depends on the type of *Storage Access* instruction being executed, or is four for instruction fetching.

- load
  An instruction that copies one or more bytes from a storage location to one or more registers (GPRs or FPRs).

- store
  An instruction that copies one or more bytes from one or more registers (GPRs or FPRs) to a storage location.

- uniprocessor
  A system that contains one PowerPC processor.

- multiprocessor
  A system that contains two or more PowerPC processors.

- shared storage multiprocessor
  A multiprocessor that contains some common storage, which all the PowerPC processors in the system can access.

- performed
  A load is performed with respect to all other processors (and mechanisms) when the value to be returned by the load can no longer be changed by a subsequent store by any processor (or other mechanism). A store is performed with respect to all other processors (and mechanisms) when any load from the same location used by the store returns the value stored (or a value stored subsequently).

- page
  A unit of storage for which protection and control attributes are independently specifiable and for which reference and change status are independently recorded.

- block
  The aligned unit of storage operated on by each *Cache Management* instruction. The size of a block can vary by instruction and by implementation. The maximum block size is one page.

- aligned storage access
  A load or store is aligned if the address of the target storage location is a multiple of the size of the transfer effected by the instruction.

- **atomic access**

  A storage access executed by a processor during which no other processor or mechanism can access any byte of the target location between the time the processor performing the access accesses any byte of the location and the time that it completes the access to all bytes of that location.

1.2 Introduction

The PowerPC User Instruction Set Architecture, discussed in Book I, defines storage as a linear array of bytes indexed from 0 to a maximum of $2^{64} - 1\{2^{32} - 1\}$. Each byte is identified by its index, called its address, and each byte contains a value. This information is sufficient to allow the programming of applications that require no special features of any particular system environment. The PowerPC Virtual Environment Architecture, described herein, expands this simple storage model to include caches, virtual storage, and shared storage multiprocessors. The PowerPC Virtual Environment Architecture, in conjunction with services based on the PowerPC Operating Environment Architecture (see Book III) and provided by the operating system, permits explicit control of this expanded storage model. A simple model for sequential execution allows at most one storage access to be performed at a time and requires that all storage accesses appear to be performed in program order. In contrast to this simple model, the PowerPC architecture specifies a relaxed model of memory consistency. In a multiprocessor system that allows multiple copies of a location, aggressive implementations of the architecture can permit intervals of time during which different copies of a location have different values. This chapter describes features of the PowerPC architecture that enable programmers to write correct programs for this memory model.

1.3 Virtual Storage

The PowerPC system implements a virtual storage model for applications. This means that a combination of hardware and software can present a storage model that allows applications to exist within a "virtual" address space larger than either the effective address space or the real address space.

Each program can access 2^{64} $\{2^{32}\}$ bytes of "effective address" (EA) space, subject to limitations imposed by the operating system. In a typical

PowerPC system, each program's EA space is a subset of a larger "virtual address" (VA) space managed by the operating system.

Each effective address is translated to a real address (i.e., to an address in real storage) before being used to access storage. The hardware accomplishes this, using the address translation mechanism described in Book III, Chapter 4, "Storage Control," on page 391. The operating system manages the real (physical) storage resources of the system, by setting up the tables and other information used by the hardware address translation mechanism.

Book II deals primarily with effective addresses that are in "ordinary segments" translated by the "segmented address translation mechanism" (see Book III, Chapter 4). Each such effective address lies in a "virtual page," which is mapped to a "real page" before data in the virtual page are accessed.

In general, main storage may not be large enough to map all the virtual pages used by the currently active applications. With support provided by hardware, the operating system can attempt to use the available real pages to map a sufficient set of virtual pages of the applications. If a sufficient set is maintained, "paging" activity is minimized. If not, performance degradation is likely.

The operating system can support restricted access to virtual pages (including read-write, read-only, and no access; see Book III, Section 4.10, "Storage Protection," on page 436), based on system standards (e.g., program code might be read-only) and application requests.

1.4 Single-Copy Atomicity

An access is *single-copy atomic,* or simply *atomic,* if it is always performed in its entirety with no visible fragmentation. Atomic accesses are thus *serialized*: each happens in its entirety in some order, even when that order is not specified in the program or enforced between processors.

In PowerPC the following single-register accesses are always atomic:

- byte accesses (all bytes are aligned on byte boundaries)
- halfword accesses aligned on halfword boundaries
- word accesses aligned on word boundaries
- doubleword accesses aligned on doubleword boundaries (64-bit implementations only)

No other accesses are guaranteed to be atomic. In particular, multiple-register loads and stores are not atomic, nor are floating-point double-word accesses on a 32-bit implementation.

The results for several combinations of loads and stores to the same or overlapping locations are described below.

1. When two processors execute atomic stores to locations that do not overlap, and no other stores are performed to those locations, the content of those locations is the same as if the two stores were performed by a single processor.

2. When two processors execute atomic stores to the same storage location, and no other store is performed to that location, the content of that location is the result stored by one of the processors.

3. When two processors execute stores that have the same target location and are not guaranteed to be atomic, and no other store is performed to that location, the result is some combination of the bytes stored by both processors.

4. When two processors execute stores to overlapping locations, and no other store is performed to those locations, the result is some combination of the bytes stored by the processors to the overlapping bytes. The portions of the locations that do not overlap contain the bytes stored by the processor storing to the location.

5. When a processor executes an atomic store to a location, a second processor executes an atomic load from that location, and no other store is performed to that location, the value returned by the load is the content of the location prior to the store or the content of the location subsequent to the store.

6. When a load and a store with the same target location can be executed simultaneously, and no other store is performed to the location, the value returned by the load is some combination of the content of the location before the store and after the store.

1.5 Memory Coherence

Coherence refers to the ordering of writes to a single location. Atomic stores to a given location are *coherent* if they are serialized in some order, and no processor is able to observe any subset of those stores as occurring in a conflicting order. This serialization order is an abstract sequence of values; the physical memory location need not assume each of the values written to it. For example, if a processor has a store-in cache, it may update a location several times before the value is written to the physical memory. The result of a store operation is not available to every processor at the same instant, and it may be that a processor observes only some of the values that are written to a location. However, when a location is accessed atomically and coherently by all processors, then, for any processor, the sequence of values it loads from the location during any interval of time forms a subsequence of the sequence of values that the location logically held during that interval. That is, a processor can never load a "newer" value first and then, later, load an "older" value.

As noted in Section 1.6, "Storage Control Attributes," on page 325, the coherence of storage locations may be managed by hardware or software depending on the setting of the Memory Coherence attribute.

Memory coherence is managed in blocks called *coherence blocks*. Their size is implementation-dependent (see the Book IV, *PowerPC Implementation Features* document for the implementation), but is usually larger than a word and often the size of a cache block.

1.5.1 Coherence Required

When a storage location is in Memory Coherence Required mode, each store to that location must be serialized with all stores to that location by all other processors that also access the location coherently. This requirement can be satisfied, for example, by implementing an ownership protocol that allows at most one processor at a time to store to the location.

Coherence does not ensure that the result of a store by one processor will be immediately visible to all other processors and mechanisms in the system. Only after a program has executed the *sync* instruction are the previous storage accesses it has executed guaranteed to have been performed with respect to all other processors and mechanisms.

Programming Note

In a single-cache system, Coherence Required mode is not necessary for correct coherent execution. In fact, in such a system, Coherence Not Required mode may give better performance.

1.5.2 Coherence Not Required

When a storage location is in Memory Coherence Not Required mode, storage coherence need not be enforced. This coherence mode may be selected by software to improve performance when it is known that the particular area of storage the processor is accessing will not be accessed by another processor or mechanism. In this mode, software must ensure that the appropriate *Cache Management* instructions have been used to put storage in a consistent state prior to changing the mode or allowing access to that storage area by a different processor or mechanism.

1.6 Storage Control Attributes

Some operating systems may provide means to allow programs to specify storage control attributes not described in Book II. The definition of these attributes can be found in Book III, Section 4.8, "Storage Access Modes," on page 429. The following describes what an operating system that supports these functions is expected to provide. The details may vary among operating systems, so the details of the specific system being used must be known before these functions can be used.

Generally, the program may use one of each of the following pairs of storage attributes:

■ **Write Through Required** or **Not Required**

■ **Caching Inhibited** or **Allowed**

■ **Memory Coherence Required** or **Not Required**

■ **Guarded** or **Not Guarded**

Not all combinations of these modes are supported; see Book III, Section 4.8.2, "Supported Storage Modes," on page 431 for further details.

A program can specify, through an operating system service, the attributes for each virtual page to which it has access. Each load or store will be performed in the following manner, depending on the setting of the storage control attributes for the page containing the addressed storage location.

Write Through

This attribute is meaningful only for Caching Allowed storage. It provides the program control over whether:

■ the processor is required to update the copy of the storage location in the cache and in main storage, or

■ the processor is allowed to update the copy of the storage location in the cache and to defer the update of main storage.

Required

Loads use the copy in the cache if it is there. Stores update the copy of the storage location in the cache if it is in the cache and also update the storage location in main storage.

Not Required

Loads and stores use the copy in the cache if it is there. The block containing the target storage location may be copied to the cache.

The storage location in main storage need not contain the value most recently stored to that location.

Caching
Inhibited
When caching is inhibited, the Write Through attribute has no meaning. The load or store is executed in the following manner:

1. The operation is performed to main storage bypassing the cache (i.e., neither the target location nor any of the block(s) containing it is copied into the cache).

2. The operation causes an access (load/store) of appropriate length (i.e., byte, halfword, word, etc.) to the target location in main storage.

It is considered a programming error if a copy of the target location of an access to Caching Inhibited storage is in the cache. Software must ensure that the location has not previously been brought into the cache or, if it has, that it has been flushed from the cache. If the programming error occurs, the result of the access is boundedly undefined.

Allowed
When caching is allowed, the access is performed in the following manner:

1. If the block containing the target storage location is in the cache, it is used.

2. If the block containing the target location is not in the cache, the block(s) of storage containing the target location may be copied to the cache and, if the access is a store, the target location is updated in the cache if it is in the cache.

Memory Coherence
This attribute provides the program control over whether the processor maintains storage coherence:
Required
Stores by all processors to the same location are serialized into some order and no processor is able to observe any subset of those stores as occurring in a conflicting order.

Not Required
The order in which one processor observes the stores performed by one or more other processors is undefined.

When coherence is required, its serialization function is effective for all supported combinations of the Write Through and Caching modes (see Book III, Section 4.8.2, "Supported Storage Modes," on page 431).

When coherence is not required, the programmer must manage the coherence of storage through use of *sync* and *Cache Management* instructions, and facilities provided by the operating system.

Guarded

This attribute provides the program control over the conditions under which data and instructions can be accessed speculatively. See Book III, Section 4.2.5, "Speculative Execution," on page 396 for a more complete definition.

Guarded

Data cannot be accessed speculatively, and instructions cannot be fetched speculatively, except under the conditions described in Book III.

Not Guarded

Data can be accessed speculatively, and instructions can be fetched speculatively.

1.7 Cache Models

The PowerPC architecture does not require any particular cache organization and allows many different implementations. However, for a program to execute correctly on all implementations, the programmer should assume that separate instruction and data caches exist, and should program to the separate cache model. The functions of these caches are affected by the storage control attributes associated with each storage access as described in Section 1.6, "Storage Control Attributes," on page 325. *Cache Management* instructions are provided so programs can manage the caches when needed. Depending on the storage control attributes specified by the program and the function being performed, the program may need to use these instructions to guarantee that the function is performed correctly. The *Cache Management* instructions are also useful to optimize the use of memory bandwidth in such applications as graphics and numerically intensive computing.

The processor is not required to maintain copies of storage locations in the instruction cache consistent with changes to storage resulting from the execution of store instructions. Program management of the cache is required when the program generates or modifies code that will be executed (i.e., when the program modifies data in storage and then attempts to execute the modified data as instructions).

The instructions provided allow the program to:

■ invalidate the copy of storage in an instruction cache block (*icbi*)

■ perform context synchronization, as described in Book III, Section 1.7.1, "Context Synchronization," on page 371 (*isync*)

■ give a hint that a block of storage should be copied into the data cache, so that the copy of the block may be in the cache when subsequent accesses to the block occur, thereby reducing delays (*dcbt, dcbtst*)

■ set the content of a data cache block to zeros (*dcbz*)

■ copy the content of a data cache block to main storage (*dcbst*)

■ copy the content of a data cache block to main storage and make the copy of the block in the data cache invalid (*dcbf*)

Programming Note

Implementations will vary as to what instructions need be executed to perform a function such as code modification. Operating systems are encouraged to provide a service (implementation-dependent) to perform the function in an efficient manner.

The function of the *Cache Management* instructions depends on the implementation of the caches and on the storage control attributes associated with the cache block that is the target of the *Cache Management* instruction.

There are many variations of cache implementations and the following sections do not attempt to describe them exhaustively. However, the variations that affect the function of the *Cache Management* instructions are discussed here.

1.7.1 Split or Dual Caches

A cache model in which there are separate caches for instructions and data is called a "Harvard-style" cache. This style is the standard PowerPC cache model; that is, it is the model assumed by this architecture, and the function of the *Cache Management* instructions depends on this model as well as on the storage control attributes of the target storage block. A copy of a target block in the cache is said to be *marked invalid* if it will not be used for subsequent accesses. The following sections describe the functions performed by each of the *Cache Management* instructions in this model.

Instruction Cache Block Invalidate

This instruction permits the program to invalidate the target storage block in the instruction cache, causing any subsequent fetch request for an instruction in the block to be sent to main storage (because the block is not found in the instruction cache). The instruction performs the following operations:

1. If the target block is not accessible to the program for loads, the system data storage error handler may be invoked.

2. Memory Coherence

Required
> If the target block is in any of the instruction caches in the system, it is marked invalid in those caches.

Not Required
> If the target block is in the instruction cache of the executing processor, it is marked invalid in that cache.

3. This access need not be recorded, but if it is it is considered a load and not a store.

Data Cache Block Touch

The two *Touch* instructions (one for reading, the other for writing) permit the program to attempt to have the target storage block in the cache prior to its first use, and thereby to avoid some of the delays due to accessing storage. These instructions are performance hints, and perform the following operations:

1. If the target block is not accessible to the program for loads, no other operation is performed.

2. Caching

Inhibited
> The target block is not copied into the data cache of the executing processor and no other operations are performed.

Allowed
Memory Coherence

> Required
>> If the target block is not in the data cache of the executing processor, the most recent version of the block may be copied

into that data cache.

Not Required
If the target block is not in the data cache of the executing processor, the block may be copied into that data cache from main storage without regard for the location of the most recently modified version.

3. This access need not be recorded, but if it is it is considered a load and not a store.

If the instruction is *Touch for Store* and the block is copied into the cache, it is copied in a manner such that a subsequent store to the block will execute efficiently.

The execution of either of these instructions *never* causes the system data storage error handler to be invoked.

Data Cache Block set to Zero

This instruction permits the program to set large areas of storage to zeros in an efficient manner. The instruction performs the following operations:

1. If the target block is not accessible to the program for stores, the system data storage error handler is invoked.

2. Write Through Required
Either each byte of the target block in main storage is set to 0x00, or the system alignment error handler is invoked.

3. Caching Inhibited
Either each byte of the target block in main storage is set to 0x00, or the system alignment error handler is invoked.

4. Memory Coherence

Required

- If the target block is in the data cache of the executing processor, each byte in the block is set to 0x00 and all copies of the block in all data caches in the system are made consistent.

- If the target block is not in the data cache of the executing processor, the block is established in that data cache without fetching it from main storage and each byte in the block is set to 0x00. All copies of the block in all data caches in the system are made consistent.

Not Required

- If the target block is in the data cache of the executing processor, each byte in the block is set to 0x00.

- If the target block is not in the data cache of the executing processor, the block is established in that data cache without fetching it from main storage and each byte in the block is set to 0x00.

5. This access must be recorded. It is considered a store.

Data Cache Block Store

This instruction permits the program to ensure that the latest version of the target storage block is in main storage. The instruction performs the following operations:

1. If the target block is not accessible to the program for loads, the system data storage error handler may be invoked.

2. Memory Coherence

Required

If the target block is in any of the data caches in the system and has been modified, it is copied to main storage.

Not Required

If the target block is in the data cache of the executing processor and has been modified, it is copied to main storage.

3. This access need not be recorded, but if it is it is considered a load and not a store.

Data Cache Block Flush

This instruction permits the program to ensure that the latest version of the target storage block is in main storage and no longer in the data cache. The instruction performs the same operations as does *Data Cache Block Store*. In addition to those operations, the following is done.

Memory Coherence

Required

If the target block is in any of the data caches in the system, it is marked invalid in those data caches.

Not Required

If the target block is in the data cache of the executing processor, it is marked invalid in that data cache.

1.7.2 Combined Cache

A combined cache implementation provides a single cache for instructions and data. For this implementation, the *Instruction Cache Block Invalidate* instruction need not perform the same operations as it would for an implementation with separate caches. The instruction is treated as a no-op, except that it is acceptable to invalidate the target block in the instruction caches of other processors if the block is in Memory Coherence Required mode.

1.7.3 Write Through Data Cache

The *Cache Management* instructions affected by the write through implementation of the data cache are listed in this section. These instructions must perform all the operations specified for a Harvard-style cache except as specified in this section. Some of the differences depend on whether the write through implementation is a write through to main storage or just a write through to a second level of cache.

Write Through to Main Storage

1. *Data Cache Block set to Zero*
The processor may invoke the system alignment error handler regardless of the setting of the storage control attributes.

2. *Data Cache Block Store*
By definition, the cache cannot contain a modified block. The processor is not required to copy the target block to main storage.

3. *Data Cache Block Flush*
By definition, the cache cannot contain a modified block. The processor is not required to copy the target block to main storage.

Write Through to Multilevel Cache

For *Data Cache Block set to Zero,* the processor may invoke the system alignment error handler regardless of the setting of the storage control attributes.

If a cache is the interface to main storage for all processors and other mechanisms that access storage, that cache can be considered main storage with respect to the *Cache Management* instructions. Otherwise, the cache instructions that cause the content of a cache block to be copied back to main storage or to be marked invalid must be performed against all levels of the cache.

1.8 Shared Storage

This architecture supports the sharing of storage between programs, between different instances of the same program on systems with one or more processors, and between processors and other mechanisms. It also supports access to a storage location by one or more programs using different effective addresses. All these cases are considered storage sharing. Storage is shared in blocks that are an integral number of pages.

When the same storage location has different effective addresses, the addresses are said to be *aliases.* Each application can be granted separate access privileges to aliased pages.

1.8.1 Storage Access Ordering

The PowerPC Architecture specifies a *weakly consistent* storage model for shared storage multiprocessor systems. This model provides an opportunity for significantly improved performance over the strongly consistent model, but places the responsibility on the program to ensure that ordering or synchronization instructions are properly placed when necessary for the correct execution of the program.

In this architecture, the order in which the processor performs storage accesses, the order in which those accesses complete in main storage, and the order in which those accesses are viewed as occurring by another processor may all be different. This property is referred to as *storage access ordering.* A means of enforcing an ordering of storage accesses is provided to allow programs or instances of programs to share storage. Similar means are needed to allow programs executing on a processor to share storage with some other mechanism, such as an I/O device, that can also access storage.

The purpose of specifying a weakly consistent storage model is to allow the processor to run very fast for most storage accesses. Two instructions, *Enforce In-order Execution of I/O* and *Synchronize,* are provided to enable the program to control the order in which storage accesses are performed by separate instructions. No ordering should be assumed for the storage accesses done by a multiple-register load or store instruction, and no means are provided for controlling that order.

Enforce In-order Execution of I/O

This instruction permits the program to control the order in which loads and stores are performed in main storage when the accessed storage has certain attributes. The data accesses affected by *eieio* are: loads and stores to storage that is both Caching Inhibited and Guarded; and stores to storage that is Write Through Required. All applicable data accesses are ordered as a single set (i.e., there is not one order for loads and stores to Caching Inhibited and Guarded storage, and another order for stores to Write Through Required storage). *eieio* does not affect the order of other data accesses, or of cache operations (whether caused explicitly by execution of a *Cache Management* instruction or implicitly by the cache coherence mechanism).

eieio ensures that all applicable data accesses to main storage previously initiated by the processor have completed with respect to main storage before any applicable storage accesses subsequently initiated by the processor access main storage. It acts like a barrier that flows through the storage queues and to main storage, preventing the reordering of storage accesses across the barrier. The *eieio* instruction may complete before previously initiated storage accesses have been performed with respect to other processors and mechanisms.

eieio can be used, for example, to ensure that the data from a sequence of stores to the control registers of an I/O device update those control registers in the order specified by the stores as ordered by *eieio*.

If stronger ordering is desired or if it is necessary to order accesses to storage that may be in the cache, the *sync* instruction must be used.

Synchronize

When a portion of storage must be forced to a known state, it is necessary to synchronize storage with respect to all processors and mechanisms. This synchronization is accomplished by requiring programs to indicate explicitly in the instruction stream, by inserting a *sync* instruction, that synchronization is required. Only when *sync* completes are the effects of all storage accesses previously executed by the program guaranteed to have been performed with respect to all other processors and mechanisms.

The *sync* instruction permits the program to ensure that all storage accesses it has initiated have been performed with respect to all other processors and mechanisms before its next instruction is executed. A program can use this instruction to ensure that all updates to a shared data structure are visible to all other processors prior to executing a store that will release the lock on that data structure. Execution of this instruction does the following:

- Performs the functions described for the *sync* instruction in Book I, "Synchronize X-form," on page 80.

- Ensures that consistency operations and the effects of *icbi, dcbz, dcbst, dcbf*, and *dcbi* instructions (see Book III, "Data Cache Block Invalidate   X-form," on page 439) previously executed by the processor executing the *sync* have completed on all other processors.

- Ensures that TLB invalidates previously executed by the processor executing the *sync* have completed on that processor. *sync* does *not* wait for such invalidates to complete on *other* processors (see Book III, Section 4.12, "Table Update Synchronization Requirements," on page 446).

- Ensures that storage accesses due to instructions previously executed by the processor executing the *sync* are recorded in the Reference and Change bits in the Page Table (see Book III, Section 4.9, "Reference and Change Recording," on page 433).

The *sync* instruction is execution synchronizing (see Book III, Section 1.7.2, "Execution Synchronization," on page 372). It is not context synchronizing (see Book III, Section 1.7.1, "Context Synchronization," on page 371), and therefore need not discard prefetched instructions.

For storage that is maintained as Memory Coherence Not Required, the only effect of *sync* on storage operations is to ensure that all previous storage accesses have completed to the level of storage specified by the Caching and Write Through storage control attributes (including the updating of Reference and Change bits).

1.8.2 Atomic Update Primitives

The *Load And Reserve* and *Store Conditional* instructions together permit atomic update of a storage location. 64-bit implementations have word and doubleword forms of each of these instructions. Described here is the operation of the word forms *lwarx* and *stwcx.*; operation of the doubleword forms *ldarx* and *stdcx.* is the same except for obvious substitutions.

These instructions function in Caching Inhibited, as well as in Caching Allowed, storage. The addressed page must, however, have the Memory Coherence Required attribute for every processor, other than the one doing the atomic update, that might execute a store to the location being atomically updated. The remainder of this section assumes that if the system is a multiprocessor, then all processors have the addressed page in Memory Coherence Required mode.

If the addressed storage is in Write Through Required mode, it is implementation-dependent whether these instructions function correctly or cause the system data storage error handler to be invoked.

The *lwarx* instruction is a load from a word-aligned location that has two side effects.

1. A nonspecific reservation for a subsequent *stwcx.* or *stdcx.* is created.

2. The storage coherence mechanism is notified that a reservation exists for the real address (see Book III, Chapter 4, "Storage Control," on page 391) corresponding to the storage location accessed by the *lwarx*.

The *stwcx.* instruction is a store to a word-aligned location that is conditioned on the existence of the reservation created by the *lwarx* or *ldarx*. To emulate an atomic operation with these instructions, it is necessary that both the *lwarx* and the *stwcx.* access the same storage location even though this requirement is not enforced by the hardware. *lwarx* and *stwcx.* are ordered by a dependence on the reservation, and the program is not required to insert other instructions to maintain the order of storage accesses by these two instructions.

A *stwcx.* performs a store to the target storage location only if the storage location accessed by the *lwarx* that established the reservation has not been stored into by another processor or mechanism between supplying a value for the *lwarx* and storing the value supplied by the *stwcx.*. In this case, CR0 is set to indicate that the store was performed.

If the *stwcx.* completes but does not perform the store because a reservation no longer exists, CR0 is set to indicate that the *stwcx.* completed but storage was not altered.

Examples of the use of *lwarx* and *stwcx.* are given in Book I, Section E.1, "Synchronization," on page 249.

When *stwcx.* to a given location succeeds, its store has been performed but may not yet be visible to all other processors and mechanisms. As a result, a subsequent load or *lwarx* from the given location on another processor may return a "stale" value. However, a subsequent *lwarx* from the given location on the other processor followed by a successful *stwcx.* on that processor is guaranteed to have returned the value stored by the first processor's *stwcx.* (in the absence of other stores to the given location).

Reservations

The ability to emulate an atomic operation using *lwarx* and *stwcx.* is based on the conditional behavior of *stwcx.*, the reservation set by *lwarx*, and the clearing of that reservation if the target location is modified by another processor or mechanism before the *stwcx.* performs its store.

A processor has at most one reservation at any time. A reservation is established by executing a *lwarx* instruction and is lost if any of the following occur:

- The processor holding the reservation executes another *lwarx* or *ldarx*; this clears the first reservation and establishes a new one.

- The processor holding the reservation executes any *stwcx.* or *stdcx.*, whether or not its address matches that of the *lwarx*.

- Some other processor executes a store or *dcbz* to the same reservation granule, or modifies a Reference or Change bit (see Book III, Section 4.9, "Reference and Change Recording," on page 433) in the same reservation granule.

- Some other mechanism modifies a storage location in the same reservation granule.

- Any additional causes of reservation loss are described in the Book IV, *PowerPC Implementation Features* document for the implementation.

Interrupts (see Book III, Chapter 5, "Interrupts," on page 453) do not clear reservations (however, system software invoked by interrupts may clear reservations). Immunity to random reservation loss ensures that programs using *lwarx* and *stwcx.* can make forward progress.

Programming Note

To ensure that a store or *stwcx.* to a given location has been performed with respect to all other processors and mechanisms, it must be followed by a *sync*. A subsequent load or *lwarx* from the given location by another processor will then return a value at least as recent as the value stored. This is often more synchronization than is actually needed to ensure program correctness.

Programming Note

One use of *lwarx* and *stwcx.* is to emulate a "Compare and Swap" primitive like that provided by the IBM System/370 Compare and Swap instruction: see Book I, "Compare and Swap," on page 252. A System/370-style Compare and Swap checks only that the old and current values of the word being tested are equal, with the result that programs that use such a Compare and Swap to control a shared resource can err if the word has been modified and the old value subsequently restored. The combination of *lwarx* and *stwcx.* improves on such a Compare and Swap, because the reservation reliably binds the *lwarx* and *stwcx.* together. The reservation is always lost if the word is modified by another processor or mechanism between the lwarx and *stwcx.*, so the *stwcx.* never succeeds unless the word has not been stored into (by another processor or mechanism) since the *lwarx.*

Programming Note

Programming convention must ensure that *lwarx* and *stwcx.* addresses match. In proper use, a *stwcx.* should be paired with a specific *lwarx* to the same real address. Situations in which a *stwcx.* may erroneously be issued after some *lwarx* other than that with which it is intended to be paired must be scrupulously avoided. For example, there must not be a context switch in which the processor holds a reservation in behalf of the old context, and the new context resumes after a *lwarx* and before the paired *stwcx.*. The *stwcx.* in the new context would complete successfully, which is not what was intended by the programmer.

Such a situation must be prevented by issuing a *stwcx.* to a dummy writable word-aligned location as part of the context switch, thereby clearing any reservation established by the old context. Executing *stwcx.* to a word-aligned location suffices to clear the reservation, whether it was obtained by *lwarx* or *ldarx*.

Guaranteeing Forward Progress

Forward progress in loops that use *lwarx* and *stwcx.* is guaranteed by a cooperative effort between hardware, operating system software, and application software. Hardware guarantees that

■ one *stwcx.* among a set of processors holding reservations to the same real address will succeed, and

■ reservations are not lost unnecessarily, i.e., when the reserved location has not been modified.

While no general rules can be given regarding operating system guarantees, programs that use the examples in Book I, Section E.1, "Synchronization," on page 249 are guaranteed forward progress.

Reservation Loss Due to Granularity

When one processor holds a reservation and another processor performs a store that might clear that reservation, the address comparison is done in a way that ignores an implementation-dependent number of low-order bits of the real addresses. The storage block corresponding to the ignored low-order bits is called the *reservation granule*. Its size is implementation-dependent (see the Book IV, *PowerPC Implementation Features* document for the implementation) but is a multiple of the *coherence block* size.

Lock words should be allocated such that contention for the locks and updates to nearby data structures do not cause excessive reservation losses from false indications of sharing that can occur due to the reservation granularity.

A processor holding a reservation on any word in a reservation granule will lose its reservation if some other processor stores anywhere in that granule. Such problems can be avoided only by ensuring that few such stores occur. This can most easily be accomplished by allocating an entire granule for a lock and wasting all but one word.

Reservation granularity may vary for each implementation. There are no architectural restrictions bounding the granularity implementations must support, so reasonably portable code must dynamically allocate aligned and padded storage for locks to guarantee absence of granularity-induced reservation loss.

Effect of Operand Placement on Performance

The placement (location and alignment) of operands in storage affects relative performance of storage accesses and may affect it significantly. The best performance is guaranteed if storage operands are aligned. In order to obtain the best performance across the widest range of implementations, the programmer should assume the performance model described in Figures 46 and 47 with respect to the placement of storage operands. Figure 46 applies when the processor is in Big-Endian mode, and Figure 47 applies when the processor is in Little-Endian mode. Performance of accesses varies depending on the following:

1. Operand Size

2. Operand Alignment

3. Endian mode (Big-Endian or Little-Endian)

4. Crossing no boundary

5. Crossing a cache block boundary

6. Crossing a page boundary that is also a protection boundary (see Book III, Section 4.10, "Storage Protection," on page 436)

7. Crossing a BAT boundary (see Book III, Section 4.7, "Block Address Translation," on page 423)

8. Crossing a segment boundary (see Book III, Section 4.2.1, "Storage Segments," on page 393)

The *Load and Store Multiple* instructions are defined to operate only on aligned operands. The *Move Assist* instructions have no alignment requirements. Both of these sets of instructions are supported only in Big-Endian mode.

For the purposes of Figures 46 and 47, crossing a boundary between pages with different storage control attributes is equivalent to crossing a segment boundary.

Operand		Boundary Crossing			
Size	Byte Alignment	None	Cache Block	Page	BAT / Segment
Integer					
8 Byte	8	optimal	–	–	–
	4	good	good	poor	poor
	<4	poor	poor	poor	poor
4 Byte	4	optimal	–	–	–
	<4	good	good	poor	poor
2 Byte	2	optimal	–	–	–
	<2	good	good	poor	poor
1 Byte	1	optimal	–	–	–
lmw, stmw	4	good	good	good	poor
string		good	good	poor	poor
Float					
8 Byte	8	optimal	–	–	–
	4	good	good	poor	poor
	<4	poor	poor	poor	poor
4 Byte	4	optimal	–	–	–
	<4	poor	poor	poor	poor

Figure 46. **Performance effects of storage operand placement, Big-Endian mode**

Operand		Boundary Crossing			
Size	Byte Alignment	None	Cache Block	Page	BAT / Segment
Integer					
8 Byte	8	optimal	–	–	–
	<8	poor	poor	poor	poor
4 Byte	4	optimal	–	–	–
	<4	poor	poor	poor	poor
2 Byte	2	optimal	–	–	–
	<2	poor	poor	poor	poor
1 Byte	1	optimal	–	–	–
Float					
8 Byte	8	optimal	–	–	–
	<8	poor	poor	poor	poor
4 Byte	4	optimal	–	–	–
	<4	poor	poor	poor	poor

Figure 47. Performance effects of storage operand placement, Little-Endian mode

2.1 Instruction Restart

If a storage access crosses a page boundary that is also a protection boundary, a BAT boundary, or a segment boundary, a number of conditions could cause the execution of the instruction to be aborted after part of the access has been performed. This may occur, for example, when a program attempts to access a page it has not previously accessed, or when the processor must check for a possible change in storage control attributes when an access crosses a page boundary. When this occurs, the implementation or the operating system may restart the instruction. If the instruction is restarted, some bytes of the location may be loaded from or stored to the target location a second time.

The following rules apply to storage accesses with regard to restarting the instruction.

Aligned Accesses
> A single-register instruction that accesses an aligned operand is never restarted.

Unaligned Accesses
> A single-register instruction that accesses an unaligned operand may be restarted if the access crosses a page, BAT, or segment boundary.

Load and Store Multiple, Move Assist
> These instructions may be restarted if, in accessing the locations specified by the instruction, a page, BAT, or segment boundary is crossed.

2.2 Atomicity and Order

Access Atomicity
> With the exception of double-precision floating-point operands in 32-bit implementations, all aligned accesses are atomic. No other access is required to be atomic. Instructions causing multiple accesses (*Load and Store Multiple* and *Move Assist*) are not atomic.

Access Order
> Since the ordering of storage accesses is not guaranteed unless the programmer inserts the appropriate ordering instructions, the order of accesses generated by a single instruction is not guaranteed. Unaligned accesses, *Load and Store Multiple* instructions, and *Move Assist* instructions have no implicit ordering characteristics. For example, processor A may store a word operand on an odd halfword boundary. It may appear to processor A that the store completed atomically. Processor or other mechanism B, executing a load from the same location, may get a result that is a combination of the value of the first halfword that existed prior to the store by processor A and the value of the second halfword stored by processor A.

Storage Control Instructions

The instructions in this chapter are not privileged. For most of them, if the applicable cache is not present the operation is a "no-op" and has no effect on any register or on storage. The only exception is the *dcbz* instruction. When the data cache does not exist, *dcbz* either zeros a certain number of bytes of main storage (which has an effect similar to zeroing bytes in a cache block which are later written to main storage) or invokes the system alignment error handler (so that its function can be simulated).

As with other storage instructions, the effect of the *Cache Management* instructions on storage is weakly consistent. If the programmer needs to ensure that *Cache Management* or other instructions have been performed with respect to all other processors and mechanisms, a *sync* instruction must be placed in the program following those instructions.

3.1 Parameters Useful to Application Programs

It is suggested that the operating system provide a service that allows an application program to obtain the following information.

1. Page size

2. Coherence block size

3. Granule size for reservations

4. An indicator of whether the processor has (a) a combined cache or no caches, or (b) some other cache configuration (split caches or one

cache only; if instruction cache fetches pass through the data cache, the cache is considered to be a split cache)

5. Instruction cache size

6. Data cache size

7. Instruction cache line size (see Book IV, *PowerPC Implementation Features*)

8. Data cache line size (see Book IV)

9. Block size for *icbi* (if no instruction cache, number of bytes zeroed by *dcbz*)

10. Block size for *dcbt* and *dcbtst* (if no data cache, number of bytes zeroed by *dcbz*)

11. Block size for *dcbz*, *dcbst*, *dcbf*, and *dcbi* [see Book III, Section 4.11.1, "Cache Management Instructions," on page 438 for a description of *dcbi* (if no data cache, number of bytes zeroed by *dcbz*)]

12. Instruction cache associativity

13. Data cache associativity

14. Factors for converting the Time Base to seconds

If the caches are combined, the same value should be given for an instruction cache attribute and the corresponding data cache attribute.

3.2 Cache Management Instructions

3.2.1 Instruction Cache Instructions

Instruction caches, if they exist, are not required to be consistent with data caches, storage, or I/O data transfers. Software must use the appropriate *Cache Management* instructions to ensure that instruction caches are kept consistent when instructions are modified by the processor or by input data transfer. When a processor alters a storage location that may be contained in an instruction cache, software must ensure that updates to storage are visible to the instruction-fetching mechanism. Although the instructions to accomplish this vary among implementations and hence many operating systems will provide a system service for this function, the following sequence is typical.

1. *dcbst* — update storage

2. *sync* — wait for update (see Book I, "Synchronize X-form," on page 80)

3. *icbi* — invalidate copy in instruction cache

4. *isync* — perform context synchronization (see Book III, Section 1.7.1, "Context Synchronization," on page 371)

These operations are necessary because the storage may be in Write Through Not Required mode. Since instruction fetching may bypass the data cache, changes made to items in the data cache may not be reflected in storage until after the instruction fetch completes.

Instruction Cache Block Invalidate   X-form

icbi   RA,RB

31	///	RA	RB	982	/
0	6	11	16	21	31

Let the effective address (EA) be the sum (RA|0)+(RB).

If the block containing the byte addressed by EA is in Coherence Required mode, and a block containing the byte addressed by EA is in the instruction cache of any processor, the block is made invalid in all such processors, so that subsequent references cause the block to be refetched.

If the block containing the byte addressed by EA is in Coherence Not Required mode, and a block containing the byte addressed by EA is in the instruction cache of this processor, the block is made invalid in this processor, so that subsequent references cause the block to be refetched.

The function of this instruction is independent of the Write Through Required/Not Required and Caching Inhibited/Allowed modes of the block containing the byte addressed by EA.

It is acceptable for the processor to treat this instruction as a load from the addressed byte with respect to address translation, storage protection, and reference and change recording. Implementations with a combined data and instruction cache treat the *icbi* instruction as a no-op, except that they may invalidate the target block in the instruction caches of other processors if the block is in Memory Coherence Required mode.

If the EA references storage outside of main storage (see Book III, Section 4.6, "Direct-Store Segments," on page 421), the instruction is treated as a no-op.

Special Registers Altered

None

Instruction Synchronize   XL-form

isync

[Power mnemonic: ics]

19	///	///	///	150	/
0	6	11	16	21	31

This instruction waits for all previous instructions to complete and then discards any prefetched instructions, causing subsequent instructions to be fetched (or refetched) from storage and to execute in the context established by the previous instructions. This instruction has no effect on other processors or on their caches.

This instruction is context synchronizing (see Book III, Section 1.7.1, "Context Synchronization," on page 371).

Special Registers Altered
```
None
```

3.2.2 Data Cache Instructions

Data caches and combined caches, if they exist, are required to be consistent with other data caches, combined caches, storage, and I/O data transfers. However, to ensure consistency, aliased effective addresses (two effective addresses that map to the same real address) must have the same page offset (see Section 1.8, "Shared Storage," on page 333).

If the effective address references storage outside of main storage (see Book III, Section 4.6, "Direct-Store Segments," on page 421), the instruction is treated as a no-op.

Programming Note

The purpose of the *dcbt* instruction is to allow the program to request a cache block fetch before it is actually needed by the program. The program can later perform loads to put data into registers. However, the processor is not obliged to load the addressed block into the data cache.

Data Cache Block Touch   X-form

dcbt   RA,RB

31	///	RA	RB	278	/
0	6	11	16	21	31

Let the effective address (EA) be the sum (RA|0)+(RB).

This instruction is a hint that performance will probably be improved if the block containing the byte addressed by EA is fetched into the data cache, because the program will probably soon load from the addressed byte. Executing *dcbt* will not cause the system error handler to be invoked.

It is acceptable for the processor to treat this instruction as a load from the addressed byte with respect to address translation, storage protection, and reference and change recording, except that the system error handler must not be invoked for a translation or protection violation.

Special Registers Altered
    None

Data Cache Block Touch for Store   X-form

dcbtst   RA,RB

31	///	RA	RB	246	/
0	6	11	16	21	31

Let the effective address (EA) be the sum (RA|0)+(RB).

This instruction is a hint that performance will probably be improved if the block containing the byte addressed by EA is fetched into the data cache, because the program will probably soon store into the addressed byte. Executing *dcbtst* will not cause the system error handler to be invoked.

It is acceptable for the processor to treat this instruction as a load from the addressed byte with respect to address translation, storage protection, and reference and change recording, except that the system error handler must not be invoked for a translation or protection violation. Since *dcbtst* does not modify storage, it must not be recorded as a store.

Special Registers Altered
    None

Programming Note

The purpose of the *dcbtst* instruction is to allow the program to request a cache block fetch before it is actually needed by the program. The program can later perform stores to put data into storage. However, the processor is not obliged to load the addressed block into the data cache.

Data Cache Block set to Zero   X-form

dcbz   RA,RB

[Power mnemonic: dclz]

31	///	RA	RB	1014	/
0	6	11	16	21	31

Let the effective address (EA) be the sum (RA|0)+(RB).

If the block containing the byte addressed by EA is in the data cache, all bytes of the block are set to zero.

If the block containing the byte addressed by EA is not in the data cache and the corresponding page is Caching Allowed, the block is

Programming Note

If the page containing
the byte addressed by EA
is Caching Inhibited or
Write Through Required,
the system alignment
error handler should set
to zero all bytes of the
area of main storage that
corresponds to the
addressed block.

See Book III, Section
5.5.2, "Machine Check
Interrupt," on page 459
for discussion of a
possible delayed Machine
Check interrupt that can
be caused by *dcbz* if the
operating system has set
up an incorrect storage
mapping.

established in the data cache without fetching the block from main storage, and all bytes of the block are set to zero.

If the page containing the byte addressed by EA is Caching Inhibited or Write Through Required, then either (a) all bytes of the area of main storage that corresponds to the addressed block are set to zero, or (b) the system alignment error handler is invoked.

If the block containing the byte addressed by EA is in Coherence Required mode, and the block exists in the data cache(s) of any other processor(s), it is kept coherent in those caches.

This instruction is treated as a store to the addressed byte with respect to address translation, storage protection, and reference and change recording.

Special Registers Altered

None

Data Cache Block Store   X-form

dcbst   RA,RB

31	///	RA	RB	54	/
0	6	11	16	21	31

Let the effective address (EA) be the sum (RA|0)+(RB).

If the block containing the byte addressed by EA is in Coherence Required mode, and a block containing the byte addressed by EA is in the data cache of any processor and has been modified, the writing of it to main storage is initiated.

If the block containing the byte addressed by EA is in Coherence Not Required mode, and a block containing the byte addressed by EA is in the data cache of this processor and has been modified, the writing of it to main storage is initiated.

The function of this instruction is independent of the Write Through Required/Not Required and Caching Inhibited/Allowed modes of the block containing the byte addressed by EA.

It is acceptable for the processor to treat this instruction as a load from the addressed byte with respect to address translation, storage protection, and reference and change recording.

Special Registers Altered

None

Data Cache Block Flush   X-form

dcbf   RA,RB

31	///	RA	RB	86	/
0	6	11	16	21	31

Let the effective address (EA) be the sum (RA|0)+(RB).

The action taken depends on the storage mode associated with the target and on the state of the block. The list below describes the action taken for the various cases.

1. Coherence Required

Unmodified Block
    Invalidate copies of the block in the caches of all processors.

Modified Block
    Copy the block to storage. Invalidate copies of the block in the caches of all processors.

Absent Block
    If modified copies of the block are in the caches of other processors, cause them to be copied to storage and invalidated. If unmodified copies are in the caches of other processors, cause those copies to be invalidated.

2. Coherence Not Required

Unmodified Block
    Invalidate the block in the processor's cache.

Modified Block
    Copy the block to storage. Invalidate the block in the processor's cache.

Absent Block
    Do nothing.

The function of this instruction is independent of the Write Through Required/Not Required and Caching Inhibited/Allowed modes of the block containing the byte addressed by EA.

It is acceptable for the processor to treat this instruction as a load from the addressed byte with respect to address translation, storage protection, and reference and change recording.

Special Registers Altered
    None

Book II   PowerPC Virtual Environment Architecture

3.3 Enforce In-order Execution of I/O Instruction

Enforce In-order Execution of I/O   X-form

eieio

31	///	///	///	854	/
0	6	11	16	21	31

The *eieio* instruction provides an ordering function for the effects of loads and stores executed by a processor. Executing an *eieio* instruction ensures that all applicable loads and stores previously initiated by the processor are complete with respect to main storage before any applicable loads and stores subsequently initiated by the processor access main storage.

eieio orders loads and stores to storage that is both Caching Inhibited and Guarded, and stores to storage that is Write Through Required. It orders all these loads and stores as a single set (i.e., there is not one order for loads and stores to Caching Inhibited and Guarded storage, and another order for stores to Write Through Required storage). *eieio* does not affect the order of other data accesses, or of cache operations (whether caused explicitly by execution of a *Cache Management* instruction or implicitly by the cache coherence mechanism).

Special Registers Altered

    None

Time Base

The Time Base (TB) is a 64-bit register (see Figure 48) containing a 64-bit unsigned integer that is incremented periodically. Each increment adds 1 to the low-order bit (bit 63). The frequency at which the integer is updated is implementation-dependent.

TBU	TBL
0 32	63

Field	Description
TBU	Upper 32 bits of Time Base
TBL	Lower 32 bits of Time Base

Figure 48. **Time Base**

The Time Base increments until its value becomes 0xFFFF_FFFF_FFFF_FFFF ($2^{64} - 1$). At the next increment, its value becomes 0x0000_0000_0000_0000. There is no explicit indication (such as an interrupt: see Book III, Chapter 5, "Interrupts," on page 453) that this has occurred.

The period of the Time Base depends on the driving frequency. As an order of magnitude example, suppose that the CPU clock is 100 MHz and that the Time Base is driven by this frequency divided by 32. Then the period of the Time Base would be

$$T_{TB} = \frac{2^{64} \times 32}{100 \text{ MHz}} = 5.90 \times 10^{12} \text{ seconds}$$

which is approximately 187,000 years.

The PowerPC Architecture does not specify a relationship between the frequency at which the Time Base is updated and other frequencies, such as the CPU clock or bus clock, in a PowerPC system. The Time Base update frequency is not required to be constant. What *is* required, so that system software can keep time of day and operate interval timers, is one of the following.

■ The system provides an (implementation-dependent) interrupt to software whenever the update frequency of the Time Base changes, and a means to determine what the current update frequency is.

■ The update frequency of the Time Base is under the control of the system software.

4.1 Time Base Instructions

Extended mnemonics

A pair of extended mnemonics is provided for the *mftb* instruction so that it can be coded with the TBR name as part of the mnemonic rather than as a numeric operand. See Book III, Appendix B, "Assembler Extended Mnemonics," on page 495.

Move From Time Base XFX-form

mftb   RT,TBR

31	RT	tbr	371	/
0	6	11	21	31

```
n ← tbr5:9 ‖ tbr0:4
if n = 268 then
   if (64-bit implementation) then RT ← TB
   else RT ← TB32:63
else if n = 269 then
   if (64-bit implementation) then RT ← 320 ‖ TB0:31
   else RT ← TB0:31
```

The TBR field denotes either the Time Base or Time Base Upper, encoded as shown in Figure 49 on page 353. The contents of the designated register are placed into register RT. When reading Time Base Upper on a 64-bit implementation, the high-order 32 bits of register RT are set to zero.

decimal	TBR*		Register name	Privileged
	$tbr_{5:9}$	$tbr_{0:4}$		
268	01000	01100	TB	no
269	01000	01101	TBU	no

*Note that the order of the two 5-bit halves of the TBR number is reversed.

Figure 49.   **TBR encodings for mftb**

If the TBR field contains any value other than one of the values shown above then one of the following occurs.

■ The system illegal instruction error handler is invoked.

■ The system privileged instruction error handler is invoked.

■ The results are boundedly undefined.

Special Registers Altered

    None

Extended Mnemonics:

Extended mnemonics for *Move From Time Base:*

Extended:	*Equivalent to:*
mftb Rt	mftb Rt,268
mftbu Rt	mftb Rt,269

4.2 Reading the Time Base on 64-bit Implementations

The contents of the Time Base may be read into a GPR by the *mftb* extended mnemonic. To read the contents of the Time Base into register Rx, execute:

    mftb   Rx

Reading the Time Base has no effect on the value it contains or on the periodic incrementing of that value.

Programming Note

mftb serves as both a basic and an extended mnemonic. The assembler will recognize an *mftb* mnemonic with two operands as the basic form, and an *mftb* mnemonic with one operand as the extended form. Another way of saying this is that if *mftb* is coded with one operand, then that operand is assumed to be RT, and TBR defaults to the value corresponding to TB.

Compiler and Assembler Note

The TBR number coded in assembler language does not appear directly as a 10-bit binary number in the instruction. The number coded is split into two 5-bit halves that are reversed in the instruction, with the high-order 5 bits appearing in bits 16:20 of the instruction and the low-order 5 bits in bits 11:15.

4.3 Reading the Time Base on 32-bit Implementations

On 32-bit implementations, it is not possible to read the entire 64-bit Time Base in a single instruction. The *mftb* extended mnemonic moves from the lower half of the Time Base (TBL) to a GPR, and the *mftbu* extended mnemonic moves from the upper half (TBU) to a GPR.

Because of the possibility of a carry from TBL to TBU occurring between reads of TBL and TBU, a sequence such as the following is necessary to read the Time Base on 32-bit implementations.

Programming Note

This sequence also works correctly on a 64-bit implementation running in either 64- or 32-bit mode.

```
loop:
      mftbu   Rx       # load from TBU
      mftb    Ry       # load from TBL
      mftbu   Rz       # load from TBU
      cmpw    Rz,Rx    # see if 'old' = 'new'
      bne     loop     # loop if carry occurred
```

The comparison and loop are necessary to ensure that a consistent pair of values has been obtained.

4.4 Computing Time of Day from the Time Base

Since the update frequency of the Time Base is implementation-dependent, the algorithm for converting the current value in the Time Base to time of day is also implementation-dependent.

As an example, assume that the Time Base is incremented at a constant rate of once for every 32 cycles of a 100 MHz CPU instruction clock. What is wanted is the pair of 32-bit values comprising a POSIX standard clock:[1] the number of whole seconds that have passed since midnight January 0, 1970, and the remaining fraction of a second expressed as a number of nanoseconds.

Assume that:

■ The value 0 in the Time Base represents the start time of the POSIX clock (if this is not true, a simple 64-bit subtraction will make it so).

---

[1] Described in POSIX Draft Standard P1003.4/D12, *Draft Standard for Information Technology — Portable Operating System Interface (POSIX)—Part 1: System Application Program Interface (API) — Amendment 1: Realtime Extension [C Language]*. Institute of Electrical and Electronics Engineers, Inc., February 1992.

■ The integer constant *ticks_per_sec* contains the value

$$\frac{100 \text{ MHz}}{32} = 3{,}125{,}000$$

which is the number of times the Time Base is updated each second.

■ The integer constant *ns_adj* contains the value

$$\frac{1{,}000{,}000{,}000}{3{,}125{,}000} = 320$$

which is the number of nanoseconds per tick of the Time Base.

64-bit Implementations

The POSIX clock can be computed with an instruction sequence such as this:

```
mftb    Ry              # Ry = Time Base
lwz     Rx,ticks_per_sec
divd    Rz,Ry,Rx        # Rz = whole seconds
stw     Rz,posix_sec
mulld   Rz,Rz,Rx        # Rz = quotient * divisor
sub     Rz,Ry,Rz        # Rz = excess ticks
lwz     Rx,ns_adj
mulld   Rz,Rz,Rx        # Rz = excess nanoseconds
stw     Rz,posix_ns
```

32-bit Implementations

On a 32-bit machine, direct implementation of the algorithm given above for 64-bit machines is awkward, due mainly to the difficulty of doing 64-bit division.[1] Such division can be avoided entirely if a time of day clock in POSIX format is updated at least once each second.

Assume that:

■ The operating system maintains the following variables:

— *posix_tb* (64 bits)

— *posix_sec* (32 bits)

— *posix_ns* (32 bits)

---

[1] See D. E. Knuth, *The Art of Computer Programming, Volume 2, Seminumerical Algorithms,* Section 4.3.1, Algorithm D. Addison-Wesley, 1981.

These variables hold the value of the Time Base and the computed POSIX second and nanosecond values from the last time the POSIX clock was computed.

■ The operating system arranges for an interrupt (see Book III, Chapter 5, "Interrupts," on page 453) to occur at least once per second, at which time it recomputes the POSIX clock values.

■ The integer constant *billion* contains the value 1,000,000,000.

The POSIX clock can be computed with an instruction sequence such as this:

```
loop:
        mftbu   Rx              # Rx = TBU
        mftb    Ry              # Ry = TBL
        mftbu   Rz              # Rz = 'new' TBU value
        cmpw    Rz,Rx           # see if 'old' = 'new'
        bne     loop            # loop if carry occurred
#           now have 64-bit TB in Rx and Ry
        lwz     Rz,posix_tb+4
        sub     Rz,Ry,Rz        # Rz = delta in ticks
        lwz     Rw,ns_adj
        mullw   Rz,Rz,Rw        # Rz = delta in ns
        lwz     Rw,posix_ns
        add     Rz,Rz,Rw        # Rz = new ns value
        lwz     Rw,billion
        cmpw    Rz,Rw           # see if past 1 second
        blt     nochange        # branch if not
        sub     Rz,Rz,Rw        # adjust nanoseconds
        lwz     Rw,posix_sec
        addi    Rw,Rw,1         # adjust seconds
        stw     Rw,posix_sec    # store new seconds
nochange:
        stw     Rz,posix_ns     # store new ns
        stw     Rx,posix_tb     # store new time base
        stw     Ry,posix_tb+4
```

Note that the upper half of the Time Base does not participate in the calculation to determine the new POSIX time of day. This is correct as long as the time change does not exceed one second.

Non-constant update frequency

In a system in which the update frequency of the Time Base may change over time, it is not possible to convert an isolated Time Base value into time of day. Instead, a Time Base value has meaning only with respect to the current update frequency and the time of day that the update frequency was last changed. Each time the update frequency changes, either the system software is notified of the change via an interrupt (see Book III, Chapter 5, "Interrupts," on page 453), or the change was instigated by the system software itself. At each such change, the system software must compute the current time of day using the old update frequency, compute a new value of *ticks_per_sec* for the new frequency, and save the time of day, Time Base value, and tick rate. Subsequent calls to compute time of day use the current Time Base value and the saved data.

Cross-Reference for Changed POWER Mnemonics

The following table lists the POWER instruction mnemonics that have been changed in the PowerPC Virtual Environment Architecture, sorted by POWER mnemonic.

To determine the PowerPC mnemonic for one of these POWER mnemonics, find the POWER mnemonic in the second column of the table: the remainder of the line gives the PowerPC mnemonic and the page on which the instruction is described, as well as the instruction names.

POWER mnemonics that have not changed are not listed.

Page	POWER		PowerPC	
	Mnemonic	Instruction	Mnemonic	Instruction
347	dclz	Data Cache Line Set to Zero	dcbz	Data Cache Block set to Zero
346	ics	Instruction Cache Synchronize	isync	Instruction Synchronize

New Instructions

The following instructions in the PowerPC Virtual Environment Architecture are new: they are not in the POWER Architecture. They exist in all PowerPC implementations.

dcbf   Data Cache Block Flush

dcbst   Data Cache Block Store

dcbt   Data Cache Block Touch

dcbtst Data Cache Block Touch for Store

eieio   Enforce In-order Execution of I/O

icbi   Instruction Cache Block Invalidate

mftb   Move From Time Base

PowerPC Virtual Environment Instruction Set

Form	Opcode		Mode Dep.[1]	Page	Mnemonic	Instruction
	Primary	Extended				
X	31	86		349	dcbf	Data Cache Block Flush
X	31	54		348	dcbst	Data Cache Block Store
X	31	278		346	dcbt	Data Cache Block Touch
X	31	246		347	dcbtst	Data Cache Block Touch for Store
X	31	1014		347	dcbz	Data Cache Block set to Zero
X	31	854		350	eieio	Enforce In-order Execution of I/O
X	31	982		345	icbi	Instruction Cache Block Invalidate
XL	19	150		346	isync	Instruction Synchronize
XFX	31	371		352	mftb	Move From Time Base

[1]All instructions in the PowerPC Virtual Environment Architecture are mode-independent, except that if the instruction refers to storage when in 32-bit mode, only the low-order 32 bits of the 64-bit effective address are used to address storage.

Book III

This book describes additional instructions and facilities beyond those of the PowerPC User Instruction Set Architecture and PowerPC Virtual Environment Architecture. It covers instructions and facilities not available to the application programmer, affecting storage control, interrupts, and timing facilities.

PowerPC Operating Environment Architecture

Introduction

1.1 Overview

Chapter 1 of Book I, *PowerPC User Instruction Set Architecture*, describes computation modes, compatibility with the POWER Architecture, document conventions, a general systems overview, instruction formats, and storage addressing. This chapter augments that description as necessary for the PowerPC Operating Environment Architecture.

1.2 Compatibility with the POWER Architecture

The PowerPC Architecture provides binary compatibility for POWER application programs, except as described in Book I, Appendix G, "Incompatibilities with the POWER Architecture," on page 271. Binary compatibility is not necessarily provided for privileged POWER instructions.

1.3 Document Conventions

The notation and terminology used in Book I apply to this Book also, with the following substitutions:

■ For "system alignment error handler" substitute "Alignment interrupt."

■ For "system data storage error handler" substitute "Data Storage interrupt."

- For "system error handler" substitute "interrupt."

- For "system floating-point assist error handler" substitute "Floating-Point Assist interrupt."

- For "system floating-point enabled exception error handler" substitute "Floating-Point Enabled Exception type Program interrupt."

- For "system floating-point unavailable error handler" substitute "Floating-Point Unavailable interrupt."

- For "system illegal instruction error handler" substitute "Illegal Instruction type Program interrupt."

- For "system instruction storage error handler" substitute "Instruction Storage interrupt."

- For "system privileged instruction error handler" substitute "Privileged Instruction type Program interrupt."

- For "system service program" substitute "System Call interrupt."

- For "system trap handler" substitute "Trap type Program interrupt."

1.3.1 Definitions and Notation

The definitions given in Book I are augmented by the following:

- The context of a program is the environment (e.g., privilege and relocation) in which the program executes. That context is controlled by the content of certain system registers, such as the MSR and SDR1, and of the address translation tables.

- An exception is an error, unusual condition, or external signal, that may set a status bit and may or may not cause an interrupt, depending upon whether or not the corresponding interrupt is enabled.

- An interrupt is the act of changing the machine state in response to an exception, as described in Chapter 5, "Interrupts," on page 453.

- A trap interrupt is an interrupt that results from execution of a *Trap* instruction.

- Hardware means any combination of hard-wired implementation, emulation assist, or interrupt for software assistance. In the last case, the interrupt may be to an architected location or to an implementation-dependent location. Any use of emulation assists or interrupts to implement the architecture is described in Book IV, *PowerPC Implementation Features*.

- /, //, ///, ... denotes a field that is reserved in an instruction, in a register, or in an architected storage table.

1.3.2 Reserved Fields

Some fields of certain storage tables may be written to automatically by hardware, e.g., Reference and Change bits in the Page Table. When the hardware writes to such a table, the following rules must be observed:

- No defined field other than the one(s) the hardware is specifically updating may be modified.

- Contents of reserved fields may be preserved by hardware or may be written as 0s. No other changes to reserved fields may be made.

The handling of reserved bits in status and control registers described in Book I, Section 1.5.2, "Reserved Fields," on page 8 applies here as well. The reader should be aware that reading and writing of some of these registers (e.g., the MSR) can occur as a side effect of processing an interrupt and of returning from an interrupt, as well as when requested explicitly by the appropriate instruction (e.g., *mtmsr*).

Programming Note

System software should initialize reserved fields in architected storage tables (Segment Table, Page Table) to 0s and not keep data in them, as the fields may be assigned a meaning in some future version of the architecture.

1.3.3 Description of Instruction Operation

The following augments the definitions given in Book I, Section 1.5.3, "Description of Instruction Operation," on page 8.

Notation	Meaning
SEGREG(x)	Segment Register x

1.4 General Systems Overview

The processor or processor unit contains the sequencing and processing controls for instruction fetch, instruction execution, and interrupt action. Instructions that the processing unit can execute fall into three classes:

- instructions executed in the Branch Processor

- instructions executed in the Fixed-Point Processor

- instructions executed in the Floating-Point Processor

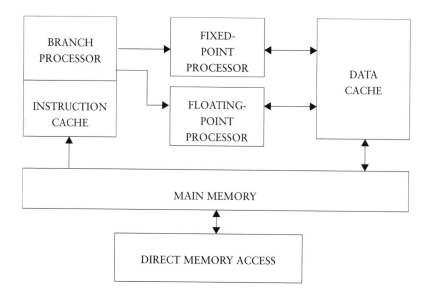

Figure 50.   **Logical view of the PowerPC processor architecture**

Almost all instructions executed in the Branch Processor, Fixed-Point Processor, and Floating-Point Processor are nonprivileged and are described in Book I, *PowerPC User Instruction Set Architecture*. Book II, *PowerPC Virtual Environment Architecture* contains some cache management instructions. Instructions related to the privileged state of the processor, control of processor resources, control of the storage hierarchy, and all other privileged instructions are described here or in Book IV, *PowerPC Implementation Features*.

1.5 Instruction Formats

See Book I, Chapter 1, "Introduction," on page 3 for a description of the instruction formats and addressing.

1.5.1 Instruction Fields

The following augments the instruction fields described in Book I, Section 1.7.1, "Instruction Fields," on page 19.

SPR (11:20)
Field used to specify a Special Purpose Register for the *mtspr* and *mfspr* instructions. The encoding is described in Section 3.4.1, "Move to/ from System Register Instructions," on page 384.

SR (12:15)
Field used to specify one of the 16 Segment Registers.

1.6 Exceptions

The following augments the list, given in Book I, Section 1.10, "Exceptions," on page 26, of exceptions that can be caused directly by the execution of an instruction.

■ the execution of a *Load* or *Store* instruction to a direct-store segment that causes a Direct-Store Error exception (Data Storage interrupt)

■ the execution of a traced instruction (Trace interrupt)

1.7 Synchronization

The synchronization described in this section refers to the state of the processor that is performing the synchronization.

1.7.1 Context Synchronization

An instruction or event is "context synchronizing" if it satisfies the requirements listed below. Such instructions and events are collectively called "context synchronizing operations." Examples of context synchronizing operations include the *sc* instruction, the *rfi* instruction, and most interrupts.

1. The operation causes instruction dispatching (the issuance of instructions by the instruction fetch mechanism to any instruction execution mechanism) to be halted.

2. The operation is not initiated or, in the case of *isync,* is not completed, until all instructions already in execution have completed to a point at which they have reported all exceptions they will cause. (If a storage access due to a previously initiated instruction may cause one or more Direct-Store Error exceptions, the determination of whether it does cause such exceptions is made before the operation is initiated.)

3. The instructions that precede the operation will complete execution in the context (privilege, relocation, storage protection, etc.) in which they were initiated.

4. If the operation directly causes an interrupt (e.g., *sc* directly causes a System Call interrupt) or is an interrupt, the operation is not initiated until no exception exists having higher priority than the exception associated with the interrupt (see Section 5.8, "Interrupt Priorities," on page 475).

5. The instructions that follow the operation will be fetched and executed in the context established by the operation. (This requirement dictates that any prefetched instructions be discarded, which in turn requires that any effects and side effects of speculatively executing them also be discarded. The only side effects of these instructions that are permitted to survive are those specified in Section 4.2.5, "Speculative Execution," on page 396.)

A context synchronizing operation is necessarily execution synchronizing; see Section 1.7.2, "Execution Synchronization." Unlike the *sync* instruction [see Book II, page 334 (under Synchronize)], a context synchronizing operation need not wait for storage-related operations to complete on other processors, nor for Reference and Change bits in the Page Table (see Section 4, "Storage Control," on page 391) to be updated.

1.7.2 Execution Synchronization

An instruction is "execution synchronizing" if all previously initiated instructions appear to have completed before the instruction is initiated or, in the case of *sync* and *isync*, before the instruction completes. Examples of execution synchronizing instructions are *sync* (see Book I, page 80) and *mtmsr*. Also, all context synchronizing instructions (see Section 1.7.1) are execution synchronizing.

Unlike a context synchronizing operation, an execution synchronizing instruction need not ensure that the instructions following that instruction will execute in the context established by that instruction. This new context becomes effective sometime after the execution synchronizing instruction completes and before or at a subsequent context synchronizing operation.

Branch Processor

2.1 Branch Processor Overview

This chapter describes the details concerning the registers and the privileged instructions implemented in the Branch Processor that are not covered in Book I, *PowerPC User Instruction Set Architecture*.

2.2 Branch Processor Registers

2.2.1 Machine Status Save/Restore Register 0

The Machine Status Save/Restore Register 0 (SRR0) is a 64-bit {32-bit} register. This register is used to save machine status on interrupts, and to restore machine status when a *Return From Interrupt* (*rfi*) instruction is executed.

On interrupt, SRR0 is set to the current or next instruction address. Thus if the interrupt occurs in 32-bit mode, the high-order 32 bits of SRR0 are set to 0. When *rfi* is executed, the contents of SRR0 are copied to the next instruction address (NIA), except that the high-order 32 bits of the NIA are set to 0 when returning to 32-bit mode.

Programming Note

In some implementations, every instruction fetch when MSR_{IR}=1, and every instruction execution requiring address translation when MSR_{DR}=1, may have the side effect of modifying SRR0 and SRR1. For further details, see the Book IV, *PowerPC Implementation Features*, document for the implementation.

SRR0	//

0　　　　　　　　　　　　　　　　　　　　　　　61　63

0　　　　　　　　　　　　　　　　　　　　　　{29}　{31}

Figure 51.　**Save/Restore Register 0**

In general, SRR0 contains either the instruction address that caused the interrupt or the instruction address to return to after an interrupt is serviced.

2.2.2 Machine Status Save/Restore Register 1

The Machine Status Save/Restore Register 1 (SRR1) is a 64-bit {32-bit} register. This register is used to save machine status on interrupts and to restore machine status when an *rfi* instruction is executed.

SRR1

0　　　　　　　　　　　　　　　　　　　　　　　　　　63 {31}

Figure 52.　**Save/Restore Register 1**

In general, when an interrupt occurs, bits 33:36 and 42:47 {1:4 and 10:15} of SRR1 are loaded with information specific to the interrupt type, and bits 0:32, 37:41, and 48:63 {0, 5:9, and 16:31} of the MSR are placed into the corresponding bit positions of SRR1.

2.2.3 Machine State Register

The Machine State Register (MSR) is a 64-bit {32-bit} register. This register defines the state of the processor. On interrupt, the MSR bits are altered in accordance with Figure 80 on page 458. The MSR can also be modified by the *mtmsr*, *sc*, and *rfi* instructions. It can be read by the *mfmsr* instruction.

MSR

0　　　　　　　　　　　　　　　　　　　　　　　　　　63 {31}

Figure 53.　**Machine State Register**

Below are shown the bit definitions for the Machine State Register. The notation "full function" on a reserved bit means that it is saved in SRR1 when an interrupt occurs. The notation "partial function" means that it is not saved.

Bit(s)	Description

0   **64-bit mode** (SF)

     0   The processor runs in 32-bit mode.

     1   The processor runs in 64-bit mode.

1:32 {0}   Reserved full function

33:36{1:4}   Reserved partial function

37:41{5:9}   Reserved full function

42:44{10:12}   Reserved partial function

45{13}   **Power Management Enable** (POW)

     0   Power management is disabled (normal operation mode).

     1   Power management is enabled (reduced power mode).

     Power management functions are implementation-dependent. For further descriptions of the effect of this bit, see the Book IV, *PowerPC Implementation Features* document for the implementation.

46{14}   Implementation-Dependent Function

     See the Book IV, *PowerPC Implementation Features* document for the implementation.

47 {15}   **Interrupt Little-Endian Mode** (ILE)
     When an interrupt is taken, this bit is copied into MSR_{LE} to select the Endian mode for the context established by the interrupt.

48{16}   **External Interrupt Enable** (EE)

     0   The processor is disabled against External and Decrementer interrupts.

     1   The processor is enabled to take an External or Decrementer interrupt.

49{17} *Problem State* (PR)

    0   The processor is privileged to execute any instruction.

    1   The processor can only execute the non-privileged instructions.

MSR$_{PR}$ also affects storage protection, as described in Chapter 4, "Storage Control," on page 391.

50{18} *Floating-Point Available* (FP)

    0   The processor cannot execute any floating-point instructions, including floating-point loads, stores, and moves.

    1   The processor can execute floating-point instructions.

51{19} *Machine Check Enable* (ME)

    0   Machine Check interrupts are disabled.

    1   Machine Check interrupts are enabled.

52{20} *Floating-Point Exception Mode 0* (FE0)

See the description on page 378.

53{21} *Single-Step Trace Enable* (SE)

    0   The processor executes instructions normally.

    1   The processor generates a Single-Step type Trace interrupt after successfully completing the execution of the next instruction (unless that instruction is *rfi*, which is never traced). Successful completion means that the instruction caused no other interrupt. See Book IV, *PowerPC Implementation Features*.

Single-step tracing may not be present on all implementations. If the function is not implemented, MSR$_{SE}$ is treated as a reserved bit.

54{22} *Branch Trace Enable* (BE)

    0   The processor executes branch instructions normally.

    1   The processor generates a Branch type Trace interrupt after completing the execution of a branch instruction, whether or not the branch is taken. See Book IV, *PowerPC Implementation Features*.

Branch tracing may not be present on all implementations. If the function is not implemented, MSR$_{BE}$ is treated as a reserved MSR bit.

Programming Note

POWER-compatible operating systems will probably write the value 1 to bit 56{24}.

55{23} *Floating-Point Exception Mode 1* (FE1)

See the description on page 378.

56 {24} Reserved full function

57{25} *Interrupt Prefix* (IP)

In the following description, **nnnnn** is the offset of the interrupt. See Figure 81 on page 459.

  0 Interrupts are vectored to the real address 0x000n_nnnn in 32-bit implementations and real address 0x0000_0000_000n_nnnn in 64-bit implementations.

  1 Interrupts are vectored to the real address 0xFFFn_nnnn in 32-bit implementations and real address 0xFFFF_FFFF_FFFn_nnnn in 64 bit implementations.

58{26} *Instruction Relocate* (IR)

  0 Instruction address translation is off.

  1 Instruction address translation is on.

59{27} *Data Relocate* (DR)

  0 Data address translation is off.

  1 Data address translation is on.

60:61 {28:29} Reserved full function

62{30} *Recoverable Interrupt* (RI)

  0 Interrupt is not recoverable.

  1 Interrupt is recoverable.

Additional information about the use of this bit is given in Sections 5.4, "Interrupt Processing," on page 456, 5.5.1, "System Reset Interrupt," on page 457, and 5.5.2, "Machine Check Interrupt," on page 459.

63{31} *Little-Endian Mode* (LE)

  0 The processor runs in Big-Endian mode.

  1 The processor runs in Little-Endian mode.

The Floating-Point Exception Mode bits FE0 and FE1 are interpreted as shown below. For further details see Book I, page 153.

FE0	FE1	Mode
0	0	Interrupts disabled
0	1	Imprecise Nonrecoverable
1	0	Imprecise Recoverable
1	1	Precise

2.3 Branch Processor Instructions

2.3.1 System Linkage Instructions

These instructions provide the means by which a program can call upon the system to perform a service, and by which the system can return from performing a service or from processing an interrupt.

These instructions are context synchronizing, as defined in Section 1.7.1, "Context Synchronization," on page 371.

The *System Call* instruction is described in Book I, page 41, but only at the level required by an application programmer. A complete description of this instruction appears below.

System Call SC-form

sc

[Power mnemonic: svca]

Compatibility Note

For a discussion of POWER compatibility with respect to instruction bits 16:29, please refer to Book I, Appendix G, "Incompatibilities with the POWER Architecture," on page 271. For compatibility with future versions of this architecture, these bits should be coded as zero.

17	///	///	///	1	/
0	6	11	16	30	31

$$SRR0 \leftarrow_{iea} CIA + 4$$
$$SRR1_{33:36\ 42:47\{1:4\ 10:15\}} \leftarrow 0$$
$$SRR1_{0:32\ 37:41\ 48:63\{0\ 5:9\ 16:31\}} \leftarrow MSR_{0:32\ 37:41\ 48:63\ \{0\ 5:9\ 16:31\}}$$
$$MSR \leftarrow new\_value\ (see\ below)$$
$$NIA \leftarrow_{iea} base\_ea + 0xC00\ (see\ below)$$

The effective address of the instruction following the *System Call* instruction is placed into SRR0. Bits 0:32, 37:41, and 48:63 {0, 5:9, and 16:31} of the MSR are placed into the corresponding bits of SRR1, and bits 33:36 and 42:47 {1:4 and 10:15} of SRR1 are set to undefined values.

Then a System Call interrupt is generated. The interrupt causes the MSR to be altered as described in Section 5.5, "Interrupt Definitions," on page 457.

The interrupt causes the next instruction to be fetched from offset 0xC00 from the base real address indicated by the new setting of MSR_{IP}.

This instruction is context synchronizing.

Special Registers Altered

```
SRR0 SRR1 MSR
```

Return From Interrupt XL-form

rfi

19	///	///	///	50	/
0	6	11	16	21	31

$MSR_{0:32\ 37:41\ 48:63\ \{0\ 5:9\ 16:31\}} \leftarrow SRR1_{0:32\ 37:41\ 48:63\ \{0\ 5:9\ 16:31\}}$
$NIA \leftarrow_{iea} SRR0_{0:61\ \{0:29\}} \parallel 0b00$

Bits 0:32, 37:41, and 48:63 {0, 5:9, and 16:31} of SRR1 are placed into the corresponding bits of the MSR. If the new MSR value does not enable any pending exceptions, then the next instruction is fetched, under control of the new MSR value, from the address $SRR0_{0:61\{0:29\}}\parallel0b00$ (32-bit implementations, and 64-bit implementations when SF=1 in the new MSR value) or $^{32}0\parallel SRR0_{32:61}\parallel0b00$ (64-bit implementations when SF=0 in the new MSR value). If the new MSR value enables one or more pending exceptions, the interrupt associated with the highest priority pending exception is generated; in this case the value placed into SRR0 by the interrupt processing mechanism (see Section 5.4, "Interrupt Processing," on page 456) is the address of the instruction that would have been executed next had the interrupt not occurred.

This instruction is privileged and context synchronizing.

Special Registers Altered

```
MSR
```

Fixed-Point Processor 3

3.1 Fixed-Point Processor Overview

This chapter describes the details concerning the registers and the privileged instructions implemented in the Fixed-Point Processor that are not covered in Book I, *PowerPC User Instruction Set Architecture*.

3.2 PowerPC Special Purpose Registers

The Special Purpose Registers are read and written via the *mfspr* (page 387) and *mtspr* (page 384) instructions. The descriptions of these instructions list the valid encodings of SPR numbers. Encodings not listed are reserved for future use or for use as implementation-specific registers.

Most SPRs are defined in other parts of this book; see the index to locate those definitions. Some SPRs are specific to an implementation. See Appendix E, "Implementation-Specific SPRs," on page 501 and Book IV, *PowerPC Implementation Features*.

3.3 Fixed-Point Processor Registers

3.3.1 Data Address Register

The Data Address Register (DAR) is a 64-bit {32-bit} register. See Section 5.5.3, "Data Storage Interrupt," on page 460 and Section 5.5.6, "Alignment Interrupt," on page 464.

When an interrupt that uses the DAR occurs, the DAR is set to the effective address associated with the interrupting instruction. If the interrupt occurs in 32-bit mode, the high-order 32 bits of the DAR are set to 0.

DAR
0   63 {31}

Figure 54.   Data Address Register

3.3.2 Data Storage Interrupt Status Register

The Data Storage Interrupt Status Register (DSISR) is a 32-bit register that defines the cause of Data Storage and Alignment interrupts. See Section 5.5.3, "Data Storage Interrupt," on page 460 and Section 5.5.6, "Alignment Interrupt," on page 464.

DSISR
0   31

Figure 55.   Data Storage Interrupt Status Register

3.3.3 Software-Use SPRs

SPRG0 through SPRG3 are 64-bit {32-bit} registers provided for operating system use.

SPRG0
SPRG1
SPRG2
SPRG3
0   63 {31}

Figure 56.   Software-use SPRs

The following list describes the conventional uses of SPRG0 through SPRG3.

SPRG0   Software may load a unique real address in this register to identify an area of storage reserved for use by the first-level interrupt handler. This area must be unique for each processor in the system.

SPRG1   This register may be used as a scratch register by the first-level interrupt handler to save the contents of a GPR. That GPR then can be loaded from SPRG0 and used as a base register to save other GPRs to storage.

SPRG2   This register may be used by the operating system as needed.

SPRG3   This register may be used by the operating system as needed.

3.3.4 Processor Version Register

The Processor Version Register is a 32-bit read-only register that contains a value identifying the specific version (model) and revision level of the PowerPC processor. The contents of the PVR can be copied to a GPR by the *mfspr* instruction. Read access to the PVR is privileged; write access is not provided.

Version	Revision
0	16 31

Figure 57.   **Processor Version Register**

The PVR contains two fields:

Version   A 16-bit number that uniquely determines a particular processor version and a version of the PowerPC Architecture. This number can be used to determine the version of a processor; it may not distinguish between different product models if more than one model uses the same processor.

Revision   A 16-bit number that distinguishes between various releases of a particular version, i.e., an Engineering Change level.

The value of the Version portion of the PVR is assigned by the PowerPC Architecture process. The value of the Revision portion of the PVR is implementation-defined.

3.4 Fixed-Point Processor Privileged Instructions

3.4.1 Move to/from System Register Instructions

The *Move To Special Purpose Register* and *Move From Special Purpose Register* instructions are described in Book I, Section 3.3.14, "Move to/from System Register Instructions," on page 128, but only at the level available to an application programmer. In particular, no mention is made there of registers that can be accessed only in privileged state. A complete description of these instructions appears below.

Extended mnemonics

A set of extended mnemonics is provided for the *mtspr* and *mfspr* instructions so that they can be coded with the SPR name as part of the mnemonic rather than as a numeric operand. See Appendix B, "Assembler Extended Mnemonics," on page 495.

Move To Special Purpose Register   XFX-form

mtspr   SPR,RS

31	RS	spr	467	/
0	6	11	21	31

```
n = spr_{5:9} || spr_{0:4}
if length(SPREG(n)) = 64 then
    SPREG(n) ← (RS)
else
    SPREG(n) ← (RS)_{32:63{0:31}}
```

The SPR field denotes a Special Purpose Register, encoded as shown in Figure 58 on page 385. The contents of register RS are placed into the designated Special Purpose Register. For Special Purpose Registers that are 32 bits long, the low-order 32 bits of RS are placed into the SPR.

For this instruction, SPRs TBL and TBU are treated as separate 32-bit registers; setting one leaves the other unaltered.

$spr_0=1$ if and only if writing the register is privileged. Execution of this instruction specifying a defined and privileged register when $MSR_{PR}=1$ will result in a Privileged Instruction type Program interrupt.

If $MSR_{PR}=1$, the only effect of executing this instruction with an SPR number that is not shown in Figure 58 and has $spr_0=1$ is to cause either an Illegal Instruction type Program interrupt or a Privileged Instruction type Program interrupt. For all other cases ($MSR_{PR}=0$ or $spr_0=0$), if the SPR field contains any value that is not shown in Figure 58 then either an Illegal Instruction type Program interrupt occurs or the results are boundedly undefined.

Special Registers Altered

See Figure 58

decimal	SPR[1] $spr_{5:9}$ $spr_{0:4}$	Register name	Privileged
1	00000 00001	XER	no
8	00000 01000	LR	no
9	00000 01001	CTR	no
18	00000 10010	DSISR	yes
19	00000 10011	DAR	yes
22	00000 10110	DEC	yes
25	00000 11001	SDR1	yes
26	00000 11010	SRR0	yes
27	00000 11011	SRR1	yes
272	01000 10000	SPRG0	yes
273	01000 10001	SPRG1	yes
274	01000 10010	SPRG2	yes
275	01000 10011	SPRG3	yes
280	01000 11000	ASR[2]	yes
282	01000 11010	EAR	yes
284	01000 11100	TBL	yes
285	01000 11101	TBU	yes

Figure 58.   **SPR encodings for mtspr**

Compiler and Assembler Note

For the *mtspr* and *mfspr* instructions, the SPR number coded in assembler language does not appear directly as a 10-bit binary number in the instruction. The number coded is split into two 5-bit halves that are reversed in the instruction, with the high-order 5 bits appearing in bits 16:20 of the instruction and the low-order 5 bits in bits 11:15. This maintains compatibility with POWER SPR encodings, in which these two instructions have only a 5-bit SPR field occupying bits 11:15.

Programming Note

For a discussion of software synchronization requirements when altering certain Special Purpose Registers, please refer to Chapter 7, "Synchronization Requirements for Special Registers and for Lookaside Buffers," on page 483.

Compatibility Note

For a discussion of POWER compatibility with respect to SPR numbers not shown in the instruction descriptions for *mtspr* and *mfspr*, please refer to Book I, Appendix G, "Incompatibilities with the POWER Architecture," on page 271. For compatibility with future versions of this architecture, only SPR numbers discussed in these instruction descriptions should be used.

decimal	SPR[1] $spr_{5:9} \; spr_{0:4}$		Register name	Privileged
528	10000 10000		IBAT0U	yes
529	10000 10001		IBAT0L	yes
530	10000 10010		IBAT1U	yes
531	10000 10011		IBAT1L	yes
532	10000 10100		IBAT2U	yes
533	10000 10101		IBAT2L	yes
534	10000 10110		IBAT3U	yes
535	10000 10111		IBAT3L	yes
536	10000 11000		DBAT0U	yes
537	10000 11001		DBAT0L	yes
538	10000 11010		DBAT1U	yes
539	10000 11011		DBAT1L	yes
540	10000 11100		DBAT2U	yes
541	10000 11101		DBAT2L	yes
542	10000 11110		DBAT3U	yes
543	10000 11111		DBAT3L	yes

[1]Note that the order of the two 5-bit halves of the SPR number is reversed.
[2]64-bit implementations only.

Figure 58. **SPR encodings for mtspr**

Move From Special Purpose Register   XFX-form

**Compiler/Assembler/
Compatibility Notes**

See the Notes that
appear with *mtspr*.

mfspr   RT,SPR

31	RT	spr	339	/
0	6	11	21	31

```
n ← spr_{5:9} ∥ spr_{0:4}
if length(SPREG(n)) = 64 then
    RT ← SPREG(n)
else
    RT ← ^{32}0 ∥ SPREG(n)
```

The SPR field denotes a Special Purpose Register, encoded as shown in Figure 59. The contents of the designated Special Purpose Register are placed into register RT. For Special Purpose Registers that are 32 bits long, the low-order 32 bits of RT receive the contents of the Special Purpose Register and the high-order 32 bits of RT are set to zero.

spr_0=1 if and only if reading the register is privileged. Execution of this instruction specifying a defined and privileged register when MSR_{PR}=1 will result in a Privileged Instruction type Program interrupt.

If MSR_{PR}=1, the only effect of executing this instruction with an SPR number that is not shown in Figure 59 and has spr_0=1 is to cause either an Illegal Instruction type Program interrupt or a Privileged Instruction type Program interrupt. For all other cases (MSR_{PR}=0 or spr_0=0), if the SPR field contains any value that is not shown in Figure 59 then either an Illegal Instruction type Program interrupt occurs or the results are boundedly undefined.

Special Registers Altered

```
None
```

decimal	SPR[1] $spr_{5:9}$ $spr_{0:4}$	Register name	Privileged
1	00000 00001	XER	no
8	00000 01000	LR	no
9	00000 01001	CTR	no
18	00000 10010	DSISR	yes
19	00000 10011	DAR	yes
22	00000 10110	DEC	yes

Figure 59.   **SPR encodings for mfspr**

decimal	SPR[1] spr$_{5:9}$ spr$_{0:4}$	Register name	Privileged
25	00000 11001	SDR1	yes
26	00000 11010	SRR0	yes
27	00000 11011	SRR1	yes
272	01000 10000	SPRG0	yes
273	01000 10001	SPRG1	yes
274	01000 10010	SPRG2	yes
275	01000 10011	SPRG3	yes
280	01000 11000	ASR[2]	yes
282	01000 11010	EAR	yes
287	01000 11111	PVR	yes
528	10000 10000	IBAT0U	yes
529	10000 10001	IBAT0L	yes
530	10000 10010	IBAT1U	yes
531	10000 10011	IBAT1L	yes
532	10000 10100	IBAT2U	yes
533	10000 10101	IBAT2L	yes
534	10000 10110	IBAT3U	yes
535	10000 10111	IBAT3L	yes
536	10000 11000	DBAT0U	yes
537	10000 11001	DBAT0L	yes
538	10000 11010	DBAT1U	yes
539	10000 11011	DBAT1L	yes
540	10000 11100	DBAT2U	yes
541	10000 11101	DBAT2L	yes
542	10000 11110	DBAT3U	yes
543	10000 11111	DBAT3L	yes

[1]Note that the order of the two 5-bit halves of the SPR number is reversed.
[2]64-bit implementations only.
Moving from the Time Base (TB and TBU) is accomplished with the ***mftb*** instruction, described in Book II, Section 4.1, "Time Base Instructions," on page 352.

Figure 59.   **SPR encodings for mfspr**

Move To Machine State Register   X-form

mtmsr   RS

31	RS	///	///	146	/
0	6	11	16	21	31

MSR ← (RS)

The contents of register RS are placed into the MSR.

This instruction is privileged and execution synchronizing.

In addition, alterations to the EE and RI bits are effective as soon as the instruction completes. Thus if MSR_{EE}=0 and an External or Decrementer interrupt is pending, executing an *mtmsr* instruction that sets MSR_{EE} to 1 will cause the External or Decrementer interrupt to be taken before the next instruction is executed if no higher priority exception exists (see Section 5.8, "Interrupt Priorities," on page 475).

Special Registers Altered

MSR

Move From Machine State Register   X-form

mfmsr   RT

31	RT	///	///	83	/
0	6	11	16	21	31

RT ← MSR

The contents of the MSR are placed into register RT.

This instruction is privileged.

Special Registers Altered

None

Programming Note

For a discussion of software synchronization requirements when altering certain MSR bits, please refer to Chapter 7, "Synchronization Requirements for Special Registers and for Lookaside Buffers," on page 483.

Storage Control

4.1 Storage Addressing

A program references storage using the effective address computed by the processor when it executes a load, store, branch, or cache instruction, and when it fetches the next sequential instruction. The effective address is translated to a real address according to procedures described in Section 4.3, "Address Translation Overview," on page 399 and following. The real address is what is sent to the memory subsystem. See Figure 60 on page 400.

For a complete discussion of storage addressing and effective address calculation, see Book I, Section 1.11, "Storage Addressing," on page 27.

Storage Control Overview

■ Page size is 2^{12} bytes (4 KB)

■ Segment size is 2^{28} bytes (256 MB)

■ 64-bit implementations:

— Maximum real memory size is 2^{64} bytes (16 EB)

— Effective Address Range is 2^{64}

— Virtual Address Range is 2^{80}

— Number of segments is 2^{52}

■ 32-bit implementations:

— Maximum real memory size is 2^{32} bytes (4 GB)

— Effective Address Range is 2^{32}

— Virtual Address Range is 2^{52}

— Number of segments is 2^{24}

■ There are two types of storage segments, based on the state of the T bit in the Segment Table Entry or Segment Register selected by the effective address:

— T=0: Ordinary segment

— T=1: Direct-store segment

4.2 Storage Model

The storage model provides the following features:

1. The architecture allows the storage implementations to take advantage of the performance benefits of weak ordering of storage access between processors or between processors and devices.

2. The architecture provides instructions that allow the programmer to ensure a consistent and ordered storage state.

■ *dcbf*	■ *lwarx*
■ *dcbst*	■ *eieio*
■ *dcbz*	■ *stdcx.*
■ *icbi*	■ *stwcx.*
■ *isync*	■ *sync*
■ *ldarx*	■ *tblsync*

3. Processor ordering: storage accesses by a single processor appear to complete sequentially from the view of the programming model but may complete out of order with respect to the ultimate destination in the storage hierarchy. Order is guaranteed at each level of the storage hierarchy for accesses to the same address from the same processor.

4. Storage consistency between processors and between a processor and I/O is controlled by software through mode bits in the Page Table or BAT register. See Section 4.8.2, "Supported Storage Modes," on page 431. Six modes are supported using the control bits:

■ Write Through

■ Caching Inhibited

■ Memory Coherence

4.2.1 Storage Segments

Storage is divided into 256 MB (2^{28}) segments. These segments can be of
two types:

■ *ordinary segment*
Address translation is controlled by the setting of the relocate bits
MSR_{DR} for data and MSR_{IR} for instructions. MSR_{IR} and MSR_{DR} are
independent bits and may be set differently. The state of these bits may
be changed by interrupts or by executing the appropriate instructions.
An effective address in these segments represents a real or virtual
address depending on the setting of the relocate bits of the MSR.

■ *direct-store segment*
Such segments may be used for access to I/O. Instruction fetch from
direct-store segments is not allowed. MSR_{DR} must be 1 when accessing data in a direct-store segment. See Section 4.6, "Direct-Store Segments," on page 421 for an explanation of direct-store segments.

The value of the T bit in the Segment Table Entry or Segment Register
distinguishes between ordinary segments and direct-store segments.

Programming Note

It is possible to provide
larger segments to
application programs by
using multiple adjacent
segments.

T	Segment type
0	Ordinary segment
1	Direct-store segment

The T bit in the Segment Table Entry or Segment Register is ignored
when fetching instructions with $MSR_{IR}=0$ or when accessing data with
$MSR_{DR}=0$. Such accesses are not considered references to direct-store
segments.
See also Section 4.6, "Direct-Store Segments," on page 421.

4.2.2 Storage Exceptions

If the appropriate relocate bit in the MSR is set to 1, each effective
address is translated to a real address before the storage access is performed. A *storage exception* occurs if the effective address is not trans-

lated by the Block Address Translation mechanism (see Section 4.7, "Block Address Translation," on page 423), and one of the following applies:

64-bit implementations:

- There is no valid entry in the Segment Table for the segment specified by the effective address.

- The appropriate Segment Table entry is found, but there is no valid entry in the Page Table for the page specified by the effective address.

- The appropriate Segment Table and Page Table entries are found, but the access is not allowed by the storage protection mechanism.

32-bit implementations:

- There is no valid entry in the Page Table for the page specified by the effective address.

- The appropriate Page Table entry is found but the access is not allowed by the storage protection mechanism.

Storage exceptions cause Instruction Storage interrupts and Data Storage interrupts that identify the address of the failing instruction.

In certain cases a storage exception may result in the "restart" of (re-execution of at least part of) a load or store instruction. See Book II, Section 2.1, "Instruction Restart," on page 341.

4.2.3 Instruction Fetch

Instructions are fetched under control of MSR_{IR}. When any context synchronizing event occurs, any prefetched instructions are discarded and then refetched using the then-current state of MSR_{IR}.

$MSR_{IR}=0$

When instruction relocation is off, $MSR_{IR}=0$, the effective address is interpreted as described in Section 4.2.7, "Real Addressing Mode," on page 399.

$MSR_{IR}=1$

Instructions are fetched using the address translated by one of the following mechanisms:

1. Segmented Address Translation Mechanism

2. Block Address Translation Mechanism

Instruction fetch from direct-store segments is not supported. An attempt to execute an instruction in a direct-store segment will result in an Instruction Storage interrupt.

Implicit Branch

Explicitly altering certain MSR bits (using *mtmsr*), or explicitly altering Segment Table Entries, Page Table Entries, or certain system registers, may have the side effect of changing the addresses, effective or real, from which the current instruction stream is being fetched. This side effect is called an *implicit branch*. For example, an *mtmsr* instruction that changes the value of MSR_{SF} may change the effective addresses from which the current instruction stream is being fetched. The MSR bits and system registers for which alteration can cause an implicit branch are indicated as such in Chapter 7, "Synchronization Requirements for Special Registers and for Lookaside Buffers," on page 483. Implicit branches are not supported by the PowerPC Architecture. If an implicit branch occurs, the results are boundedly undefined.

4.2.4 Data Storage Access

Data accesses are controlled by MSR_{DR}. When the state of MSR_{DR} changes, subsequent accesses are made using the new state of MSR_{DR}.

$MSR_{DR}=0$
When data relocation is off, $MSR_{DR}=0$, the effective address is interpreted as described in Section 4.2.7, "Real Addressing Mode," on page 399.

$MSR_{DR}=1$
When address relocation is on, $MSR_{DR}=1$, the effective address is translated by one of the following mechanisms:

1. Segmented Address Translation Mechanism

2. Block Address Translation Mechanism

3. Direct-Store Segment Translation Mechanism

4.2.5 Speculative Execution

Data Access

A *speculative operation* is one that a program "might" perform and that the hardware decides to execute out of order on the *speculation* that the result will be needed. If subsequent events indicate that the speculative instruction would not have been executed, the processor abandons any result the instruction produced. Typically, hardware executes instructions speculatively when it has resources that would otherwise be idle, so that the operation is done without cost or almost so.

Most operations can be performed speculatively, as long as the machine appears to follow a simple sequential model such as that presented in Book I, Section 2.2, "Instruction Fetching," on page 31. Certain speculative operations are not permitted:

■ A speculative store may not be performed in such a manner that the alteration of the target location can be observed by other processors or mechanisms until it can be determined that the store is no longer speculative.

■ Speculative loads from Guarded storage (see below) are prohibited, except that if a load or store operation will be executed, the entire cache block(s) containing the referenced data may be loaded into the cache.

■ No error of any kind other than Machine Check may be reported due to the speculative execution of an instruction, until such time as it is known that execution of the instruction is required.

Speculative loads are allowed from any storage that is not Guarded. If a Machine Check exception results, a Machine Check interrupt may be generated even if the data access that caused the Machine Check exception would not have been performed because a previous uncompleted operation would have changed the execution path.

Only one side effect (other than Machine Check) of speculative execution is permitted when a speculative instruction's result is abandoned: the Reference bit(s) in the referenced Page Table Entry(s) may be set due to a speculative load.

Instruction Prefetch

The processor typically fetches instructions ahead of the one(s) currently being executed in order to avoid delay. Such *instruction prefetching* is a speculative operation in that prefetched instructions may not be executed due to intervening branches or interrupts.

Most prefetching is permitted, as long as the machine appears to follow a simple sequential model such as that presented in Book I, Section 2.2, "Instruction Fetching," on page 31. Certain prefetching is not permitted:

■ Prefetching from Guarded storage (see below) is prohibited, except that if an instruction in a cache block will be executed, the entire cache block may be loaded into the cache.

■ No error of any kind other than Machine Check may be reported due to instruction prefetching, until such time as the instruction that is the target of such prefetch becomes the instruction to be executed.

Speculative instruction fetches are allowed from any storage that is not Guarded. If a Machine Check exception results, a Machine Check interrupt may be generated even if the instruction fetch that caused the Machine Check exception would not have been executed because a previous uncompleted operation would have changed the execution path.

Only one side effect (other than Machine Check) of instruction prefetching is permitted: the Reference bit(s) in the referenced Page Table Entry(s) may be set.

Guarded Storage

Storage is said to be "Guarded" if either (a) the G bit is 1 in the relevant PTE or DBAT register, or (b) MSR bit IR or DR is 0 for instruction fetches or data loads respectively. (In case (b) all of storage is Guarded.)

Storage in a Guarded area may not be well behaved with regard to prefetching and other speculative storage operations. Such storage may represent an I/O device, and a speculative load or instruction fetch directed to such a device may cause the device to perform unexpected or incorrect operations.

Storage addresses in a Guarded area may not have successors; that is, there may be "holes" in a Guarded area of the real address space. On any system, the highest real address has no successor. Lack of a successor address means that speculative sequential operations such as instruction prefetching may fail and may result in a Machine Check.

As used below, "branch path" means the execution path as determined by *Branch* instructions.

Load or Store Instruction

A load or store instruction may not speculatively access Guarded storage unless one of the following conditions exists:

Programming Note

A *Trap*, *sc*, or *rfi* instruction will not necessarily prevent access to Guarded storage. When an access to Guarded storage is to be made based on some condition, the access must be protected by a *Branch* instruction.

1. The target storage location is in a cache. In this case, the location may be accessed in the cache or in main storage.

2. The target storage is Caching Allowed (I=0) and it is guaranteed that the load or store is on the branch path that will be executed (in the absence of any intervening interrupts). In this case, the entire cache block containing the target storage location may be loaded into the cache.

3. The target storage is Caching Inhibited (I=1), the load or store is on the branch path that will be executed, and no prior instructions can cause an interrupt.

Instruction Fetch

Instructions may not be speculatively fetched from Guarded storage unless one of the following conditions exists:

1. The target storage location is in a cache. In this case, the location may be accessed in the cache or in main storage.

2. $MSR_{IR}=1$ and an instruction has previously been fetched from the page.

3. It is guaranteed that the instruction to be fetched is on the branch path that will be taken (in the absence of any intervening interrupts). If $MSR_{IR}=0$, only the cache block containing the target instruction may be fetched.

4.2.6 32-Bit Mode on a 64-Bit Implementation

The computation of the 64-bit effective address is independent of mode. When a 64-bit implementation executes in 32-bit mode ($MSR_{SF}=0$), the high-order 32 bits of the 64-bit effective address are treated as zero for the purpose of addressing storage. This applies to both data accesses and instruction fetches. It applies when address translation is disabled, and to both translation modes (Segmented Address Translation and Block Address Translation) when address translation is enabled. This truncation of the EA is the only respect in which storage accesses are mode-dependent.

4.2.7 Real Addressing Mode

Whether address translation is enabled is controlled by MSR_{IR} for instruction fetching and by MSR_{DR} for data loads and stores. If address translation is disabled for a particular access (fetch, load, or store), the effective address is treated as the real address and is passed directly to the memory subsystem.

The EA is a 64-bit {32-bit} quantity computed by the CPU. The width of the real address supported by a particular implementation will be less than or equal to this quantity. If it is less, the high-order bits of the EA are *ignored* when the real address is formed.

Accesses in real mode bypass all storage protection checks (see Section 4.10) and do not cause the recording of reference and change information (see Section 4.9). Real mode data accesses are performed as though the storage access mode bits "WIMG" were 0011 (see Section 4.8). Real mode instruction fetches are performed as though the "WIMG" bits were either 0001 or 0011.

Access to direct-store segments (see Section 4.6) is not possible when translation is disabled, as Segment Table Entries (see "Segment Table," on page 404) or Segment Registers (see "Segment Registers," on page 413) are not checked for a T=1 specification.

Warning: An attempt to fetch from, load from, or store to a real address that is not physically present in the machine may result in a Machine Check interrupt or a Checkstop (see Section 5.5.2, "Machine Check Interrupt," on page 459).

STEGs in the Segment Table on a 64-bit implementation. These STEGs can be used to emulate the 32-bit implementation's Segment Registers.

4.3 Address Translation Overview

Figure 60 on page 400 gives an overview of the address translation process on PowerPC.

The *effective address* (EA) is the address generated by the processor for load and store instructions or for instruction fetch. This address is passed simultaneously to two translation mechanisms:

■ *Segmented Address Translation*, described in Section 4.4 on page 401 for 64-bit implementations and in Section 4.5 on page 412 for 32-bit implementations, and

■ *Block Address Translation*, described in Section 4.7 on page 423.

A typical effective address will be successfully translated by just one of

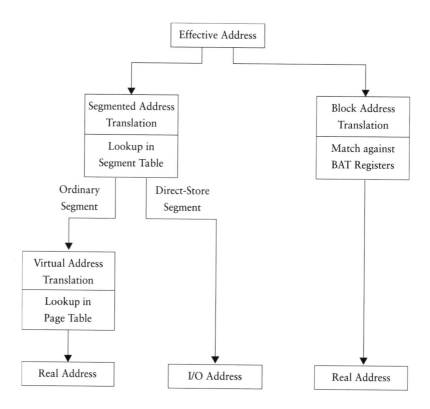

Figure 60.   **PowerPC address translation**

these mechanisms. If neither mechanism is successful, a *storage exception* (see page 393) results. If both mechanisms are successful, Block Address Translation takes precedence.

An effective address that translates successfully via the Segmented Address Translation mechanism (but not by the Block Address Translation mechanism) is a reference to one of two types of segments:

■ A *direct-store segment,* in which case the address is converted directly to an I/O address and is passed to the I/O subsystem for further action, or

■ An *ordinary segment,* in which case the address is converted to a *real address* that is then used to access storage.

An effective address that translates successfully via the Block Address Translation mechanism is converted directly to a *real address* that is then used to access storage.

4.4 Segmented Address Translation, 64-Bit Implementations

Figure 61 shows the steps involved in translating from an effective address to a real address on a 64-bit implementation.

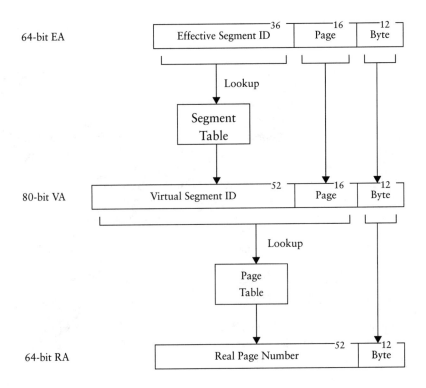

Figure 61.   Address translation overview (64-bit implementations)

If an access is translated by the Block Address Translation mechanism (BAT, see Section 4.7 on page 423), the BAT takes precedence and the results of segmented address translation are not used. If an access is not translated by a BAT, segmented address translation proceeds as follows.

The effective address (EA) is a 64-bit quantity computed by the processor. Bits 0:35 of the EA are the Effective Segment ID (ESID); these are looked up in the Segment Table to produce a Virtual Segment ID (VSID). Bits 36:51 of the EA are the Page Number within the segment; these are concatenated with the VSID from the Segment Table to form the Virtual

Page Number (VPN). The VPN is looked up in the Page Table to produce a Real Page Number (RPN). Bits 52:63 of the EA are the byte offset within the page; these are concatenated with the RPN to form the real address (RA) that is used to access storage.

If the processor is executing in 32-bit mode (MSR$_{SF}$=0), the translation process described above is followed except that the high-order 32 bits of the 64-bit effective address (that is, bits 0:31 of the ESID) are forced to zero before the lookup in the Segment Table starts. Bits 32:35 of the EA, which are the high-order 4 bits of the lower 32 bits of the EA, thus constitute the ESID.

If the selected Segment Table Entry identifies the segment as a direct-store segment, the Page Table is not referred to. Rather, translation continues as described in Section 4.6, "Direct-Store Segments," on page 421.

For ordinary segments the translation moves in two steps from effective address to virtual address (which never exists as a specific entity but can be considered to be the concatenation of the VPN and byte offset), and from virtual address to real address.

The first step in segmented address translation is to convert the effective address to a virtual address, as described in Section 4.4.1 on page 402. The second step, conversion of the virtual address to a real address, is described in Section 4.4.2 on page 406.

4.4.1 Virtual Address Generation, 64-Bit Implementations

Conversion of a 64-bit effective address to a virtual address is done by searching a hashed segment table pointed to by the Address Space Register, as shown in Figure 62 on page 403.

Address Space Register

The ASR is shown in Figure 63 on page 404. This 64-bit special-purpose register holds the real address of the Segment Table. The Segment Table defines the set of segments than can be addressed at any one time.

Access to the ASR is privileged. The ASR may be read or written by the *mfspr* and *mtspr* instructions. See "Move From Special Purpose Register XFX-form," on page 387 and "Move To Special Purpose Register XFX-form," on page 384.

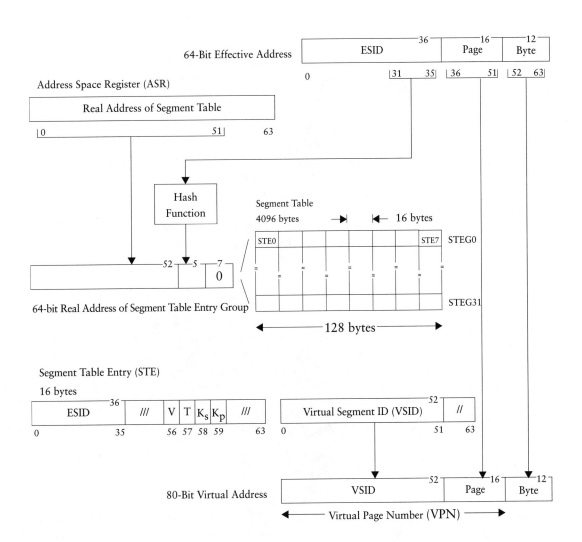

Figure 62. **Translation of 64-bit effective address to virtual address**

Real address of Segment Table	///
0 51	63

Figure 63.   **Address Space Register**

Segment Table

The Segment Table (STAB) is a one-page data structure that defines the mapping between Effective Segment IDs and Virtual Segment IDs. The STAB must be on a page boundary.

The STAB contains 32 Segment Table Entry Groups (STEGs). An STEG contains 8 Segment Table Entries (STEs) of 16 bytes each; each STEG is thus 128 bytes long. STEGs are entry points for searches of the Segment Table.

See Section 4.12, "Table Update Synchronization Requirements," on page 446 for the rules that software must follow when updating the Segment Table.

Segment Table Entry

Each Segment Table Entry (STE) maps one ESID to one VSID. Additional information in the STE controls the STAB search process and provides input to the storage protection mechanism. Figure 64 on page 405 shows the layout of an STE.

See Section 4.10, "Storage Protection," on page 436 for a discussion of the storage key bits.

Segment Table Search

An outline of the STAB search process is shown in Figure 62 on page 403. The detailed algorithm is as follows:

1. Primary Hash: Bits 0:51 of the ASR are concatenated with bits 31:35 of the effective address (the low 5 bits of the ESID) and with a field of seven 0s to form the 64-bit real address of a Segment Table Entry Group. This operation, referred to as the "Primary STAB Hash," identifies a particular STEG, each of whose 8 STEs will be tested in turn.

2. The first STE in the selected STEG is tested for a match with the EA. In order for a match to exist, the following must be true:

- $STE_V = 1$

Dword	Bit(s)	Name	Description	Dword	Bit(s)	Name	Description
0	0:35	ESID	Effective Segment ID	1	0:51	VSID	Virtual SID
	56	V	Entry valid if V=1				
	57	T	Direct-store segment if T=1		0:63	IO	I/O specific
	58	K_s	Supervisor state storage key				
	59	K_p	Problem state storage key				

All other fields are reserved.

Figure 64. **Segment Table Entry format**

- $STE_{ESID} = EA_{0:35}$

If a match is found, the STE search terminates successfully.

3. Step 2 is repeated for each of the other 7 STEs in the STEG. The first matching STE terminates the search. If none of the 8 STEs match, the secondary hash must be tried.

4. Secondary Hash: Bits 0:51 of the ASR are concatenated with the one's complement of bits 31:35 of the effective address and with a field of seven 0s to form the 64-bit real address of a Segment Table Entry Group. This operation is referred to as the "Secondary STAB Hash."

5. The first STE in the selected STEG is tested for a match with the EA. In order for a match to exist, the following must be true:

- $STE_V = 1$

- $STE_{ESID} = EA_{0:35}$

If a match is found, the STE search terminates successfully.

6. Step 5 is repeated for each of the other 7 STEs in the STEG. The first matching STE terminates the search. If none of the 8 STEs match, the search fails.

Programming Notes

1. Segment Table entries may or may not be cached in an SLB.

2. Segment Table lookups are done using real addresses and storage access mode M=1 (Memory Coherence required).

3. It is possible that the hardware implements two SLB arrays (one for data and one for instructions). In this case, the size, shape and values contained by the arrays may be different.

4. The ASR must point to a valid Segment Table whenever address relocation is enabled (MSR_{IR}=1 or MSR_{DR}=1 or both) and the effective address is not covered by BAT translation.

5. Use the *slbie* or *slbia* instruction to ensure that the SLB no longer contains a mapping for a particular segment.

6. See Chapter 7, "Synchronization Requirements for Special Registers and for Lookaside Buffers," on page 483, for the synchronization requirements that must be satisfied when a program changes the contents of the ASR.

7. Hardware never modifies the Segment Table.

If the Segment Table search succeeds, the Virtual Page Number (VPN) is formed by concatenating the VSID from the matching STE with bits 36:51 of the effective address (the page number). The complete 80-bit virtual address (VA) is formed by concatenating the VPN with bits 52:63 of the EA (the byte offset).

If the search fails, a *page fault* interrupt is taken. This will be an Instruction Storage interrupt or a Data Storage interrupt, depending on whether the effective address is for an instruction fetch or for data access.

If the selected STE has T=1, the reference is to a direct-store segment. No reference is made to the Page Table; processing continues as described in Section 4.6, "Direct-Store Segments," on page 421.

Segment Lookaside Buffer

Conceptually, the Segment Table is searched by the address relocation hardware to translate every reference. For performance reasons, the hardware usually keeps a Segment Lookaside Buffer (SLB) that holds STEs that have recently been used. The SLB is searched prior to searching the Segment Table. As a consequence, when software makes changes to the Segment Table, it must perform the appropriate SLB invalidate operations to maintain the consistency of the SLB with the tables.

4.4.2 Virtual to Real Translation, 64-Bit Implementations

Conversion of an 80-bit virtual address to a real address is done by searching a hashed page table located by SDR1 as shown in Figure 65 on page 407.

Generation of the 80-bit virtual address that is input to this stage of the translation process is described in Section 4.4.1, "Virtual Address Generation, 64-Bit Implementations," on page 402.

Page Table

The Hashed Page Table (HTAB) is a variable-sized data structure that defines the mapping between Virtual Page Numbers and Real Page Numbers. The HTAB's size must be a power of 2, and its starting address must be a multiple of its size.

The layout of the HTAB is similar to that of the Segment Table, except that the HTAB's size is variable while the STAB's size is exactly one page. The HTAB contains a number of Page Table Entry Groups (PTEGs). A PTEG contains eight Page Table Entries (PTEs) of 16 bytes each; each

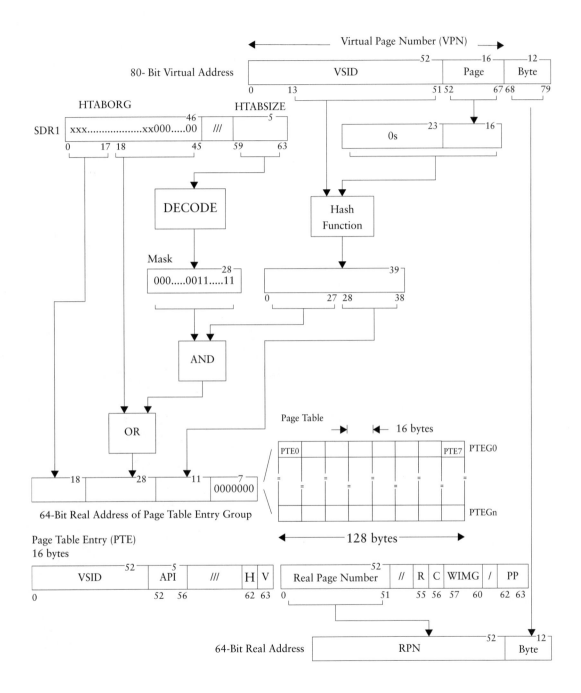

Figure 65. **Translation of 80-bit virtual address to 64-bit real address**

PTEG is thus 128 bytes long. PTEGs are entry points for searches of the Page Table.

See Section 4.12, "Table Update Synchronization Requirements," on page 446 for the rules that software must follow when updating the Page Table.

Page Table Entry

Each Page Table Entry (PTE) maps one VPN to one RPN. Additional information in the PTE controls the HTAB search process and provides input to the storage protection mechanism. Figure 66 shows the layout of a PTE.

0		52	56		62	63
VSID		API	///		H	V
RPN		//	R	C	WIMG	/	PP

| 0 | 51 | 55 | 56 | 57 | 60 | 62 | 63 |

Dword	Bit(s)	Name	Description
0	0:51	VSID	Virtual Segment ID
	52:56	API	Abbreviated Page Index
	62	H	Hash function identifier
	63	V	Entry valid (V=1) or invalid (V=0)
1	0:51	RPN	Real Page Number
	55	R	Reference bit
	56	C	Change bit
	57:60	WIMG	Storage access controls
	62:63	PP	Page Protection bits

All other fields are reserved.

Figure 66.   Page Table Entry, 64-bit implementations

The PTE contains an Abbreviated Page Index rather than the complete Page field. At least 11 of the low-order bits of the VPN are used in the hash function to select a PTEG. These bits are not repeated in the PTEs of that PTEG.

Page Table Size

The number of entries in the Page Table directly affects performance because it influences the hit ratio in the Page Table and thus the rate of page fault interrupts. If the table is too small, it is possible that not all the virtual pages that actually have real pages assigned can be mapped via the Page Table. This can happen if too many hash collisions occur and there are more than 16 entries for the same primary/secondary pair of PTEGs. While this situation cannot be guaranteed not to occur for any size Page Table, making the Page Table larger than the minimum size will reduce the frequency of occurrence of such collisions.

Storage Description Register 1

The SDR1 register is shown in Figure 67.

HTABORG	///	HTABSIZE
0 45	59	63

Bits	Name	Description
0:45	HTABORG	Real address of Page Table
59:63	HTABSIZE	Encoded size of Page Table

All other fields are reserved.

Figure 67.   **SDR1, 64-bit implementations**

The *HTABORG* field in SDR1 contains the high-order 46 bits of the 64-bit real address of the Page Table. The Page Table is thus constrained to lie on a 2^{18} byte (256 KB) boundary at a minimum. At least 11 bits from the hash function (see Figure 65 on page 407) are used to index into the Page Table. The minimum size Page Table is 256 KB (2^{11} PTEGs of 128 bytes each).

The Page Table can be any size 2^n where $18 \leq n \leq 46$. As the Page Table size is increased, more bits are used from the hash to index into the table and the value in HTABORG must have more of its low-order bits equal to 0.

The *HTABSIZE* field in SDR1 contains an integer giving the number of bits from the hash that are used in the Page Table index. HTABSIZE is used to generate a mask of the form 0b00...011...1, which is a string of 28 – HTABSIZE 0-bits followed by a string of HTABSIZE 1-bits. The 1-bits determine which additional bits (beyond the minimum of 11) from

Programming Note

It is recommended that the number of PTEGs in the Page Table be at least one-half the number of real pages to be accessed.

As an example, if the amount of real memory to be accessed is 2^{31} bytes (2 GB), then we have $2^{31-12} = 2^{19}$ real pages. The minimum recommended Page Table size would be 2^{18} PTEGs, or 2^{25} bytes (32 MB).

the hash are used in the index; HTABORG must have this same number of low-order bits equal to 0. See Figure 65 on page 407.

Example: Suppose that the Page Table is 16,384 (2^{14}) 128-byte PTEGs, for a total size of 2^{21} bytes (2 MB). A 14-bit index is required. Eleven bits are provided from the hash to start with, so 3 additional bits from the hash must be selected. Thus the value in HTABSIZE must be 3 and the value in HTABORG must have its low-order 3 bits (bits 31:33 of SDR1) equal to 0. This means that the Page Table must begin on a $2^{3+11+7} = 2^{21}$ = 2 MB boundary.

Hashed Page Table Search

An outline of the HTAB search process is shown in Figure 65 on page 407. The detailed algorithm is as follows:

1. Primary Hash: A 39-bit hash value is computed by Exclusive ORing the low-order 39 bits of the VSID with a 39-bit value formed by concatenating 23 bits of 0 with the page index.

2. The 64-bit real address of a PTEG is formed by concatenating the following values:

- Bits 0:17 of SDR1 (the 18 high-order bits of HTABORG).

- Bits 0:27 of the value formed in step 1 ANDed with the mask generated from bits 59:63 of SDR1 (HTABSIZE) and then ORed with bits 18:45 of SDR1 (the 28 low-order bits of HTABORG).

- Bits 28:38 of the value formed in step 1.

- A 7-bit field of 0s.

This operation, referred to as the "Primary HTAB Hash," identifies a particular PTEG, each of whose 8 PTEs will be tested in turn.

3. The first PTE in the selected PTEG is tested for a match with VPN. In order for a match to exist, the following must be true:

- $PTE_H=0$

- $PTE_V=1$

- $PTE_{VSID}=VA_{0:51}$

- $PTE_{API}=VA_{52:56}$

If a match is found, the PTE search terminates successfully.

4. Step 3 is repeated for each of the other 7 PTEs in the PTEG. The first matching PTE terminates the search. If none of the 8 PTEs match, the secondary hash must be tried.

5. **Secondary Hash:**   A 39-bit hash value is computed by taking the one's complement of the Exclusive OR of the low-order 39 bits of the VSID with a 39-bit value formed by concatenating 23 bits of 0 with the page index.

6. The 64-bit real address of a PTEG is formed by concatenating the following values:

   ■ Bits 0:17 of SDR1 (the 18 high-order bits of HTABORG).

   ■ Bits 0:27 of the value formed in step 5 ANDed with the mask generated from bits 59:63 of SDR1 (HTABSIZE) and then ORed with bits 18:45 of SDR1 (the 28 low-order bits of HTABORG).

   ■ Bits 28:38 of the value formed in step 5.

   ■ A 7-bit field of 0s.

   This operation is referred to as the "Secondary HTAB Hash."

7. The first PTE in the selected PTEG is tested for a match with VPN. In order for a match to exist, the following must be true:

   ■ $PTE_H = 1$

   ■ $PTE_V = 1$

   ■ $PTE_{VSID} = VA_{0:51}$

   ■ $PTE_{API} = VA_{52:56}$

   If a match is found, the PTE search terminates successfully.

8. Step 7 is repeated for each of the other 7 PTEs in the PTEG. The first matching PTE terminates the search. If none of the 8 PTEs match, the search fails.

If the Page Table search succeeds, the content of the PTE that translates the EA is returned. The real address (RA) is formed by concatenating the RPN from the matching PTE with bits 52:63 of the effective address (the byte offset).

If the search fails, a *page fault* interrupt is taken. This will be an Instruction Storage interrupt or a Data Storage interrupt, depending on whether the effective address is for an instruction fetch or for data access.

Programming Notes

1. Page Table Entries may or may not be cached in a TLB.

2. Page Table lookups are done using real addresses and storage access mode M=1 (Memory Coherence).

3. It is possible that the hardware implements two TLB arrays (one for data and one for instructions). In this case, the size, shape, and values contained by the arrays may be different.

4. Use the *tlbie* or *tlbia* instruction to ensure that the TLB no longer contains a mapping for a particular page.

5. Refer to Book IV, *PowerPC Implementation Features*, for the procedure to be used to invalidate the entire TLB.

Translation Lookaside Buffer

Conceptually, the Page Table is searched by the address relocation hardware to translate every reference. For performance reasons, the hardware usually keeps a Translation Lookaside Buffer (TLB) that holds PTEs that have recently been used. The TLB is searched prior to searching the Page Table. As a consequence, when software makes changes to the Page Table it must perform the appropriate TLB invalidate operations to maintain the consistency of the TLB with the Page Table.

4.5 Segmented Address Translation, 32-Bit Implementations

Figure 68 shows the steps involved in translating from an effective address to a real address on a 32-bit implementation.

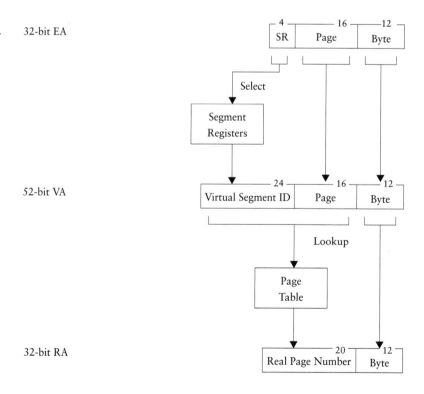

Figure 68.   Address translation overview (32-bit implementations)

If an access is translated by the Block Address Translation mechanism (BAT, see Section 4.7 on page 423), the BAT takes precedence and the results of segmented address translation are not used. If an access is not translated by a BAT, segmented address translation proceeds as follows.

The effective address (EA) is a 32-bit quantity computed by the processor. Bits 0:3 of the EA are the Segment Register number. These are used to select a Segment Register, from which is extracted a Virtual Segment ID (VSID). Bits 4:19 of the EA are the Page Number within the segment; these are concatenated with the VSID from the Segment Register to form the Virtual Page Number (VPN). The VPN is looked up in the Page Table to produce a Real Page Number (RPN). Bits 20:31 of the EA are the byte offset within the page; these are concatenated with the RPN to form the real address (RA) that is used to access storage.

If the selected Segment Register identifies the segment as a direct-store segment, the Page Table is not referred to. Rather, translation continues as described in Section 4.6, "Direct-Store Segments," on page 421.

For ordinary segments the translation moves in two steps from effective address to virtual address (which never exists as a specific entity but can be considered to be the concatenation of the VPN and byte offset) and from virtual address to real address.

The first step in segmented address translation is to convert the effective address to a virtual address, as described in Section 4.5.1. The second step, conversion of the virtual address to a real address, is described in Section 4.5.2 on page 415.

4.5.1 Virtual Address Generation, 32-Bit Implementations

Conversion of a 32-bit effective address to a virtual address is done by using the four high-order bits of the EA to select a Segment Register, as shown in Figure 69 on page 414.

Segment Registers

The 16 32-bit Segment Registers are present only in 32-bit implementations. Figure 70 on page 415 shows the layout of a Segment Register. The fields in the Segment Register are interpreted according to the value of bit 0 (the T bit).

If an access is translated by the Block Address Translation mechanism (BAT, see Section 4.7 on page 423), the BAT takes precedence and the results of translation using Segment Registers are not used. If an access is

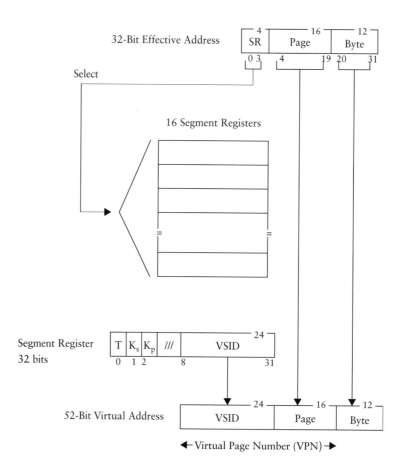

Figure 69.   Translation of 32-bit effective address to virtual address

not translated by a BAT, and T=0 in the selected Segment Register, the effective address is a reference to an ordinary segment. The 52-bit virtual address (VA) is formed by concatenating

- the 24-bit VSID field from the Segment Register,

- the 16-bit page index, $EA_{4:19}$, and

- the 12-bit byte offset, $EA_{20:31}$.

The VA is then translated to a real address as described in the next section.

If T=1 in the selected Segment Register (and the access is not translated by a BAT), the effective address is a reference to a direct-store segment. No reference is made to the Page Table; processing continues as described in Section 4.6, "Direct-Store Segments," on page 421.

T	K$_s$	K$_p$	///	VSID
0	1	2	8	31

Bit(s)	Name	Description
0	T	T = 0 selects this format
1	Ks	Supervisor state storage key
2	K$_p$	Problem state storage key
8:31	VSID	Virtual Segment ID

All other fields are reserved.

T	K$_s$	K$_p$	BUID	controller specific
0	1	2	3	12	31

Bit(s)	Name	Description
0	T	T = 1 selects this format
1	K$_s$	Supervisor state storage key
2	K$_p$	Problem state storage key
3:11	BUID	Bus Unit ID
12:31		Device dependent data for I/O controller

Figure 70. **Segment Register format**

4.5.2 Virtual to Real Translation, 32-Bit Implementations

Conversion of a 52-bit virtual address to a real address is done by searching a hashed page table located by SDR1, as shown in Figure 71 on page 416.

Generation of the 52-bit virtual address that is input to this stage of the translation process is described in Section 4.5.1, "Virtual Address Generation, 32-Bit Implementations," on page 413.

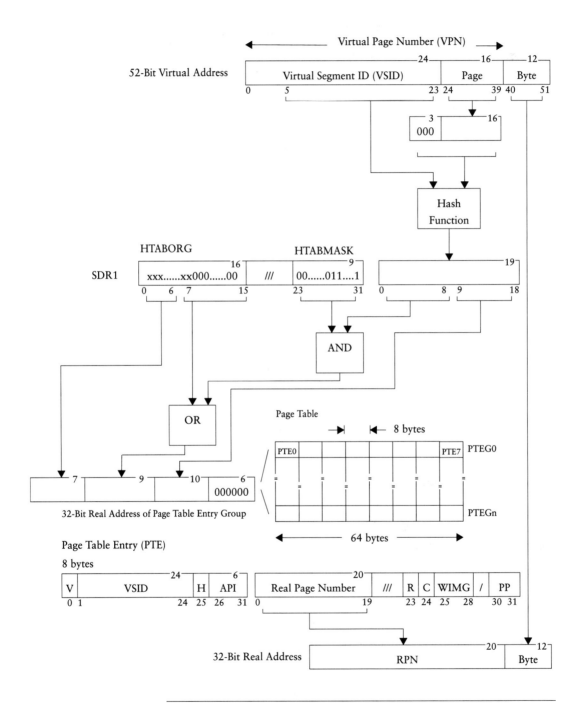

Figure 71. **Translation of 52-bit virtual address to 32-bit real address**

Page Table

The Hashed Page Table (HTAB) is a variable-sized data structure that defines the mapping between Virtual Page Numbers and Real Page Numbers. The HTAB's size must be a power of 2, and its starting address must be a multiple of its size.

The HTAB contains a number of Page Table Entry Groups (PTEGs). A PTEG contains eight Page Table Entries (PTEs) of eight bytes each; each PTEG is thus 64 bytes long. PTEGs are entry points for searches of the Page Table.

See Section 4.12, "Table Update Synchronization Requirements," on page 446 for the rules that software must follow when updating the Page Table.

Page Table Entry

Each Page Table Entry (PTE) maps one VPN to one RPN. Additional information in the PTE controls the HTAB search process and provides input to the storage protection mechanism. Figure 72 shows the layout of a PTE.

```
0    1                                    25   26              31
┌───┬──────────────────────────────┬─────┬─────────────────────┐
│ V │            VSID               │  H  │        API          │
├───┴──────────────────┬────┬───┬───┼────┬──────┬────┬──────────┤
│         RPN          │ // │ R │ C │WIMG│  /   │ PP │          │
└──────────────────────┴────┴───┴───┴────┴──────┴────┴──────────┘
0                     19    23  24  25   28          30  31
```

Word	Bit(s)	Name	Description
0	0	V	Entry valid (V=1) or invalid (V=0)
	1:24	VSID	Virtual Segment ID
	25	H	Hash function identifier
	26:31	API	Abbreviated Page Index
1	0:19	RPN	Real Page Number
	23	R	Reference Bit
	24	C	Change bit
	25:28	WIMG	Storage access control
	30:31	PP	Page protection bits

All other fields are reserved.

Figure 72.   **Page Table Entry, 32-bit implementations**

Programming Note

It is recommended that
the number of PTEGs in
the Page Table be at least
one-half the number of
real pages to be accessed.

As an example, if the
amount of real memory
to be accessed is 2^{29} bytes
(512 MB), then we have
$2^{29-12} = 2^{17}$ real pages.
The minimum
recommended Page Table
size would be 2^{16} PTEGs,
or 2^{22} bytes (4 MB).

The PTE contains an Abbreviated Page Index rather than the complete Page field. At least 10 of the low-order bits of the Page field are used in the hash function to select a PTEG. These bits are not repeated in the PTEs of that PTEG.

Page Table Size

The number of entries in the Page Table directly affects performance because it influences the hit ratio in the Page Table and thus the rate of page fault interrupts. If the table is too small, it is possible that not all the virtual pages that actually have real pages assigned can be mapped via the Page Table. This can happen if too many hash collisions occur and there are more than 16 entries for the same primary/secondary pair of PTEGs. While this situation cannot be guaranteed not to occur for any size Page Table, making the Page Table larger than the minimum size will reduce the frequency of such collisions.

Storage Description Register 1

The SDR1 register is shown in Figure 73.

HTABORG	///	HTABMASK
0 15	23	31

Bit(s)	Name	Description
0:15	HTABORG	Real address of Page Table
23:31	HTABMASK	Mask for Page Table address

All other fields are reserved.

Figure 73.   **SDR1, 32-bit implementations**

The *HTABORG* field in SDR1 contains the high-order 16 bits of the 32-bit real address of the Page Table. The Page Table is thus constrained to lie on a 2^{16} byte (64 KB) boundary at a minimum. At least 10 bits from the hash function (see Figure 71 on page 416) are used to index into the Page Table. The minimum size Page Table is 64 KB (2^{10} PTEGs of 64 bytes each).

The Page Table can be any size 2^n where $16 \leq n \leq 25$. As the table size is increased, more bits are used from the hash to index into the table and the value in HTABORG must have more of its low-order bits equal to 0.

The *HTABMASK* field in SDR1 contains a mask value that determines how many bits from the hash are used in the Page Table index. This mask must be of the form 0b00...011...1, that is, a string of 0-bits followed by a string of 1-bits. The 1-bits determine how many additional bits (beyond the minimum of 10) from the hash are used in the index; HTABORG must have this same number of low-order bits equal to 0. See Figure 71 on page 416.

Example: Suppose that the Page Table is 8,192 (2^{13}) 64-byte PTEGs, for a total size of 2^{19} bytes (512 KB). A 13-bit index is required. Ten bits are provided from the hash to start with, so 3 additional bits from the hash must be selected. Thus the value in HTABMASK must be 0x007 and the value in HTABORG must have its low-order 3 bits (bits 13:15 of SDR1) equal to 0. This means that the Page Table must begin on a $2^{3+10+6} = 2^{19} = 512$ KB boundary.

Hashed Page Table Search

An outline of the HTAB search process is shown in Figure 71 on page 416. The detailed algorithm is as follows:

1. A 19-bit hash value is computed by Exclusive ORing the low-order 19 bits of the VSID with a 19-bit value formed by concatenating 3 bits of 0 with the page index.

2. Primary Hash: The 32-bit real address of a PTEG is formed by concatenating the following values:

- Bits 0:6 of SDR1 (the 7 high-order bits of HTABORG).

- Bits 0:8 of the value formed in step 1 ANDed with bits 23:31 of SDR1 (the value of HTABMASK) and then ORed with bits 7:15 of SDR1 (the 9 low-order bits of HTABORG).

- Bits 9:18 of the value formed in step 1.

- A 6-bit field of 0s.

This operation, referred to as the "Primary HTAB Hash," identifies a particular PTEG, each of whose 8 PTEs will be tested in turn.

3. The first PTE in the selected PTEG is tested for a match with VPN. In order for a match to exist, the following must be true:

- $PTE_H = 0$

- $PTE_V = 1$

- $PTE_{VSID}=VA_{0:23}$

- $PTE_{API}=VA_{24:29}$

If a match is found, the PTE search terminates successfully.

4. Step 3 is repeated for each of the other 7 PTEs in the PTEG. The first matching PTE terminates the search. If none of the 8 PTEs match, the secondary hash must be tried.

5. A 19-bit hash value is computed by taking the one's complement of the Exclusive OR of the low-order 19 bits of the VSID with a 19-bit value formed by concatenating 3 bits of 0 with the page index.

6. Secondary Hash: The 32-bit real address of a PTEG is formed by concatenating the following values:

- Bits 0:6 of SDR1 (the 7 high-order bits of HTABORG).

- Bits 0:8 of the value formed in step 5 ANDed with bits 23:31 of SDR1 (the value of HTABMASK) and then ORed with bits 7:15 of SDR1 (the 9 low-order bits of HTABORG).

- Bits 9:18 of the value formed in step 5.

- A 6-bit field of 0s.

This operation is referred to as the "Secondary HTAB Hash."

7. The first PTE in the selected PTEG is tested for a match with VPN. In order for a match to exist, the following must be true:

- $PTE_H=1$

- $PTE_V=1$

- $PTE_{VSID}=VA_{0:23}$

- $PTE_{API}=VA_{24:29}$

If a match is found, the PTE search terminates successfully.

8. Step 7 is repeated for each of the other 7 PTEs in the PTEG. The first matching PTE terminates the search. If none of the 8 PTEs match, the search fails.

If the Page Table search succeeds, the content of the PTE that translates the EA is returned. The Real Address (RA) is formed by concatenating the RPN from the matching PTE with bits 20:31 of the effective address (the byte offset).

If the search fails, a *page fault* interrupt is taken. This will be an Instruction Storage interrupt or a Data Storage interrupt, depending on whether the effective address is for an instruction fetch or for data access.

Translation Lookaside Buffer

Conceptually, the Page Table is searched by the address relocation hardware to translate every reference. For performance reasons, the hardware usually keeps a Translation Lookaside Buffer (TLB) that holds PTEs that have recently been used. The TLB is searched prior to searching the Page Table. As a consequence, when software makes changes to the Page Table it must perform the appropriate TLB invalidate operations to maintain the consistency of the TLB with the Page Table.

4.6   Direct-Store Segments

A *direct-store* segment is a mapping of effective addresses onto an external address space, typically an I/O bus.

Effective addresses that lie within direct-store segments complete only the first step of segmented address translation.

■ In 64-bit implementations, this is the search of the Segment Table. If the resulting Segment Table Entry has T=1, the reference is to a direct-store segment.

■ In 32-bit implementations, this is the selection of the Segment Register. If the Segment Register has T=1, the reference is to a direct-store segment.

Direct-store data accesses are performed as though the storage access mode bits "WIMG" were 0101 (see Section 4.8).

4.6.1 Completion of Direct-Store Access

If an access is translated by the Block Address Translation mechanism (BAT, see Section 4.7), the BAT takes precedence and the results of segmented address translation are not used. If an access is not translated by a BAT, and the segmented address translation process has discovered that the segment has T=1, translation terminates. No reference is made to the Page Table; Reference and Change bits are not updated. The following data are sent to the storage controller:

Programming Notes

1. Page Table Entries may or may not be cached in a TLB.

2. Page Table lookups are done using real addresses and storage access mode M=1 (Memory Coherence).

3. It is possible that the hardware implements two TLB arrays (one for data and one for instructions). In this case, the size, shape, and values contained by the arrays may be different.

4. Use the *tlbie* or *tlbia* instruction to ensure that the TLB no longer contains a mapping for a particular page.

5. Refer to Book IV, *PowerPC Implementation Features*, for the procedure to be used to invalidate the entire TLB.

Compatibility Note

Direct-store segments are provided for POWER compatibility. Applications that require low-latency load/store access to an external address space should consider more traditional methods.

For 64-bit implementations:

- A one-bit field representing the privilege of the storage access, computed as follows:

  $Key \leftarrow (K_p \ \& \ MSR_{PR}) \ | \ (K_s \ \& \ \neg MSR_{PR})$

- The 32-bit IO field from bits 32:63 of the second doubleword of the STE

- The low-order 28 bits of the effective address, $EA_{36:63}$

For 32-bit implementations:

- A one-bit field representing the privilege of the storage access, computed as follows:

  $Key \leftarrow (K_p \ \& \ MSR_{PR}) \ | \ (K_s \ \& \ \neg MSR_{PR})$

- The contents of bits 3:31 of the Segment Register, which is the BUID field concatenated with the "controller specific" field

- The low-order 28 bits of the effective address, $EA_{4:31}$

An implementation of the PowerPC Architecture may cause multiple address/data transfers for a single instruction. The address for each transfer will be handled in the same manner that addresses for access to main storage are handled.

4.6.2 Direct-Store Segment Protection

Page-level protection as described in Section 4.10.1, "Page Protection," on page 437 is not provided by the PowerPC processor for direct-storage segments. The appropriate key bit (K_s or K_p) from the STE or Segment Register is sent to the storage controller, but it is up to the storage controller to implement any protection mechanism. Frequently no such mechanism will be provided; the fact that a direct-store segment is mapped into the address space of a process may be regarded as sufficient authority to access the segment.

4.6.3 Instructions Not Supported for T=1

The following instructions are not supported when they specify an effective address in a segment where T=1:

- *lwarx*   ■ *stwcx.*
- *ldarx*   ■ *stdcx.*
- *eciwx*   ■ *ecowx*

If one of these instructions is executed specifying an effective address in a segment where T=1, either a Data Storage interrupt occurs or the results are boundedly undefined.

4.6.4 Instructions with No Effect for T=1

The following instructions are treated as no-ops when they specify an effective address in a segment where T=1:

- *dcbt*   ■ *dcbst*
- *dcbtst*   ■ *dcbz*
- *dcbf*   ■ *icbi*
- *dcbi*

For further details of storage references to direct-store segments, refer to Book IV, *PowerPC Implementation Features*.

4.7 Block Address Translation

The *Block Address Translation* (BAT) mechanism provides a means for mapping ranges of virtual addresses larger than a single page onto contiguous areas of real storage. Such areas can be used for data that are not subject to normal virtual storage handling (paging), such as a memory-mapped display buffer or an extremely large array of numeric data.

4.7.1 Recognition of Addresses in BAT Areas

Block Address Translation is enabled only when address translation is enabled (MSR_{IR}=1 or MSR_{DR}=1 or both).

Special Purpose Registers (SPRs) called BAT registers define the starting addresses and sizes of BAT areas. The BAT registers are accessed in parallel with segmented address translation to determine whether a particular EA corresponds to a BAT area. If an EA is within a BAT area, the real address for storage access is determined as described below.

It is possible to set up the BAT registers and the segmented address translation mechanism such that a particular effective address is within a BAT area and also is covered by page translation. When this happens, the BAT takes precedence over entries in the Segment Table or the content of a Segment Register (including the T bit).

Programming Note

It is possible for a BAT area to overlay part of an ordinary segment, such that the BAT portion is nonpageable while the rest of the segment is pageable. If this is done, it is not necessary to supply Page Table Entries for the portion of the segment overlaid by the BAT.

Programming Note

If the same storage address is to be mapped via BAT for both I-fetch and data load and store, it is necessary to load the mapping into both an IBAT pair and a DBAT pair. This is true even on an implementation that does not have split I and D caches.

The BAT areas are defined by pairs of SPRs. These SPRs can be read or written by the *mfspr* and *mtspr* instructions; see pages 384 and 387. Access to these SPRs is privileged. The layout of the BAT registers is shown in Figure 74 on page 425 for 64-bit implementations and in Figure 75 on page 426 for 32-bit implementations.

Four pairs of BAT registers are provided for translating instruction addresses (the IBAT registers), and four pairs are provided for translating data addresses (the DBAT registers).

It is an error for system software to set up the BAT registers such that an effective address is translated by more than one IBAT pair or by more than one DBAT pair. If this error occurs, the results are undefined and may include a violation of the storage protection mechanism, a Machine Check interrupt, or a Checkstop.

Each pair of BAT registers defines the starting address of a BAT area in effective address space, the length of the area, and the start of the corresponding area in real address space. If an effective address is within the range of EAs defined by a pair of BAT registers that is valid (see below) for the access, its real address is developed by (conceptually) subtracting the starting effective address of the BAT area from the EA and adding the starting real address of the BAT area.

BAT areas are restricted to a finite set of allowable lengths, all of which are powers of 2. The smallest BAT area defined is 128 KB (2^{17} bytes). The largest BAT area defined is 256 MB (2^{28} bytes). The starting address of a BAT area in both EA space and RA space must be a multiple of the area's length.

4.7.2 BAT Registers

See Section 3.4.1, "Move to/from System Register Instructions," on page 384 for a list of the SPR numbers for the BAT registers. See Appendix B, "Assembler Extended Mnemonics," on page 495 for a list of extended mnemonics for use with the BAT registers.

Upper BAT Register

BEPI	///	BL	V_s	V_p
BRPN	///	WIMG	/	PP

Lower BAT Register

Register	Bit(s)	Name	Description
Upper	0:46	BEPI	Block Effective Page Index
	51:61	BL	Block Length
	62	V_s	Supervisor state valid bit
	63	V_p	Problem state valid bid
Lower	0:46	BRPN	Block Real Page Number
	57:60	WIMG	Storage access controls Bit 60 is reserved in IBATs
	62:63	PP	Protection bits for BAT area

All other fields are reserved.

Figure 74.   **BAT registers, 64-bit implementations**

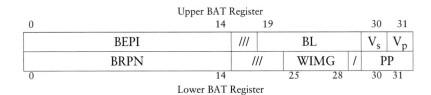

Register	Bit(s)	Name	Description
Upper	0:14	BEPI	Block Effective Page Index
	19:29	BL	Block Length
	30	V_s	Supervisor state valid bit
	31	V_p	Problem state valid bid
Lower	0:14	BRPN	Block Real Page Number
	25:28	WIMG	Storage access controls Bit 28 is reserved in IBATs
	30:31	PP	Protection bits for BAT area

All other fields are reserved.

Figure 75. BAT registers, 32-bit implementations

The equation for determining whether a BAT entry is valid for a particular access is:

```
BAT_entry_valid = (Vs & ¬MSRPR) | (Vp & MSRPR)
```

If a BAT entry is not valid for a given access, it does not participate in address translation for that access.

Two BAT entries may not map an overlapping effective address range and be valid at the same time.

The BL field in the upper BAT register is a mask that encodes the length of the BAT area.

BAT Area Length	BL
128 KB	000 0000 0000
256 KB	000 0000 0001
512 KB	000 0000 0011
1 MB	000 0000 0111
2 MB	000 0000 1111
4 MB	000 0001 1111
8 MB	000 0011 1111
16 MB	000 0111 1111
32 MB	000 1111 1111
64 MB	001 1111 1111
128 MB	011 1111 1111
256 MB	111 1111 1111

Only the values shown are valid for BL. The rightmost bit of BL is aligned with bit 46 {14} of the EA.

An effective address is determined to be within a BAT area if EA matches BEPI. The boundary between the string of 0s and the string of 1s in BL determines the bits of EA that participate in the comparison with BEPI. A match occurs if the following expression is true on a 64-bit implementation:

$$EA_{0:35} \mid\mid (EA_{36:46} \text{ \& } \neg BL) = BEPI$$

Note: In 32-bit mode, $EA_{0:31}$ are treated as zeros.

A match occurs if the following expression is true on a 32-bit implementation:

$$EA_{0:3} \mid\mid (EA_{4:14} \text{ \& } \neg BL) = BEPI$$

Bits in EA corresponding to 1s in BL, concatenated with the 17 bits of EA to the right of BL, form the offset within the BAT area.

The value in BL must be one of those given in the table above, and the values in BEPI and BRPN must have at least as many low-order 0s as there are 1s in BL. If these rules are violated, the results are undefined.

BAT Storage Protection

If an effective address is determined to be within a BAT area that is valid for the access, the access is next validated by the storage protection scheme described in Section 4.10.2, "BAT Protection," on page 438. If this protection mechanism rejects the EA, a page fault (Data Storage interrupt or Instruction Storage interrupt) is generated.

BAT Real Address

If the protection mechanism accepts the access, then a real address is formed as shown in Figure 76 for 64-bit implementations, and in Figure 77 on page 429 for 32-bit implementations.

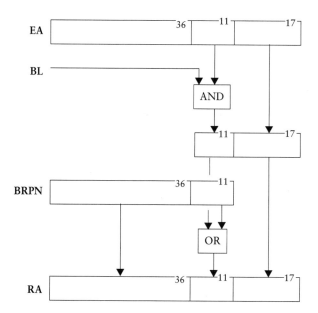

Figure 76.   **Formation of real address via BAT, 64-bit implementations**

Access to the real memory of the BAT area is made according to the storage mode defined by the "WIMG" bits in the lower BAT register. These bits apply to the entire BAT area rather than to an individual page. See Section 4.8.2, "Supported Storage Modes," on page 431 for an explanation of these bits.

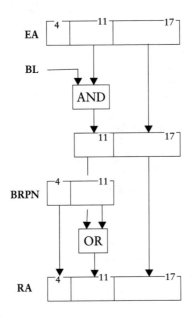

Figure 77. **Formation of real address via BAT, 32-bit implementations**

4.8 Storage Access Modes

When address relocation is enabled and the effective address generated by a storage access is translated by the Segmented Address Translation mechanism or by the Block Address Translation mechanism, the access is performed under the control of the Page Table Entry or BAT entry used to translate the effective address. Each Page Table Entry or DBAT entry contains four mode control bits, W, I, M, and G, that specify the storage mode for all accesses translated by the entry. The IBAT entry contains the W, I, and M bits, but not the G bit. The W and I bits control how the processor executing the access uses its own cache. The M bit specifies whether the processor executing the access must use the storage coherence protocol to ensure that all copies of the addressed storage location are made consistent. The G bit controls whether speculative data and instruction fetching is permitted. For an access translated by an IBAT entry, G is assumed to be 0.

The mode control bits only have meaning when an effective address is translated in the processor performing a storage access. When an access is performed for which coherence is required, the processor performing the access must inform the coherence mechanism that the access requires memory coherence. Other processors affected by the access must respond to the coherence mechanism. However, since these mode control bits are only relevant when an effective address is translated and have no direct relation to data in the cache, processors responding to the coherence request are able to respond without knowledge of the state of these bits.

4.8.1 W, I, M, and G bits

The *W*, *I*, *M*, and *G* bits in a Page Table Entry or DBAT entry, or the *W*, *I*, and *M* bits in an IBAT entry, control the way in which the processor accesses cache and main storage. Each bit controls a separate aspect of storage references.

W   **Write Through**

If the data are in the cache, a store must update that copy of the data. In addition, if W=1 the update must be written to the home storage location (see below).

Store combining optimizations are allowed except when the store instructions are separated by *sync* or *eieio*. The architecture presumes that data present in the cache are valid and a store may cause any part of that data to be copied back to main storage.

The definition of the home storage location is dependent upon the implementation of the memory system but can be illustrated by the following examples:

- RAM Storage
  The store must be sent to the RAM controller to be written into the target RAM.

- I/O Adapter Card
  The store must be sent to the adapter card to be written to the target register or storage location.

In systems with multilevel caching, the store must be written to a depth in the memory hierarchy that is seen by all processors and devices.

I   **Caching Inhibited**

If I=1, the storage access is completed by referencing the location in main storage, bypassing the cache. During the access, the accessed location is not brought into the cache nor is the location allocated in the cache.

Load/store combining optimizations are allowed except when the accesses are separated by *sync*, or by *eieio* when the storage access is also Guarded.

M   **Memory Coherence**

This mode control is provided to allow improved performance in systems in which accesses to storage kept consistent by hardware are slower than accesses to storage not kept consistent by hardware, and in which software is able to enforce the required consistency. When the mode is off (M=0), the hardware need not enforce data coherence. When the mode is on (M=1), the hardware must enforce data coherence. Because instruction storage need not be consistent with data storage, it is permissible for an implementation to ignore the M bit for instruction fetches.

G   **Guarded Storage**

If G=1, accesses to storage must conform to the restrictions described in Section 4.2.5, "Speculative Execution," on page 396.

4.8.2 Supported Storage Modes

The combinations of the Write Through bit, the Caching Inhibited bit, and the Memory Coherence bit define eight different storage modes. Six of these modes are supported. For each, the G bit may be 0 or 1.

■ WIM = 000

1. Data may be cached.

2. Loads or stores for which the target location is in the cache may use that copy of the location.

3. Exclusive ownership of the block containing the target location is not required for store accesses, and consistency operations for the block may be ignored when fetching the block, storing it back, or changing its state from shared to exclusive.

■ WIM = 001

1. Data may be cached.

2. Loads or stores for which the target location is in the cache may use that copy of the location.

3. Exclusive ownership of the block containing the target location is required before store accesses are allowed. When fetching the block, the processor must indicate that consistency is to be enforced on the bus transaction. If the state of the block is read shared, the processor must gain exclusive use of the block before storing into it.

■ WIM = 010

Caching is inhibited. The storage access goes to storage bypassing the cache. Hardware-enforced storage consistency is not required.

■ WIM = 011

Caching is inhibited. The storage access goes to storage bypassing the cache. Storage consistency is enforced by hardware.

■ WIM = 100

1. Data may be cached.

2. Loads for which the target location is in the cache may use that copy of the location.

3. Stores must be written to main storage. The target location of the store may be cached and must be updated if there.

4. Exclusive ownership of the block containing the target location is not required for store accesses, and consistency operations for the block may be ignored when fetching the block, storing it back, or changing its state from shared to exclusive.

■ WIM = 101

1. Data may be cached.

2. Loads for which the target location is in the cache may use that copy of the location.

3. Stores must be written to main storage. The target location of the store may be cached and must be updated if there.

4. Exclusive ownership of the block containing the target location is required before store accesses are allowed. When fetching the block, the processor must indicate that consistency is to be enforced on the bus transaction. If the state of the block is read shared, the processor must gain exclusive use of the block before storing into it.

■ WIM = 110

This mode would represent memory that is Write Through, Caching Inhibited, and Memory Coherence Not Required. This mode is **not supported**.

■ WIM = 111

This mode would represent memory that is Write Through, Caching Inhibited, and Memory Coherence Required. This mode is **not supported**.

4.8.3 Mismatched WIMG Bits

Accesses to the same storage location using two effective addresses for which the Write Through mode (W bit) differs must meet the memory coherence requirements described in Book II, Section 1.5, "Memory Coherence," on page 323.

Accesses to the same storage location using two effective addresses for which the Caching mode (I bit) differs must meet the requirement that a copy of the target location of an access to Caching Inhibited storage not be in the cache. Violation of this requirement is considered a programming error; software must ensure that the location has not previously been brought into the cache or, if it has, that it has been flushed from the cache. If the programming error occurs, the result of the access is boundedly undefined.

Accesses to the same storage location using two effective addresses for which the Memory Coherence mode (M bit) or the Guarded mode (G bit) differ are always permitted.

4.9 Reference and Change Recording

If address translation is enabled ($MSR_{IR}=1$ or $MSR_{DR}=1$), Reference (R) and Change (C) bits are maintained in the Page Table Entry for each real page for accesses due to Segment and Page Table address translation. Reference and change recording is not performed for translations due to BAT or for direct-store (T=1) segments.

The R and C bits are set automatically by hardware or by software assist in conjunction with normal Page Table processing as follows:

Reference Bit

As a result of Page Table processing for a storage access (load, store, cache instruction, or instruction fetch), the Reference bit may be set to 1 immediately, or its setting may be delayed until the storage access is determined to be successful.

The Reference bit may be set for a speculatively executed access. The Reference bit may also be set for accesses that are not performed when the access is prohibited by page protection, or if the access is the result of a string operation of zero length, or if the access is a *Store Conditional* but no store is performed because a reservation does not exist.

Change Bit

Whenever a data store is executed successfully, as part of the TLB lookup procedure the Change bit in the TLB is checked. If it is already set to 1, no further action is taken. If the TLB Change bit is 0, it is set to 1 and the corresponding Change bit in the Page Table Entry is set to 1.

The PowerPC Architecture requires that the Change bit be set to 1 only if the store is allowed by storage protection and all branches prior to the store that will cause the Change bit to be set have been resolved and it has been determined that the store is on the path that is to be executed.

Furthermore, the Change bit may be set even when a store is not performed successfully in the following cases:

1. A *Store Conditional* (*stwcx.* or *stdcx.*) is executed and is allowed by the storage protection mechanism, but no store is performed because a reservation does not exist.

2. A *Store String Word Indexed* (*stswx*) is executed and is allowed by the storage protection mechanism, but no store is performed because the length is zero.

3. The store operation is not performed because the instruction stream is interrupted before the store is performed.

Execution of either of the *Data Cache Block Touch* instructions (*dcbt*, *dcbtst*) may result in setting the R bit for a page. Neither instruction may result in setting the C bit for a page.

Figure 78 on page 435 summarizes the rules for setting the Reference and Change bits. The table applies to each atomic storage reference. It should be read from the top down; the first line matching a given situation applies. For example, if *stwcx.* fails due to both a storage protection violation and the lack of a reservation, the Change bit must not be altered.

Status of access	R	C
Storage protection violation	Acc[1]	No
Speculative I-fetch or load-type instruction		
Beyond an unresolved branch	Acc	No
Beyond a possible interrupt	Acc	No
Speculative store-type instruction		
Beyond an unresolved branch	Acc	No
Beyond a possible interrupt	Acc	Acc[2]
Zero-length load (*lswx*)	Acc	No
Zero-length store (*stswx*)	Acc	Acc[2]
Store Conditional fails due to lack of a reservation	Acc	Acc[2]
Other non-speculative access:		
I-fetch	Yes[3]	No
Ordinary load or *eciwx*	Yes	No
Ordinary store, *ecowx*, or *dcbz*	Yes	Yes
icbi, dcbt, dcbtst, dcbst, dcbf	Acc[1]	No
dcbi	Acc[1]	Acc[1,2]

"Acc" means that it is acceptable to set the R bit, or that it is acceptable to set the C bit if a store to the location would not violate storage protection.
[1]It is preferable not to set the bit.
[2]If C is set, R must also be set.
[3]This includes the case in which the instruction was speculatively fetched and R was not set to 1.

Figure 78.   Setting the Reference and Change bits

In the figure, the "load-type" instructions are the load instructions described in Book I, *eciwx*, and the *Cache Management* instructions that are permitted to be treated as a load with respect to address translation. The "store-type" instructions are the store instructions described in Book I, *ecowx*, and the *Cache Management* instructions that are treated as a store with respect to address translation. The "ordinary" load and store instructions are those described in Book I.

When the hardware does an implied load from the Page Table Entry due to a TLB miss, or updates the Reference and Change bits in the Page Table Entry, the accesses are done in real mode, so there are no Reference or Change bits to update. If software refers to a Page Table Entry when $MSR_{DR}=1$, then Reference and Change bits in the associated Page Table Entries are set as for ordinary loads and stores. See Section 4.12, "Table Update Synchronization Requirements," on page 446 for the rules software must follow when updating the Reference and Change bits in the Page Table.

4.9.1 Synchronization of Reference and Change Bit Updates

If processor A executes a load or store that causes a Reference bit and/or Change bit update, the following conditions must be met with respect to setting the bits and performing the access:

1. If processor A subsequently executes a *sync*, both the updates to the bits and the access must be performed with respect to all other processors and mechanisms before the *sync* completes on processor A.

2. If processor B subsequently executes a *tlbie* that invalidates the TLB entry in processor A that was used to translate the access, and processor B then executes a *tlbsync* that is broadcast, both the updates to the bits and the access must be performed with respect to all other processors and mechanisms before the *tlbsync* completes on processor A.

Updates to the Reference and Change bits may not be immediately visible to the program after executing a load, store, or instruction fetch that sets them indirectly.

4.10 Storage Protection

The storage protection mechanism provides a means for selectively granting read access, granting read/write access, and prohibiting access to areas of storage based on a number of control criteria.

Since the protection mechanism operates as part of the address translation mechanism, storage protection applies to translated accesses only. Instruction storage access protection is active only when $MSR_{IR}=1$. Data storage access protection is active only when $MSR_{DR}=1$.

Protection domains are defined only when the appropriate relocate bit

Programming Note

If it is important that the program that loads from the PTE retrieve the correct R and C bits, a *sync* instruction must be executed between a load, store, or instruction fetch that indirectly sets an R or C bit and the load of these bits from the PTE.

Programming Note

On systems with Translation Lookaside Buffers, the Reference and Change bits are set only on the basis of TLB activity. When software resets these bits to zero it must synchronize the TLB's actions by invalidating the TLB entries associated with the pages whose Reference and Change bits were reset.

in the MSR (IR or DR) is 1. A protection domain is a page within an ordinary segment, an area of storage defined by a BAT entry, or a direct-store segment. A *protection boundary* is a boundary between protection domains.

For ordinary translated accesses to memory via the Page Table, the page protection mechanism described in the next section is active. Different mechanisms are used for Block Address Translation (BAT) accesses (see Section 4.10.2, "BAT Protection," on page 438) and for direct-store segments (see Section 4.6.2, "Direct-Store Segment Protection," on page 422).

4.10.1 Page Protection

The page protection mechanism provides protection at the granularity of a page (4 KB). It is controlled by the following inputs:

- MSR_{PR}, which distinguishes between supervisor state and problem state

- K_s and K_p, supervisor and problem key bits in the Segment Table Entry or Segment Register

- PP bits in the Page Table Entry

A reference made via the segmented address translation mechanism is associated with a Segment Table Entry (STE) or Segment Register and with a Page Table Entry (PTE) by the address translation mechanism. The K bits, the PP bits, and the MSR_{PR} bit are used as follows:

A Key value is developed according to the following formula:

```
Key ← (Kp & MSRPR) | (Ks & ¬MSRPR)
```

Using the generated Key, the table in Figure 79 on page 438 is applied. When a reference is not permitted because of the protection mechanism one of the following occurs:

- A Data Storage interrupt is generated and bit 4 of the DSISR is set to 1.

- An Instruction Storage interrupt is generated and bit 36 {4} of SRR1 is set to 1.

Key	PP	Page Type	Load Access Permitted	Store Access Permitted
0	00	read/write	yes	yes
0	01	read/write	yes	yes
0	10	read/write	yes	yes
0	11	read only	yes	no
1	00	no access	no	no
1	01	read only	yes	no
1	10	read/write	yes	yes
1	11	read only	yes	no

Key   Key selected by state of MSR_{PR} bit
PP   PTE page protection bits

Figure 79.   **Protection Key processing**

4.10.2 BAT Protection

The BAT protection mechanism operates on an entire BAT area, not on individual pages. If an effective address is determined to be within a BAT area that is valid for the access, the operations described above in Section 4.10.1, "Page Protection," on page 437 are performed, with these exceptions:

■ For BATs, no Key value is defined; Figure 79 is used with an assumed Key=1.

■ The PP bits from the lower BAT register are used, not bits from a Page Table Entry.

4.11 Storage Control Instructions

4.11.1 Cache Management Instructions

This section contains the only privileged cache management instruction and additional specifications for the other cache management instructions described in Book II, Section 3.2, "Cache Management Instructions," on page 344.

If the effective address references a direct-store segment, the instruction is treated as a no-op.

When data relocate is off, $MSR_{DR}=0$, the *Data Cache Block set to Zero* instruction establishes a block in the cache and may not verify that the real address is valid. If a block is created for an invalid real address, a Machine Check may result when an attempt is made to write that block back to storage. The block could be written back as the result of the execution of an instruction that causes a cache miss and the invalid address block is the target for replacement, or as the result of a *Data Cache Block Store* instruction.

Data Cache Block Invalidate   X-form

dcbi   RA,RB

31	///	RA	RB	470	/
0	6	11	16	21	31

Let the effective address (EA) be the sum (RA|0)+(RB).

The action taken is dependent on the storage mode associated with the target and on the state of the block. The list below describes the action to take if the block containing the byte addressed by EA is or is not in the cache.

1. Coherence Not Required

Unmodified Block
  Invalidate the block in the local cache.

Modified Block
  Invalidate the block in the local cache. (Discard the modified contents.)

Absent Block
  No action is taken.

2. Coherence Required

Unmodified Block
  Invalidate copies of the block in the caches of all processors.

Modified Block
  Invalidate copies of the block in the caches of all processors. (Discard the modified contents.)

Absent Block
  If copies of the block are in the caches of any other processor, cause the copies to be invalidated. (Discard any modified contents.)

When data address translation is enabled, $MSR_{DR}=1$, and the virtual address has no translation, a Data Storage Interrupt occurs. See Section 5.5.3, "Data Storage Interrupt," on page 460.

The function of this instruction is independent of the Write Through Required/Not Required and Caching Inhibited/Allowed modes of the block containing the byte addressed by EA.

This instruction is treated as a store to the addressed byte with respect to address translation and storage protection, except that the Change bit need not be set, and if the Change bit is not set then the Reference bit need not be set.

This instruction is privileged.

Special Registers Altered

    None

4.11.2 Segment Register Manipulation Instructions

Programming Note

For a discussion of software sychronization requirements when altering Segment Registers, please refer to Chapter 7, "Synchronization Requirements for Special Registers and for Lookaside Buffers," on page 483.

Move To Segment Register   X-form

mtsr   SR,RS

31	RS	/	SR	///	210	/
0	6	11	12 16	21		31

SEGREG(SR) ← (RS)

The contents of register RS are placed into Segment Register SR.

This instruction is privileged.

This instruction is defined only for 32-bit implementations. Using it on a 64-bit implementation will cause an Illegal Instruction type Program interrupt.

Special Registers Altered

    None

Move To Segment Register Indirect   X-form

mtsrin   RS,RB

[Power mnemonic: mtsri]

31	RS	///	RB	242	/
0	6	11	16	21	31

SEGREG((RB)$_{0:3}$) ← (RS)

The contents of register RS are copied to the Segment Register selected by bits 0:3 of register RB.

This instruction is privileged.

This instruction is defined only for 32-bit implementations. Using it on a 64-bit implementation will cause an Illegal Instruction type Program interrupt.

Special Registers Altered

None

Move From Segment Register   X-form

mfsr   RT,SR

31	RT	/	SR	///	595	/
0	6	11	12	16	21	31

RT ← SEGREG(SR)

The contents of Segment Register SR are placed into register RT.

This instruction is privileged.

This instruction is defined only for 32-bit implementations. Using it on a 64-bit implementation will cause an Illegal Instruction type Program interrupt.

Special Registers Altered

None

Programming Note

The RA field is not defined for the *mtsrin* and *mfsrin* instructions in this architecture. However, *mtsrin* and *mfsrin* will perform the same function in PowerPC as do *mtsri* and *mfsri* in POWER if RA is 0 in the POWER instructions.

Move From Segment Register Indirect   X-form

mfsrin   RT,RB

31	RT	///	RB	659	/
0	6	11	16	21	31

RT ← SEGREG((RB)$_{0:3}$)

The contents of the Segment Register selected by bits 0:3 of register RB are copied into register RT.

This instruction is privileged.

This instruction is defined only for 32-bit implementations. Using it on a 64-bit implementation will cause an Illegal Instruction type Program interrupt.

Special Registers Altered

None

4.11.3 Lookaside Buffer Management Instructions (Optional)

While the PowerPC Architecture describes logically separate instruction fetch and fixed-point (including effective address computation) execution units, the programming model is that there is one translation mechanism and, for 32-bit implementations, one set of Segment Registers.

For performance reasons, most implementations will implement a Segment Lookaside Buffer (SLB) (64-bit implementations) and a Translation Lookaside Buffer (TLB). These are caches of portions of the Segment Table and Page Table, respectively. As changes are made to the address translation tables, it is necessary to force the SLB and TLB into line with the updated tables. This is done by invalidating SLB and TLB entries, or occasionally by invalidating the entire SLB or TLB, and allowing the translation caching mechanism to refetch from the tables.

Each PowerPC implementation that has an SLB *must* provide means for doing the following:

■ invalidating an individual SLB entry

■ invalidating the entire SLB

Each PowerPC implementation that has a TLB *must* provide means for doing the following:

- invalidating an individual TLB entry

- invalidating the entire TLB

An implementation may choose to provide one or more of the instructions listed in this section in order to satisfy requirements in the preceding list. If an instruction is implemented that matches the semantics of an instruction described here, the implementation should be as specified here. Alternatively, an algorithm may be given that performs one of the functions listed above (a loop invalidating individual SLB entries may be used to invalidate the entire SLB, for example), or instructions with different semantics may be implemented. Such algorithms or instructions must be described in Book IV, *PowerPC Implementation Features*.

It is permissible for an instruction described here to be implemented so that more is done than absolutely required. For example, an instruction whose semantics are to purge an SLB entry may be implemented so as to purge an entire congruence class or perhaps even the entire SLB. Such additional actions should be described in Book IV.

If a 64-bit implementation does not implement an SLB, it treats the corresponding instructions (*slbie* and *slbia*) either as no-ops or as illegal instructions. Similarly, if any implementation does not implement a TLB, it treats the corresponding instructions (*tlbie, tlbia,* and *tlbsync*) either as no-ops or as illegal instructions.

SLB Invalidate Entry   X-form

slbie   RB

31	///	///	RB	434	/
0	6	11	16	21	31

```
EA ← (RB)
if SLB entry exists for EA then
    SLB entry ← invalid
```

Let the effective address (EA) be the contents of register RB. If the Segment Lookaside Buffer (SLB) contains an entry corresponding to EA, that entry is made invalid (i.e., removed from the SLB).

The SLB search is done regardless of the settings of MSR_{IR} and MSR_{DR}.

Block Address Translation for EA, if any, is ignored.

This instruction is privileged.

This instruction is optional in the PowerPC Architecture.

This instruction is defined only for 64-bit implementations. Using it on

Programming Note

Because the presence, absence, and exact semantics of the various *Lookaside Buffer Management* instructions are model-dependent, it is recommended that system software "encapsulate" uses of such instructions into subroutines to minimize the impact of moving from one implementation to another.

Programming Note

For a discussion of software synchronization requirements when invalidating SLB and TLB entries, please refer to Chapter 7, "Synchronization Requirements for Special Registers and for Lookaside Buffers," on page 483.

Programming Note

It is not necessary that the ASR point to a valid Segment Table when issuing *slbie*.

a 32-bit implementation will cause an Illegal Instruction type Program interrupt.

Special Registers Altered

    None

Programming Note

It is not necessary that the ASR point to a valid Segment Table when issuing *slbia*.

SLB Invalidate All   X-form

slbia

31	///	///	///	498	/
0	6	11	16	21	31

    All SLB entries ← invalid

The entire SLB is made invalid (i.e., all entries are removed).

The SLB is invalidated regardless of the settings of MSR_{IR} and MSR_{DR}.

This instruction is privileged.

This instruction is optional in the PowerPC Architecture.

This instruction is defined only for 64-bit implementations. Using it on a 32-bit implementation will cause an Illegal Instruction type Program interrupt.

Special Registers Altered

    None

TLB Invalidate Entry   X-form

tlbie   RB

[Power mnemonic: tlbi]

31	///	///	RB	306	/
0	6	11	16	21	31

    VPI ← (RB)36:51 (4:19)
    Identify TLB entries corresponding to VPI
    Each such TLB entry ← invalid

Let the effective address (EA) be the contents of register RB. If the Translation Lookaside Buffer (TLB) contains an entry corresponding to EA, that entry is made invalid (i.e., removed from the TLB).

The TLB search is done regardless of the settings of MSR_{IR} and MSR_{DR}. The search is done based on a portion of the Virtual Page Index, including the least significant bits, without reference to the SLB, Segment Table, or Segment Register. All entries matching the search criteria are invalidated.

Block Address Translation for EA, if any, is ignored.

This instruction is privileged.

This instruction is optional in the PowerPC Architecture.

See Section 4.12, "Table Update Synchronization Requirements," on page 446 for a description of other requirements associated with the use of this instruction.

Programming Note

Nothing is guaranteed about instruction fetching in other processors if *tlbie* deletes the TLB entry for the page in which some other processor is currently executing.

Special Registers Altered

None

TLB Invalidate All   X-form

tlbia

31	///	///	///	370	/
0	6	11	16	21	31

All TLB entries ← invalid

The entire TLB is invalidated (i.e., all entries are removed).

The TLB is invalidated regardless of the settings of MSR_{IR} and MSR_{DR}.

This instruction is privileged.

This instruction is optional in the PowerPC Architecture.

Programming Notes

It is not necessary that the ASR point to a valid Segment Table or that SDR 1 point to a valid Page Table when issuing *tlbia*.

Nothing is guaranteed about instruction fetching in other processors if *tlbia* deletes the TLB entry for the page in which some other processor is currently executing.

Special Registers Altered

None

TLB Synchronize   X-form

tlbsync

31	///	///	///	566	/
0	6	11	16	21	31

The *tlbsync* instruction does not complete until all previous *tlbie* and *tlbia* instructions executed by the processor executing this instruction have been received and completed by all other processors.

This instruction is privileged.

This instruction is optional in the PowerPC Architecture, but it must be implemented if any of the following are true:

■ A TLB invalidation instruction that broadcasts is implemented.

■ The *eciwx* or *ecowx* instructions are implemented.

See Section 4.12, "Table Update Synchronization Requirements," on page 446 for a description of other requirements associated with the use of this instruction.

Special Registers Altered
   None

4.12 Table Update Synchronization Requirements

This section describes the steps that software must take when updating the tables involved in address translation. Updates to these tables include:

■ Adding a new Page Table Entry (PTE)

■ Modifying an existing PTE, including the special case of modifying the PTE's Reference bit

■ Deleting a PTE

■ Adding a new Segment Table Entry (STE)

■ Modifying an existing STE

■ Deleting an STE

In a multiprocessor system it is critical that these rules be followed to ensure that all processors see a consistent set of tables. Even in a uniprocessor system certain rules must be followed, notably those regarding Reference and Change bit updates, because software changes must be synchronized with automatic updates by the hardware.

A *sync* instruction ensures that all prior *tlbie* instructions executed by the processor executing the *sync* instruction have completed on that processor.

To ensure that a *tlbie* instruction executed by one processor has completed on all other processors, the sequence *tlbie* followed by *sync* is not sufficient. This sequence must be followed by a *tlbsync* instruction and then a *sync* instruction on the processor that executed the *tlbie* to ensure that:

1. the prior *tlbie* instructions have completed on other processors, and

2. the *tlbsync* has completed on the processor executing this sequence.

When *tlbie* is executed on one processor, software must ensure that the following sequence of instructions is executed on that processor before a *tlbie* is executed on a second processor:

1. *sync*

2. *tlbsync*

3. *sync*

Other instructions may be interleaved with this sequence of instructions, but these instructions must appear in the order shown.

The code sequences shown in Sections 4.12.1 and 4.12.2 assume that a context synchronizing operation has occurred before the sequence is executed (e.g., that the sequence is executed within the Data Storage interrupt handler).

Page Table Entries and Segment Table Entries must not be changed in a manner that causes an implicit branch.

4.12.1 Page Table Updates

HTAB entries must be locked on multiprocessors. Access to HTAB entries must be appropriately synchronized by software locking of (i.e., guaranteeing exclusive access to) entries or groups of entries if more than one processor can modify the table at once.

On uniprocessors, HTAB entries need not be locked. To adapt the examples given below for the uniprocessor case, simply delete the "lock()" and "unlock()" lines. The *sync* instructions shown are still required even on uniprocessors.

TLBs are noncoherent caches of the HTAB. TLB entries must be flushed explicitly with one of the *TLB Invalidate* instructions. The *sync* instruction waits until all prior TLB invalidates by this processor are complete. This may cost a *sync* per HTAB entry update.

Unsynchronized lookups in the HTAB continue even while it is being modified. Any processor, including the processor modifying the HTAB, may look in the HTAB at any time in an attempt to reload a TLB entry. An inconsistent HTAB entry must never accidentally become visible, thus there must be synchronization between modifications to the Valid bit and any other modifications. This costs as many as two *sync*s per HTAB entry update.

Processors write Reference and Change bits with unsynchronized atomic byte stores. This requires that the V, R, and C bits be in distinct bytes. It also requires extreme care to ensure that no store overwrites one of these bytes accidentally.

In the examples below,

■ "lock()" and "unlock()" refer to software locks for exclusive access to the table entry in question,

■ sync refers to the *sync* instruction,

■ tlbsync refers to the *tlbsync* instruction, and

■ tlbie refers to the *tlbie* instruction.

Adding a Page Table Entry

This is the simplest Page Table case. It requires no synchronization with the hardware, just a lock on the PTE in a multiprocessor system. We fill in the entries in the PTE except for the Valid bit, issue a *sync* to ensure that the updates have all made it to storage, and turn on the Valid bit.

```
lock(PTE)
PTE_VSID,H,API ← new values
PTE_RPN,R,C,WIMG,PP ← new values
sync
PTE_V ← 1
unlock(PTE)
```

Modifying a Page Table Entry

General case

In this case a currently valid PTE must be changed. To do this we must lock the PTE, mark it invalid, flush it from the TLB, update the information in the PTE, mark it valid again, and unlock, using *sync* at appropriate times to wait for modifications to complete.

```
lock(PTE)
PTE_V ← 0
sync
tlbie(PTE)
sync
tlbsync
sync
PTE_VSID,H,API ← new values
```

```
PTE_RPN,R,C,WIMG,PP ← new values
sync
PTE_V ← 1
unlock(PTE)
```

Resetting the Reference bit

In the case where the PTE is modified only to set the Reference bit to 0, a much simpler algorithm suffices because the Reference bit need not be maintained exactly.

```
lock(PTE)
oldR ← PTE_R
if oldR = 1 then
    PTE_R ← 0
    tlbie(PTE)
unlock(PTE)
```

Since only the R and C bits are modified by hardware, and since R and C are in different bytes, the R bit can be set to 0 by reading the current contents of the byte in the PTE containing R (bits 48:55 of the second doubleword on 64-bit implementations, bits 16:23 of the second word on 32-bit implementations), ANDing the value with 0xFE, and storing the byte back into the PTE.

Modifying the virtual address

If the virtual address is being changed to a different address within the same TLB hash class, it suffices to:

```
lock(PTE)
val ← PTE_VSID,API,H,V
insert new VSID into val
PTE_VSID,API,H,V ← val
sync
tlbie(PTE)
sync
tlbsync
sync
unlock(PTE)
```

Here we take advantage of the fact that the store into the first double-word (word, on 32-bit systems) of the PTE is performed atomically.

Deleting a Page Table Entry

Here we just lock the entry, mark it invalid, wait for the change to complete, and unlock.

```
lock(PTE)
PTE_V ← 0
```
sync
tlbie(PTE)
sync
tlbsync
sync
```
unlock(PTE)
```

4.12.2 Segment Table Updates

These updates are similar to Page Table updates, but without the complication of hardware updates to Reference and Change bits.

STAB entries must be locked on multiprocessors. Access to STAB entries must be appropriately synchronized by software locking of (i.e., guaranteeing exclusive access to) entries or groups of entries if more than one processor can modify the table at once.

On uniprocessors, STAB entries need not be locked. To adapt the examples given below for the uniprocessor case, simply delete the "lock()" and "unlock()" lines. The *sync* instructions shown are still required even on uniprocessors.

SLBs are noncoherent caches of the STAB. SLB entries must be flushed explicitly with one of the *SLB Invalidate* instructions. The *sync* instruction waits until all prior SLB invalidates by this processor are complete. This may cost a *sync* per STAB entry update.

Unsynchronized lookups in the STAB continue even while it is being modified. Any processor, including the processor modifying the STAB, may look in the STAB at any time in an attempt to reload an SLB entry. An inconsistent STAB entry must never accidentally become visible, thus there must be synchronization between modifications to the Valid bit and any other modifications. This costs as many as two *syncs* per STAB entry update.

In the examples below,

■ "lock()" and "unlock()" refer to software locks for exclusive access to the table entry in question,

■ sync refers to the *sync* instruction, and

■ slbie refers to the *slbie* instruction.

Adding a Segment Table Entry

We fill in the entries in the STE except for the Valid bit, issue a *sync* to ensure that the updates have all made it to storage, and turn on the Valid bit.

```
lock(STE)
STE_ESID,T,Ks,Kp ← new values
if T = 0
    then STE_VSID ← new value
    else STE_IO ← new value
sync
STE_V ← 1
unlock(STE)
```

Modifying a Segment Table Entry

In this case a currently valid STE must be changed. To do this we must lock the STE, mark it invalid, flush it from the SLB, update the information in the STE, mark it valid again, and unlock, using *sync* at appropriate times to wait for modifications to complete.

```
lock(STE)
STE_V ← 0
sync
slbie(STE)
sync
STE_ESID,T,Ks,Kp ← new values
if T = 0
    then STE_VSID ← new value
    else STE_IO ← new value
sync
STE_V ← 1
unlock(STE)
```

Deleting a Segment Table Entry

Here we just lock the entry, mark it invalid, wait for the change to complete, and unlock.

```
lock(STE)
STE_V ← 0
sync
slbie(STE)
sync
unlock(STE)
```

4.12.3 Segment Register Updates

On an implementation that provides Segment Registers rather than a Segment Table, there is no table to be locked but there are certain synchronization requirements that must be satisfied when using the *Move To Segment Register* instructions. See Chapter 7, "Synchronization Requirements for Special Registers and for Lookaside Buffers," on page 483.

Interrupts

5.1 Overview

The PowerPC architecture provides an interrupt mechanism to allow the processor to change state as a result of external signals, errors, or unusual conditions arising in the execution of instructions.

System Reset and Machine Check interrupts are not ordered. All other interrupts are ordered such that only one interrupt is reported, and when it is processed (taken) no program state is lost. Since save/restore registers SRR0 and SRR1 are serially reusable resources used by most interrupts, program state may be lost when an unordered interrupt is taken.

5.2 Interrupt Synchronization

When an interrupt occurs, SRR0 is set to point to an instruction such that all preceding instructions have completed execution, no subsequent instruction has begun execution, and the instruction addressed by SRR0 may or may not have completed execution, depending on the interrupt type.

With the exception of System Reset and Machine Check interrupts, all interrupts are context synchronizing as defined in Section 1.7.1, "Context Synchronization," on page 371. System Reset and Machine Check interrupts are context synchronizing if they are recoverable (i.e., if bit 62 {30} of SRR1 is set to 1 by the interrupt). If a System Reset or Machine Check interrupt is not recoverable (i.e., if bit 62 {30} of SRR1 is set to 0 by the interrupt), it acts like a context synchronizing operation with respect to subsequent instructions. That is, a non-recoverable System Reset or Machine Check interrupt need not satisfy items 1 through 3 of Section 1.7.1, but does satisfy items 4 and 5.

5.3 Interrupt Classes

Interrupts are classified by whether they are directly caused by the execution of an instruction or are caused by some other system exception. Those that are "system-caused" are:

- System Reset

- Machine Check

- External

- Decrementer

External and Decrementer are maskable interrupts. While $MSR_{EE}=0$, the interrupt mechanism ignores the exceptions that generate these interrupts. Therefore, software may delay the generation of these interrupts by setting $MSR_{EE}=0$ or by failing to set $MSR_{EE}=1$ after processing an interrupt. When any interrupt is taken, MSR_{EE} is set to 0 by the interrupt mechanism, delaying the recognition of any further exceptions causing these interrupts.

System Reset and Machine Check exceptions are not maskable. These exceptions will be recognized regardless of the setting of the MSR.

"Instruction-caused" interrupts are further divided into two classes, *precise* and *imprecise*.

5.3.1 Precise Interrupt

Except for the Imprecise Mode Floating-Point Enabled Exception interrupt, all instruction-caused interrupts are precise. When the fetching or execution of an instruction causes a precise interrupt, the following conditions exist at the interrupt point:

1. SRR0 addresses either the instruction causing the exception or the immediately following instruction. Which instruction is addressed can be determined from the interrupt type and status bits.

2. An interrupt is generated such that all instructions preceding the instruction causing the exception appear to have completed with respect to the executing processor. However, some storage accesses generated by these preceding instructions may not have been performed with respect to all other processors and mechanisms.

3. The instruction causing the exception may appear not to have begun execution (except for causing the exception), may have partially completed, or may have completed, depending on the interrupt type.

4. Architecturally, no subsequent instruction has begun execution.

5.3.2 Imprecise Interrupt

This architecture defines one imprecise interrupt, the Imprecise Mode Floating-Point Enabled Exception interrupt.

When the execution of an instruction causes an imprecise interrupt, the following conditions exist at the interrupt point:

1. SRR0 addresses either the instruction causing the exception or some instruction following the instruction causing the exception that generated the interrupt.

2. An interrupt is generated such that all instructions preceding the instruction addressed by SRR0 appear to have completed with respect to the executing processor.

3. If the imprecise interrupt is forced by the context synchronizing mechanism, due to an instruction that causes another interrupt (e.g., Alignment, Data Storage), then SRR0 addresses the interrupt-forcing instruction, and the interrupt-forcing instruction may have been partially executed (see Section 5.6, "Partially Executed Instructions," on page 472).

4. If the imprecise interrupt is forced by the execution synchronizing mechanism, due to executing an execution synchronizing instruction other than *sync* or *isync*, then SRR0 addresses the interrupt-forcing instruction, and the interrupt-forcing instruction appears not to have begun execution (except for its forcing the imprecise interrupt). If the imprecise interrupt is forced by a *sync* or *isync* instruction, then SRR0 may address either the *sync* or *isync* instruction or the following instruction.

5. If the imprecise interrupt is not forced by either the context synchronizing mechanism or the execution synchronizing mechanism, then the instruction addressed by SRR0 appears not to have begun execution, if it is not the excepting instruction.

6. No instruction following the instruction addressed by SRR0 appears to have begun execution.

All Floating-Point Enabled Exception interrupts are maskable using the MSR bits FE0 and FE1. Although these interrupts are maskable, they differ significantly from the other maskable interrupts in that the masking of these interrupts is usually controlled by the application program, whereas the masking of External and Decrementer interrupts is controlled by the operating system.

5.4 Interrupt Processing

Associated with each kind of interrupt is an *interrupt vector*, which contains the initial sequence of instructions that is executed when the corresponding interrupt occurs.

Interrupt processing consists of saving a small part of the processor's state in certain registers, identifying the cause of the interrupt in another register, and continuing execution at the corresponding interrupt vector location. When an exception exists that will cause an interrupt to be generated and it has been determined that the interrupt can be taken, the following actions are performed:

Programming Note

In some implementations, every instruction fetch when $MSR_{IR}=1$, and every instruction execution requiring address translation when $MSR_{DR}=1$, may have the side effect of modifying SRR0 and SRR1. For further details, see the Book IV, *PowerPC Implementation Features* document for the implementation.

1. SRR0 is loaded with an instruction address that depends on the type of interrupt; see the specific interrupt description for details.

2. Bits 33:36 and 42:47 {1:4 and 10:15} of SRR1 are loaded with information specific to the interrupt type.

3. Bits 0:32, 37:41, and 48:63 {0, 5:9, and 16:31} of SRR1 are loaded with a copy of the corresponding bits of the MSR, except for the Machine Check interrupt, for which these bits are set to implementation-dependent values.

4. The MSR is set as described in Figure 80 on page 458. The new values take effect beginning with the first instruction following the interrupt. MSR bits of particular interest are:

- MSR_{IR} and MSR_{DR} are set to 0 for all interrupt types. Thus relocate is turned off for both instruction fetch and data access beginning with the first instruction following the acceptance of the interrupt. See Chapter 4, "Storage Control," on page 391.

- MSR_{SF} is set to 1 in 64-bit implementations and execution after the interrupt begins in 64-bit mode. This bit does not exist in 32-bit implementations.

5. Instruction fetch and execution resumes, using the new MSR value, at a location specific to the interrupt type. The location is determined by adding the interrupt vector's offset (see Figure 81 on page 459) to the base address determined by MSR_{IP} (see Interrupt Prefix on page 377). For a Machine Check that occurs when $MSR_{ME}=0$, the Checkstop state is entered (the machine stops executing instructions). See Section 5.5.2, "Machine Check Interrupt," on page 459.

Interrupts do not clear reservations obtained with *lwarx* or *ldarx*. The operating system should do so at appropriate points, such as at process switch.

5.5 Interrupt Definitions

Figure 80 on page 458 shows all the types of interrupts and the values assigned to the MSR for each. Figure 81 on page 459 shows the offset of the interrupt vector for each interrupt type.

5.5.1 System Reset Interrupt

System Reset begins with a System Reset interrupt.

If the System Reset exception caused the processor state to be corrupted such that the contents of SRR0 or SRR1 are not valid or other processor resources are corrupt and would preclude reliable resumption of program execution, then the processor sets SRR1 bit 62 {30} (where MSR_{RI} is normally placed) to 0, to indicate to the interrupt handler that the interrupt is not recoverable.

The following registers are set:

SRR0 Set to the effective address of the instruction that the processor would have attempted to execute next if no interrupt conditions were present.

SRR1
    33:36 {1:4}   Set to 0.
    42:47 {10:15} Set to 0.
    62 {30}   Loaded from bit 62 {30} of the MSR if the processor is in a recoverable state, otherwise set to 0.
    Others   Loaded from the MSR.

MSR   See Figure 80 on page 458.

Programming Note

In general, at process switch, due to possible process interlocks and possible data availability requirements, the operating system needs to consider executing the following:

- *stwcx.*, to clear the reservation if one is outstanding, to ensure that a *lwarx* or *ldarx* in the "old" process is not paired with a *stwcx.* or *stdcx.* in the "new" process.

- *sync*, to ensure that all storage operations of an interrupted process are complete with respect to other processors before that process begins executing on another processor.

- *isync* or *rfi*, to ensure that the instructions in the "new" process execute in the "new" context.

Programming Note

In order to handle Machine Check and System Reset interrupts correctly, the operating system should manage MSR_{RI} as follows.

- In the Machine Check and System Reset interrupt handlers, interpret SRR1 bit 62 {30} (where MSR_{RI} is placed) as:

    —0: interrupt is not recoverable

—1: interrupt is recoverable

■ In each interrupt handler, when enough state has been saved that a Machine Check or System Reset interrupt can be recovered from, set MSR_{RI} to 1.

■ In each interrupt handler, do the following (in order) just before returning:

1. Set MSR_{RI} to 0.

2. Set SRR0 and SRR1 to the values to be used by *rfi*. The new value of SRR1 should have bit 62 {30} set to 1 (which will happen naturally if SRR1 is restored to the value saved there by the interrupt, because the interrupt handler will not be executing this sequence unless the interrupt is recoverable).

3. Execute *rfi*.

MSR_{RI} can be managed similarly to handle interrupts other than Machine Check and System Reset that occur within interrupt handlers.

This Note describes only the management of MSR_{RI}. It is not intended to be a full description of the requirements for an interrupt handler.

Interrupt Type	MSR bit				
	IP	ILE	LE	ME	SF{}
System Reset	—	—	(1)	—	1
Machine Check	—	—	(1)	0	1
Data Storage	—	—	(1)	—	1
Instruction Storage	—	—	(1)	—	1
External	—	—	(1)	—	1
Alignment	—	—	(1)	—	1
Program	—	—	(1)	—	1
FP Unavailable	—	—	(1)	—	1
Decrementer	—	—	(1)	—	1
System Call	—	—	(1)	—	1
Trace	—	—	(1)	—	1
Floating-Point Assist	—	—	(1)	—	1

0   bit is set to 0
1   bit is set to 1
—   bit is not altered
(1)   bit is copied from ILE

Defined bits not shown above (BE, DR, EE, FE0, FE1, FP, IR, POW, PR, RI, and SE) are set to 0.

Reserved bits are set as if written as 0.

Figure 80   **MSR setting due to interrupt**

Execution resumes at offset 0x00100 from the base real address indicated by MSR_{IP}.

Each implementation provides a means for software to distinguish power-on Reset from other types of System Reset, and describes it in the Book IV, *PowerPC Implementation Features* document for the implementation.

Offset (hex)	Interrupt Type
00000	Reserved
00100	System Reset
00200	Machine Check
00300	Data Storage
00400	Instruction Storage
00500	External
00600	Alignment
00700	Program
00800	Floating-Point Unavailable
00900	Decrementer
00A00	Reserved
00B00	Reserved
00C00	System Call
00D00	Trace
00E00	Floating-Point Assist
00E10	Reserved
. . .	. . .
00FFF	Reserved
01000	Reserved, implementation-specific
. . .	. . .
02FFF	(end of interrupt vector locations)

Programming Note

Use of any of the locations shown as reserved in Figure 81 risks incompatibility with future implementations.

Figure 81.   **Offset of interrupt vector by interrupt type**

5.5.2 Machine Check Interrupt

Machine Check interrupts are enabled when $MSR_{ME}=1$. If $MSR_{ME}=0$ and a Machine Check occurs, the processor enters the Checkstop state.

Programming Note

On some implementations a Machine Check interrupt may occur due to referencing an invalid (nonexistent) real address, either directly (with MSR$_{DR}$=0) or through an invalid translation. On such a system, execution of *Data Cache Block set to Zero* can cause a delayed Machine Check interrupt by introducing a block into the data cache that is associated with an invalid real address. A Machine Check interrupt could eventually occur when and if a subsequent attempt is made to store that block to main storage.

Disabled Machine Check (Checkstop State)

When a processor is in Checkstop state, instruction processing is suspended and generally cannot be restarted without resetting the processor. Some implementations may preserve some or all of the internal state of the processor when entering Checkstop state, so that the state can be analyzed as an aid in problem determination.

Enabled Machine Check

If the Machine Check exception caused the processor state to be corrupted such that the contents of SRR0 or SRR1 are not valid or other processor resources are corrupt and would preclude reliable resumption of program execution, then the processor sets SRR1 bit 62 {30} (where MSR$_{RI}$ is normally placed) to 0, to indicate to the interrupt handler that the interrupt is not recoverable.

In some systems, the operating system may attempt to identify and log the cause of the Machine Check. If the exception that caused the Machine Check does not preclude continued execution (i.e., if SRR1 bit 62 {30} is set to 1 for the interrupt handler), the processor must be able to continue execution at the Machine Check interrupt vector address.

The following registers are set:

SRR0 Set on a "best effort" basis to the effective address of some instruction that was executing or was about to be executed when the Machine Check exception occurred. For further details see the Book IV, *PowerPC Implementation Features* document for the implementation.

SRR1
62 {30}   Loaded from bit 62 {30} of the MSR if the processor is in a recoverable state, otherwise set to 0.

Others   See the Book IV, *PowerPC Implementation Features* document for the implementation.

MSR   See Figure 80 on page 458.

Execution resumes at offset 0x00200 from the base real address indicated by MSR$_{IP}$.

5.5.3 Data Storage Interrupt

A Data Storage interrupt occurs when no higher priority exception exists and a data storage access cannot be performed for any of the following reasons:

■ The instruction results in a Direct-Store Error exception.

■ The effective address of a *Load, Store, icbi, dcbz, dcbst, dcbf, dcbi, eciwx,* or *ecowx* instruction cannot be translated.

■ The instruction is not supported for the type of storage addressed.

— *lwarx, ldarx, stwcx.,* or *stdcx.* to a location that is Write Through Required (if the interrupt does not occur then the instruction executes correctly: see Book II, Section 1.8.2, "Atomic Update Primitives," on page 336).

— *lwarx, ldarx, stwcx., stdcx., eciwx,* or *ecowx* to a direct-store segment (if the interrupt does not occur then the results are boundedly undefined: see Section 4.6.3, "Instructions Not Supported for T=1," on page 422).

■ The access violates storage protection.

■ Execution of an *eciwx* or *ecowx* instruction is disallowed because $EAR_E=0$.

Such accesses can be generated by load/store type instructions (discussed in Book I, *PowerPC User Instruction Set Architecture*), certain storage control instructions, certain cache control instructions (discussed in Book II, *PowerPC Virtual Environment Architecture*), and the *eciwx* and *ecowx* instructions.

If a *stwcx.* or *stdcx.* has an effective address for which a normal *Store* would cause a Data Storage interrupt, but the processor does not have the reservation from *lwarx* or *ldarx*, then it is implementation-dependent whether a Data Storage interrupt occurs.

If a *Move Assist* instruction has a length of zero (in the XER), a Data Storage interrupt does not occur, regardless of the effective address.

The following registers are set:

SRR0   Set to the effective address of the instruction that caused the interrupt.

SRR1
   33:36 {1:4}   Set to 0.
   42:47 {10:15} Set to 0.
   Others   Loaded from the MSR.

MSR   See Figure 80 on page 458.

DSISR
   0   Set to 1 if a load or store instruction results in a Direct-Store Error exception, otherwise 0.

   1   Set to 1 if the translation of an attempted access is not found in the hashed primary HTEG, or in the rehashed secondary HTEG, or in the range of a DBAT register; otherwise 0.

   2:3   Set to 0.

   4   Set to 1 if a storage access is not permitted by the page or DBAT protection mechanism described on page 436, otherwise 0.

   5   Set to 1 if the access was due to an *eciwx, ecowx, lwarx, ldarx, stwcx.,* or *stdcx.* that addresses a direct-store segment (T=1 in Segment Register or Segment Table Entry), or if the access was due to a *lwarx, ldarx, stwcx.,* or *stdcx.* that addresses Write Through storage; set to 0 otherwise.

   6   Set to 1 for a store operation and to 0 for a load operation.

   7:8   Set to 0.

   9   Reserved for DABR (see the Book IV, *PowerPC Implementation Features* document for the implementation).

   10   Set to 1 if the Segment Table search fails to find a translation for the effective address, otherwise set to 0.

   11   Set to 1 if execution of an *eciwx* or *ecowx* instruction was attempted when $EAR_E=0$, otherwise set to 0.

   12:31 Set to 0.

DAR Set to the effective address of a storage element as described in the following list.

- A byte in the first word accessed in the page that caused the Data Storage interrupt, for a byte, halfword, or word access to an ordinary segment.
- A byte in the first doubleword accessed in the page that caused the Data Storage interrupt, for a doubleword access to an ordinary segment.
- A byte in the first word accessed in the BAT area that caused the Data Storage interrupt, for a byte, halfword, or word access to a BAT area.
- A byte in the first doubleword accessed in the BAT area that caused the Data Storage interrupt, for a doubleword access to a BAT area.
- A byte in the block that caused the Data Storage interrupt, for *icbi, dcbz, dcbst, dcbf,* or *dcbi.*
- Any effective address in the range of storage being addressed,

for a Direct-Store Error exception.

■ The effective address computed by the instruction, for attempted execution of *eciwx* or *ecowx* when $EAR_E=0$.

If the interrupt occurs in 32-bit mode on a 64-bit implementation, the high-order 32 bits of the DAR are set to 0.
Execution resumes at offset 0x00300 from the base real address indicated by MSR_{IP}.

5.5.4 Instruction Storage Interrupt

An Instruction Storage interrupt occurs when no higher priority exception exists and an attempt to fetch the next instruction to be executed cannot be performed for any of the following reasons:

■ The effective address cannot be translated.

■ The fetch access is to a direct-store segment.

■ The fetch access violates storage protection.

Such accesses can only be generated by instruction fetches.
The following registers are set:

SRR0   Set to the effective address of the instruction that the processor would have attempted to execute next if no interrupt conditions were present (if the interrupt occurs on attempting to fetch a branch target, SRR0 is set to the branch target address).

SRR1
  33 {1}   Set to 1 if the translation of an attempted access is not found in the hashed primary HTEG, or in the rehashed secondary HTEG, or in the range of an IBAT register; otherwise 0.
  34 {2}   Set to 0.
  35 {3}   Set to 1 if the fetch access was to a direct-store segment (T=1 in Segment Register or Segment Table Entry); set to 0 otherwise.
  36 {4}   Set to 1 if a storage access is not permitted by the page or IBAT protection mechanism described on page 436, otherwise 0.
  42 {10} Set to 1 if the Segment Table search fails to find a translation for the effective address, otherwise set to 0.
  43:47 {11:15} Set to 0.
  Others   Loaded from the MSR.

MSR   See Figure 80 on page 458.

Execution resumes at offset 0x00400 from the base real address indicated by MSR_{IP}.

5.5.5 External Interrupt

An External interrupt occurs when no higher priority exception exists, an External interrupt exception is presented to the interrupt mechanism, and $MSR_{EE}=1$. The occurrence of the interrupt does *not* cancel the request.
The following registers are set:

SRR0   Set to the effective address of the instruction that the processor would have attempted to execute next if no interrupt conditions were present.

SRR1
33:36 {1:4}	Set to 0.
42:47 {10:15}	Set to 0.
Others	Loaded from the MSR.

MSR   See Figure 80 on page 458.

Execution resumes at offset 0x00500 from the base real address indicated by MSR_{IP}.

5.5.6 Alignment Interrupt

An Alignment interrupt occurs when no higher priority exception exists and the implementation cannot perform a storage access for one of the reasons listed below.

■ The operand of a floating-point load or store is not word-aligned.

■ The operand of a fixed-point doubleword load or store is not word-aligned.

■ The operand of *lmw, stmw, lwarx, ldarx, stwcx., stdcx., eciwx,* or *ecowx* is not aligned.

■ The operand of a single-register load or store is not aligned and the processor is in Little-Endian mode.

■ The instruction is *lmw, stmw, lswi, lswx, stswi,* or *stswx* and the processor is in Little-Endian mode.

■ The operand of a floating-point load or store is in a direct-store segment (T=1).

■ The operand of an elementary or string load or store crosses a protection boundary.

■ The operand of *lmw* or *stmw* crosses a segment or BAT boundary.

■ The operand of *dcbz* is in storage that is Write Through Required or Caching Inhibited, or *dcbz* is executed in an implementation that has either no data cache or a Write Through data cache.

For *lmw, stmw, lswi, lswx, stswi,* and *stswx* in Little-Endian mode, an Alignment interrupt always occurs. For *lmw* and *stmw* with an operand that is not aligned in Big-Endian mode, and for *lwarx, ldarx, stwcx., stdcx., eciwx,* and *ecowx* with an operand that is not aligned in either Endian mode, an implementation may yield boundedly undefined results instead of causing an Alignment interrupt (for *eciwx* and *ecowx* when $EAR_E=0$, a third alternative is to cause a Data Storage interrupt). For all other cases listed above, an implementation may execute the instruction correctly instead of causing an Alignment interrupt. (For *dcbz*, "correct" execution means setting each byte of the block in main storage to 0x00.)

The following registers are set:

SRR0 Set to the effective address of the instruction that caused the interrupt.

SRR1
    33:36 {1:4}   Set to 0.
    42:47 {10:15}   Set to 0.
    Others   Loaded from the MSR.

MSR See Figure 80 on page 458.

DSISR
    0:11   Set to 0.
    12:13   Set to bits 30:31 of the instruction if DS-form.
        Set to 0b00 if D- or X-form. (Set to 0b00 on 32-bit implementations.)
    14   Set to 0.
    15:16   Set to bits 29:30 of the instruction if X-form.
        Set to 0b00 if D- or DS-form.
    17   Set to bit 25 of the instruction if X-form.
        Set to bit 5 of the instruction if D- or DS-form.

Programming Note

The architecture does not support the use of an unaligned effective address by *lwarx, ldarx, stwcx., stdcx., eciwx,* and *ecowx*. If an Alignment interrupt occurs because one of these instructions specifies an unaligned effective address, the Alignment interrupt handler must not attempt to simulate the instruction, but instead should treat the instruction as a programming error.

18:21   Set to bits 21:24 of the instruction if X-form.
          Set to bits 1:4 of the instruction if D- or DS-form.
22:26   Set to bits 6:10 of the instruction (RT/RS/FRT/FRS), except
          undefined for *dcbz*.
27:31   Set to bits 11:15 of the instruction (RA) for update form in-
          structions; set to either bits 11:15 of the instruction or to any
          register number not in the range of registers to be loaded for
          a valid form *lmw, lswi,* or *lswx*; otherwise undefined.

DAR   Set to the effective address of the data access as computed by the
      instruction causing the Alignment exception, except that if the in-
      terrupt occurs in 32-bit mode on a 64-bit implementation, the
      high-order 32 bits of the DAR are set to 0.

For an X-form *Load* or *Store*, it is acceptable to set the DSISR to the
same value that would have resulted if the corresponding D- or DS-form
instruction had caused the interrupt. Similarly, for a D- or DS-form *Load*
or *Store*, it is acceptable to set the DSISR to the value that would have
resulted for the corresponding X-form instruction. For example, an
unaligned *lwax* (that crosses a protection boundary) would normally, following the description above, cause the DSISR to be set to binary:

000000000000 00 0 01 0 0101 ttttt ?????

where "ttttt" denotes the RT field, and "?????" denotes undefined bits.
However, it is acceptable if it causes the DSISR to be set as for *lwa*, which
is

000000000000 10 0 00 0 1101 ttttt ?????

If there is no corresponding alternative form instruction (e.g., for *lwaux*),
the value described above must be set in the DSISR.

The instruction pairs that may use the same DSISR value are:

lbz/lbzx	lbzu/lbzux	lhz/lhzx	lhzu/lhzux
lha/lhax	lhau/lhaux	lwz/lwzx	lwzu/lwzux
lwa/lwax	ld/ldx	ldu/ldux	
stb/stbx	stbu/stbux	sth/sthx	sthu/sthux
stw/stwx	stwu/stwux	std/stdx	stdu/stdux
lfs/lfsx	lfsu/lfsux	lfd/lfdx	lfdu/lfdux
stfs/stfsx	stfsu/stfsux	stfd/stfdx	stfdu/stfdux

Execution resumes at offset 0x00600 from the base real address indicated by MSR_{IP}.

5.5.7 Program Interrupt

A Program interrupt occurs when no higher priority exception exists and one of the following exceptions arises during execution of an instruction:

Floating-Point Enabled Exception

A Floating-Point Enabled Exception type Program interrupt is generated when the expression

$$(MSR_{FE0} \mid MSR_{FE1}) \ \& \ FPSCR_{FEX}$$

is 1. $FPSCR_{FEX}$ is turned on by the execution of a floating-point instruction that causes an enabled exception or by the execution of a *Move To FPSCR* instruction that results in both an exception bit and its corresponding enable bit being 1.

Illegal Instruction

An Illegal Instruction type Program interrupt is generated when execution is attempted of an illegal instruction, or of a reserved or optional instruction that is not provided by the implementation.

An Illegal Instruction type Program interrupt may be generated when execution is attempted of any of the following kinds of instruction. If the interrupt is not generated, the alternative is shown in parentheses.

- an instruction that is in invalid form (boundedly undefined results)

- an *lswx* instruction for which RA or RB is in the range of registers to be loaded (boundedly undefined results)

- an *mtspr* or *mfspr* instruction with an SPR field that does not contain one of the defined values:

  — $MSR_{PR}=1$ and $spr_0=1$
  (Privileged Instruction type Program interrupt)

  — $MSR_{PR}=0$ or $spr_0=0$
  (boundedly undefined results)

- an unimplemented floating-point instruction that is not optional (Floating-Point Assist interrupt)

Privileged Instruction

The following applies when $MSR_{PR}=1$.

A Privileged Instruction type Program interrupt is generated when execution is attempted of a privileged instruction, or of an *mtspr* or *mfspr* instruction with an SPR field that contains one of the defined values having $spr_0=1$. It may be generated when execution is attempted of an *mtspr* or *mfspr* instruction with an SPR field that does not contain one of the defined values but has $spr_0=1$; in this case an Illegal Instruction type Program interrupt may be generated instead.

Trap

A Trap type Program interrupt is generated when any of the conditions specified in a *Trap* instruction is met.

The following registers are set:

SRR0 For all Program interrupts except a Floating-Point Enabled Exception when in one of the Imprecise modes, set to the effective address of the instruction that caused the Program interrupt.

For an Imprecise Mode Floating-Point Enabled Exception, set to the effective address of the excepting instruction or to the effective address of some subsequent instruction. If it points to a subsequent instruction, that instruction has not been executed. If a subsequent instruction is *Synchronize* (*sync*) or *Instruction Synchronize* (*isync*), SRR0 will not point more than four bytes beyond the *sync* or *isync* instruction.

If $FPSCR_{FEX}=1$ but Floating-Point Enabled Exception interrupts are disabled by having both MSR_{FE0} and $MSR_{FE1} = 0$, a Floating-Point Enabled Exception interrupt will occur prior to or at the next synchronizing event if these MSR bits are altered by any instruction that can set the MSR so that the expression

$$(MSR_{FE0} \mid MSR_{FE1}) \mathrel{\&} FPSCR_{FEX}$$

is 1. When this occurs, SRR0 is loaded with the address of the instruction that would have executed next, not with the address of the instruction that modified the MSR causing the interrupt.

SRR1

33:36 {1:4}	Set to 0.
42 {10}	Set to 0.
43 {11}	Set to 1 for a Floating-Point Enabled Exception type Program interrupt, otherwise 0.
44 {12}	Set to 1 for an Illegal Instruction type Program interrupt, otherwise 0.
45 {13}	Set to 1 for a Privileged Instruction type Program interrupt, otherwise 0.
46 {14}	Set to 1 for a Trap type Program interrupt, otherwise 0.
47 {15}	Set to 0 if SRR0 contains the address of the instruction causing the exception, and to 1 if SRR0 contains the address of a subsequent instruction.
Others	Loaded from the MSR.

Only one of bits 43:46 {11:14} can be set to 1.

MSR See Figure 80 on page 458.

Execution resumes at offset 0x00700 from the base real address indicated by MSR_{IP}.

5.5.8 Floating-Point Unavailable Interrupt

A Floating-Point Unavailable interrupt occurs when no higher priority exception exists, an attempt is made to execute a floating-point instruction (including floating-point loads, stores, and moves), and $MSR_{FP}=0$.

The following registers are set:

SRR0 Set to the effective address of the instruction that caused the interrupt.

SRR1

33:36 {1:4}	Set to 0.
42:47 {10:15}	Set to 0.
Others	Loaded from the MSR.

MSR See Figure 80 on page 458.

Execution resumes at offset 0x00800 from the base real address indicated by MSR_{IP}.

5.5.9 Decrementer Interrupt

A Decrementer interrupt occurs when no higher priority exception exists, the Decrementer exception exists, and $MSR_{EE}=1$. The occurrence of the interrupt cancels the request.

The following registers are set:

SRR0 Set to the effective address of the instruction that the processor would have attempted to execute next if no interrupt conditions were present.

SRR1
   33:36 {1:4}   Set to 0.
   42:47 {10:15} Set to 0.
   Others   Loaded from the MSR.

MSR   See Figure 80 on page 458.

Execution resumes at offset 0x00900 from the base real address indicated by MSR_{IP}.

5.5.10 System Call Interrupt

A System Call interrupt occurs when a *System Call* instruction is executed.

The following registers are set:

SRR0 Set to the effective address of the instruction following the *System Call* instruction.

SRR1
   33:36 {1:4}   Set to 0.
   42:47 {10:15} Set to 0.
   Others   Loaded from the MSR.

MSR   See Figure 80 on page 458.

Execution resumes at offset 0x00C00 from the base real address indicated by MSR_{IP}.

5.5.11 Trace Interrupt

The Trace interrupt may optionally be implemented.

If implemented, a Trace interrupt occurs when no higher priority exception exists and either $MSR_{SE}=1$ and any instruction except *rfi* is successfully completed, or $MSR_{BE}=1$ and a *Branch* instruction is completed. Successful completion means that the instruction caused no other interrupt. Thus a Trace interrupt never occurs for a *System Call* instruction, nor for a *Trap* instruction that traps.

The following registers are set:

SRR0   Set to the effective address of the instruction that the processor would have attempted to execute next if no interrupt conditions were present.

SRR1
    33:36 and 42:47 {1:4 and 10:15} See the Book IV, *PowerPC Implementation Features* document for the implementation.
    Others Loaded from the MSR.

MSR   See Figure 80 on page 458.

For further details see the Book IV, *PowerPC Implementation Features* document for the implementation.

Execution resumes at offset 0x00D00 from the base real address indicated by MSR_{IP}.

5.5.12 Floating-Point Assist Interrupt

The Floating-Point Assist interrupt may optionally be implemented. Its purpose is to allow software assistance for the following cases.

■ Implemented floating-point instructions that need software assistance in order to complete certain operations such those involving denormalized numbers.

■ Unimplemented floating-point instructions that are not optional.
   It is permissible for the processor to generate an Illegal Instruction type Program interrupt instead of a Floating-Point Assist interrupt in this case.

The following registers are set:

SRR0   Set to the effective address of the instruction that caused the Floating-Point Assist interrupt.

SRR1
    33:36 and 42:47 {1:4 and 10:15} See the Book IV, *PowerPC Implementation Features* document for the implementation.

Others Loaded from the MSR.

MSR   See Figure 80 on page 458.

For further details see the Book IV, *PowerPC Implementation Features* document for the implementation.

Execution resumes at offset 0x00E00 from the base real address indicated by MSR_{IP}.

5.6 Partially Executed Instructions

The architecture permits certain instructions to be partially executed when an Alignment or Data Storage interrupt occurs, or when an imprecise interrupt is forced by an instruction that causes an Alignment or Data Storage exception. These instructions are:

1. *Load Multiple* or *Load String* that causes an Alignment or Data Storage interrupt: some registers in the range of registers to be loaded may have been loaded.

2. *Store Multiple* or *Store String* that causes an Alignment or Data Storage interrupt: some bytes of storage in the range addressed may have been updated.

3. An elementary (non-multiple and non-string) store that causes an Alignment or Data Storage interrupt: some bytes just before the boundary may have been updated. If the instruction normally alters CR0 (*stwcx.*, *stdcx.*), CR0 is set to an undefined value. For update forms, the update register (RA) is not altered.

4. A floating-point load that causes an Alignment or Data Storage interrupt: the target register (FRT) may be altered. For update forms, the update register (RA) is not altered.

5. A load or store to a direct-store segment that causes a Data Storage interrupt due to a Direct-Store Error exception: some of the associated address/data transfers may not have been initiated. All initiated transfers are completed before the exception is reported, and the non-initiated transfers are aborted. Thus the instruction completes before the Data Storage interrupt occurs.

In the cases above, the questions of how many registers and how much storage is altered are implementation-, instruction-, and boundary-dependent. However, storage protection is not violated. Furthermore, if some of the data accessed is in direct-store (T=1) and the instruction is not supported for direct-store, the locations in direct-store are not accessed.

In the following situation, partial execution is not allowed (this preserves restartability):

> An elementary (non-multiple and non-string) fixed-point load that causes an Alignment or Data Storage interrupt: the target register (RT) is not altered. For update forms, the update register (RA) is not altered.

5.7 Exception Ordering

Since multiple exceptions can exist at the same time and the architecture does not provide for reporting more than one interrupt at a time, the generation of more than one interrupt is prohibited. Also, some exceptions would be lost if they were not recognized and handled when they occurred. For example, if an External interrupt was generated when a Data Storage exception existed, the Data Storage exception would be lost. If the Data Storage exception was caused by a *Store Multiple* instruction that spanned a page boundary and the exception was a result of attempting to access the second page, the store could have modified locations in the first page even though it appeared that the *Store Multiple* instruction was never executed.

In addition, the architecture defines imprecise interrupts that must be recoverable, cannot be lost, and can occur at any time with respect to the executing instruction stream. Some of the maskable and nonmaskable exceptions are persistent and can be deferred. The following exceptions persist even though some other interrupt is generated:

■ Floating-Point Enabled Exceptions

■ External

■ Decrementer

For the above reasons, all exceptions are prioritized with respect to other exceptions that may exist at the same instant to prevent the loss of any exception that is not persistent. Some exceptions cannot exist at the same instant as some others.

5.7.1 Unordered Interrupt Conditions

The exceptions listed here are unordered, meaning that they may occur at any time regardless of the state of the interrupt mechanism. These exceptions must be recognized and processed when presented.

1. System Reset

2. Machine Check

All other interrupts are ordered with respect to the interrupt mechanism resources.

5.7.2 Ordered Exceptions

The exceptions described here are ordered, meaning that only one can be reported. However, the single ordered exception that can be reported may exist in concert with unordered exceptions. Ordered exceptions may or may not be instruction-caused. The two lists identify the ordered interrupts by type. The order within the lists does not imply priority but only lists the possible exceptions that may be reported.

System-caused or Imprecise

1. Program
   — Imprecise Mode Floating-Point Enabled Exception

2. External

3. Decrementer

Instruction-caused and Precise

1. Instruction Storage

2. Program
   — Illegal Instruction
   — Privileged Instruction

3. Function Dependent
   3.a Fixed-Point
      1a   Program
          — Trap
      1b   System Call
      1c.1 Alignment

1c.2 Data Storage
2   Trace (if implemented)
3.b Floating-Point
1   FP Unavailable
2a   Program
         — Precise Mode Floating-Point Enabled Exception
2b   Floating-Point Assist (if implemented)
2c.1 Alignment
2c.2 Data Storage
3   Trace (if implemented)

For implementations that execute multiple instructions in parallel using pipeline or superscalar techniques, or combinations of these, it can be difficult to understand the ordering of exceptions. To understand this ordering it is useful to consider a model in which an instruction is fetched, decoded, and then executed. In this model, the exceptions a single instruction would generate are in the order shown in the list of instruction-caused exceptions. Exceptions with different numbers have different ordering. Exceptions with the same numbering but different lettering are mutually exclusive and cannot be caused by the same instruction.

Even on processors that are capable of executing several instructions simultaneously, or out of order, instruction-caused interrupts (precise and imprecise) occur in program order.

5.8 Interrupt Priorities

This section describes the relationship of nonmaskable, maskable, precise, and imprecise interrupts. In the following descriptions, the interrupt mechanism waiting for all possible exceptions to be reported includes only exceptions caused by previously initiated instructions (e.g., it does not include waiting for the Decrementer to step through zero). The exceptions are listed in order of highest to lowest priority.

1. System Reset
   System Reset exception has the highest priority of all exceptions. If this exception exists, the interrupt mechanism ignores all other exceptions and generates a System Reset interrupt.

   Once the System Reset interrupt is generated, no nonmaskable interrupts are generated due to exceptions caused by instructions issued prior to the generation of this interrupt.

2. Machine Check

Machine Check exception is the second highest priority exception. If this exception exists and a System Reset exception does not exist, the interrupt mechanism ignores all other exceptions and generates a Machine Check interrupt.

Once the Machine Check interrupt is generated, no nonmaskable interrupts are generated due to exceptions caused by instructions issued prior to the generation of this interrupt.

3. Instruction Dependent

This exception is the third highest priority exception. When this exception is created, the interrupt mechanism waits for all possible Imprecise exceptions to be reported. It then generates the appropriate ordered interrupt if no higher priority exception exists when the interrupt is to be generated. Within this category a particular instruction may present more than a single exception. When this occurs, those exceptions are ordered in priority as indicated in the following lists.

A. Fixed-Point Loads and Stores

    a. Alignment
    b. Data Storage
    c. Trace (if implemented)

B. Floating-Point Loads and Stores
    a. Floating-Point Unavailable
    b. Alignment
    c. Data Storage
    d. Trace (if implemented)

C. Other Floating-Point Instructions
    a. Floating-Point Unavailable
    b. Program — Precise Mode Floating-Point Enabled Exception
    c. Floating-Point Assist (if implemented)
    d. Trace (if implemented)

D. *rfi* and *mtmsr*
    a. Program — Privileged Instruction
    b. Program — Precise Mode Floating-Point Enabled Exception
    c. Trace (if implemented), for *mtmsr* only

If the MSR bits FE0 and FE1 are set such that Precise Mode Floating-Point Enabled Exception interrupts are enabled and FPSCR bit FEX is set, a Program interrupt will result prior to or at the next synchronizing event.

E. Other exceptions
These exceptions are mutually exclusive and have the same priority:
- Program — Trap
- System Call
- Program — Privileged Instruction
- Program — Illegal Instruction

F. Instruction Storage
This exception has the lowest priority in this category. It is recognized only when all instructions prior to the instruction causing this exception appear to have completed and that instruction is to be executed.

The priority of this interrupt is specified for completeness and to ensure that it is not given more favorable treatment. It is acceptable for an implementation to treat this interrupt as though it had a lower priority.

4. Program — Imprecise Mode Floating-Point Enabled Exception
This exception is the fourth highest priority exception. When this exception is created, the interrupt mechanism waits for all other possible exceptions to be reported. It then generates this interrupt if no higher priority exception exists when the interrupt is to be generated.

5. External
This exception is the fifth highest priority exception. When this exception is created, the interrupt mechanism waits for all other possible exceptions to be reported. It then generates this interrupt if no higher priority exception exists when the interrupt is to be generated.

6. Decrementer
This exception is the lowest priority exception. When this exception is created, the interrupt mechanism waits for all other possible exceptions to be reported. It then generates this interrupt if no higher priority exception exists when the interrupt is to be generated.

Timer Facilities

6.1 Overview

The Time Base and the Decrementer provide timing functions for the system. A specific instruction is provided for reading the Time Base, while the Decrementer is manipulated as an SPR and the Time Base is written as an SPR. Both are volatile resources and must be initialized during startup.

Time Base (TB)

> The Time Base provides a long-period counter driven by an implementation-dependent frequency.

Decrementer (DEC)

> The Decrementer, a counter that is updated at the same rate as the Time Base, provides a means of signaling an interrupt after a specified amount of time has elapsed unless

- the Decrementer is altered by software in the interim, **or**

- the Time Base update frequency changes.

6.2 Time Base

The Time Base (TB) is a 64-bit register (see Figure 82, "Time Base," on page 480) containing a 64-bit unsigned integer that is incremented periodically. Each increment adds 1 to the low-order bit (bit 63). The frequency at which the integer is updated is implementation-dependent.

There is no automatic initialization of the Time Base; system software must perform this initialization.

Programming Notes

Assuming that the operating system initializes the Time Base on power-on to some reasonable value and that the update frequency of the Time Base is constant, the Time Base can be used as a source of values that increase at a constant rate, such as for time stamps in trace entries.

Even if the update frequency is not constant, values read from the Time Base are monotonically increasing (except when the Time Base wraps from $2^{64}-1$ to 0). If a trace entry is recorded each time the update frequency changes, the sequence of Time Base values can be post-processed to become actual time values.

On an implementation that performs speculative execution, the Time Base may be read arbitrarily far "ahead" of the point at which it appears in the instruction stream. If it is important that this not occur, a context synchronizing operation such as the *isync* instruction should be placed immediately before the instructions that read the Time Base.

See Book II, Section 4.4, "Computing Time of Day from the Time Base," on page 354 for ways to

TBU	TBL

0   32   63

Field	Description
TBU	Upper 32 bits of Time Base
TBL	Lower 32 bits of Time Base

Figure 82 Time Base

The Time Base increments until its value becomes 0xFFFF_FFFF_FFFF_FFFF ($2^{64}-1$). At the next increment, its value becomes 0x0000_0000_0000_0000. There is no interrupt or other indication when this occurs.

The period of the Time Base depends on the driving frequency. As an order of magnitude example, suppose that the CPU clock is 100 MHz and that the Time Base is driven by this frequency divided by 32. Then the period of the Time Base would be

$$T_{TB} = \frac{2^{64} \times 32}{100 \text{ MHz}} = 5.90 \times 10^{12} \text{ seconds}$$

which is approximately 187,000 years.

The Time Base must be implemented such that the following requirements are satisfied.

1. Loading a GPR from the Time Base shall have no effect on the accuracy of the Time Base.

2. Storing a GPR to the Time Base shall replace the value in the Time Base with the value in the GPR.

The PowerPC Architecture does not specify a relationship between the frequency at which the Time Base is updated and other frequencies, such as the CPU clock or bus clock in a PowerPC system. The Time Base update frequency is not required to be constant. What *is* required, so that system software can keep time of day and operate interval timers, is one of the following.

■ The system provides an (implementation-dependent) interrupt to software whenever the update frequency of the Time Base changes, and a means to determine what the current update frequency is.

■ The update frequency of the Time Base is under the control of the system software.

compute time of day in POSIX format.

6.2.1 Writing the Time Base

Writing the Time Base is privileged. Reading the Time Base is *not* privileged; it is discussed in Book II, Chapter 4, "Time Base," on page 351.

It is not possible to write the entire 64-bit Time Base using a single instruction. The *mttbl* and *mttbu* extended mnemonics write the lower and upper halves of the Time Base (TBL and TBU), respectively, preserving the other half. These are extended mnemonics for the *mtspr* instruction; see page 495.

The Time Base can be written by a sequence such as:

```
lwz     Rx,upper    # load 64-bit value for
lwz     Ry,lower    #   TB into Rx and Ry
li      Rz,0
mttbl   Rz          # force TBL to 0
mttbu   Rx          # set TBU
mttbl   Ry          # set TBL
```

Loading 0 into TBL prevents the possibility of a carry from TBL to TBU while the Time Base is being initialized.

Programming Note

The instructions for writing the Time Base are implementation- and mode-independent. Thus code written to set the Time Base on a 32-bit implementation will work correctly on a 64-bit implementation running in either 64- or 32-bit mode.

6.3 Decrementer

The Decrementer (DEC) is a 32-bit decrementing counter that provides a mechanism for causing a Decrementer interrupt after a programmable delay.

DEC

0   31

Figure 83 **Decrementer**

The Decrementer is driven by the same frequency as the Time Base. The period of the Decrementer will depend on the driving frequency, but if the same values are used as given above for the Time Base (see Section 6.2), and if the Time Base update frequency is constant, the period would be

$$T_{DEC} = \frac{2^{32} \times 32}{100 \text{ MHz}} = 1.37 \times 10^3 \text{ seconds}$$

which is approximately 23 minutes.

The Decrementer counts down, causing an interrupt (unless masked) when passing through zero. The Decrementer must be implemented such that the following requirements are satisfied.

1. The operation of the Time Base and the Decrementer is coherent, i.e., the counters are driven by the same fundamental time base.

2. Loading a GPR from the Decrementer shall have no effect on the accuracy of the Decrementer.

3. Storing a GPR to the Decrementer shall replace the value in the Decrementer with the value in the GPR.

4. Whenever bit 0 of the Decrementer changes from 0 to 1, an interrupt request is signaled. If multiple Decrementer Interrupt requests are received before the first can be reported, only one interrupt is reported. The occurrence of a Decrementer interrupt cancels the request.

5. If the Decrementer is altered by software and the content of bit 0 is changed from 0 to 1, an interrupt request is signaled.

6.3.1 Writing and Reading the Decrementer

The content of the Decrementer can be read or written using the *mfspr* and *mtspr* instructions, both of which are privileged when they refer to the Decrementer. Using an extended mnemonic (see page 495), the Decrementer may be written from register GPR Rx using:

```
mtdec  Rx
```

The Decrementer may be read into GPR Rx using:

```
mfdec  Rx
```

Copying the Decrementer to a GPR has no effect on the Decrementer content or interrupt mechanism.

7

Synchronization Requirements for Special Registers and for Lookaside Buffers

Changing the value in certain system registers, and invalidating SLB and TLB entries, can have the *side effect* of altering the context in which data addresses and instruction addresses are interpreted, and in which instructions are executed. For example, changing MSR_{IR} from 0 to 1 has the side effect of enabling translation of instruction addresses. These side effects need not occur in program order, and therefore may require explicit synchronization by software. (Program order is defined in Book II, Section 1.1, "Definitions and Notation," on page 319.)

An instruction that alters the context in which data addresses or instruction addresses are interpreted, or in which instructions are executed, is called a "context-altering instruction." This chapter covers all the context-altering instructions. The software synchronization required for them is shown in Table 12 on page 485 (for data access) and Table 13 on page 486 (for instruction fetch and execution).

The notation "CSI" in the tables means any context synchronizing instruction (i.e., *sc, isync,* or *rfi*). A context synchronizing interrupt (i.e., any interrupt except non-recoverable System Reset or non-recoverable Machine Check) can be used instead of a context synchronizing instruction. If it is, phrases like "the synchronizing instruction," below, should be interpreted as meaning the instruction at which the interrupt occurs. If no software synchronization is required before (after) a context-altering instruction, "the synchronizing instruction before (after) the context-altering instruction" should be interpreted as meaning the context-altering instruction itself.

The synchronizing instruction before the context-altering instruction ensures that all instructions up to and including that synchronizing instruction are fetched and executed in the context that existed before the alteration.   The synchronizing instruction after the context-altering instruction ensures that all instructions after that synchronizing instruction are fetched and executed in the context established by the alteration. Instructions after the first synchronizing instruction, up to and including the second synchronizing instruction, may be fetched or executed in either context.

If a sequence of instructions contains context-altering instructions and contains no instructions that are affected by any of the context alterations, no software synchronization is required within the sequence.

No software synchronization is required before altering the MSR (except perhaps when altering the POW or LE bits: see the tables), because *mtmsr* is execution synchronizing. No software synchronization is required before most of the other alterations shown in Table 13 on page 486, because all instructions before the context-altering instruction are fetched and decoded before the context-altering instruction is executed (the processor must determine whether any of the preceding instructions are context synchronizing).

Programming Note

Sometimes advantage can be taken of the fact that certain instructions that occur naturally in the program, such as the *rfi* at the end of an interrupt handler, provide the required synchronization.

Instruction or Event	Required Before	Required After	Notes
interrupt	none	none	
rfi	none	none	
sc	none	none	
mtmsr (SF)	none	CSI	
mtmsr (ILE)	none	none	
mtmsr (PR)	none	CSI	
mtmsr (ME)	none	CSI	1
mtmsr (DR)	none	CSI	
mtmsr (LE)	—	—	3
mtsr[in]	CSI	CSI	
mtspr (ASR)	CSI	CSI	
mtspr (SDR1)	*sync*	CSI	6, 7
mtspr (DBAT)	CSI	CSI	
mtspr (DABR)	—	—	5
mtspr (EAR)	CSI	CSI	
slbie	CSI	CSI or *sync*	8
slbia	CSI	CSI or *sync*	8
tlbie	CSI	CSI or *sync*	8, 9
tlbia	CSI	CSI or *sync*	8, 9

Table 12.   **Synchronization requirements for data access**

Instruction or Event	Required Before	Required After	Notes
interrupt	none	none	
rfi	none	none	
sc	none	none	
mtmsr (SF)	none	CSI	10
mtmsr (POW)	—	—	2
mtmsr (ILE)	none	none	
mtmsr (EE)	none	none	4
mtmsr (PR)	none	CSI	
mtmsr (FP)	none	CSI	
mtmsr (ME)	none	CSI	1
mtmsr (FE0, FE1)	none	CSI	
mtmsr (SE, BE)	none	CSI	
mtmsr (IP)	none	none	
mtmsr (IR)	none	CSI	11
mtmsr (RI)	none	none	
mtmsr (LE)	—	—	3
mtsr[in]	none	CSI	11
mtspr (ASR)	none	CSI	11
mtspr (SDR1)	*sync*	CSI	6, 7
mtspr (IBAT)	none	CSI	11
mtspr (DEC)	none	none	12
slbie	none	CSI or *sync*	8
slbia	none	CSI or *sync*	8
tlbie	none	CSI or *sync*	8, 9
tlbia	none	CSI or *sync*	8, 9

Table 13. **Synchronization requirements for instruction fetch and/or execution**

Notes:

1. A context synchronizing instruction is required after altering the ME bit to ensure that the alteration takes effect for subsequent Machine Check interrupts, which may not be recoverable and therefore may not be context synchronizing.

2. Synchronization requirements for changing the power conserving mode are implementation-dependent, and are specified in the Book IV, *PowerPC Implementation Features* document for the implementation.

3. Synchronization requirements for changing from one Endian mode to the other are implementation-dependent, and are specified in the Book IV, *PowerPC Implementation Features* document for the implementation.

4. The effect of changing the EE bit is immediate.

   ■ If an *mtmsr* instruction sets the EE bit to 0, neither an External interrupt nor a Decrementer interrupt occurs after the *mtmsr* is executed.

   ■ If an *mtmsr* instruction changes the EE bit from 0 to 1 when an External, Decrementer, or higher priority exception exists, the corresponding interrupt occurs immediately after the *mtmsr* is executed, and before the next instruction is executed in the program that set EE to 1.

5. Synchronization requirements for changing the Data Address Breakpoint Register are implementation-dependent, and are specified in the Book IV, *PowerPC Implementation Features* document for the implementation.

6. SDR1 must not be altered when $MSR_{DR}=1$ or $MSR_{IR}=1$; if it is, the results are undefined.

7. A *sync* instruction is required before the *mtspr* instruction because SDR1 identifies the Page Table and thereby the location of Reference and Change bits. To ensure that Reference and Change bits are updated in the correct Page Table, SDR1 must not be altered until all Reference and Change bit updates due to instructions before the *mtspr* have completed. A *sync* instruction guarantees this synchronization of Reference and Change bit updates, while neither a context synchronizing operation nor the instruction fetching mechanism does so.

Programming Note

Regarding Note 8, the following sequence illustrates why it is necessary, for data accesses, to ensure that all storage accesses due to instructions before the *slbie, slbia, tlbie,* or *tlbia* have completed to a point at which they have reported all exceptions they will cause. Assume that valid Segment Table and Page Table entries exist for the target storage location when the sequence starts.

1. A program issues a load or store to a segment (page).

2. The same program marks the entry for the target segment (page) invalid in the Segment Table (Page Table).

3. The same program executes an *slbie* or *slbia* (*tlbie* or *tlbia*) that invalidates the corresponding SLB entry (TLB entry).

4. The load or store instruction finally executes, and gets a segment fault (page fault).

The segment fault or page fault is semantically incorrect. In order to prevent it, a context synchronizing instruction must be executed between steps 1 and 2

8. For data accesses, the context synchronizing instruction before the *slbie, slbia, tlbie,* or *tlbia* instruction ensures that all storage accesses due to preceding instructions have completed to a point at which they have reported all exceptions they will cause.

   The context synchronizing instruction after the *slbie, slbia, tlbie,* or *tlbia* ensures that subsequent storage accesses (data and instruction) will not use the SLB or TLB entry(s) being invalidated. It does *not* ensure that all storage accesses previously translated by the SLB or TLB entry(s) being invalidated have completed with respect to storage or, for *tlbie* or *tlbia*, that Reference and Change bit updates associated with those storage accesses have completed; if these completions must be ensured, the *slbie, slbia, tlbie,* or *tlbia* must be followed by a *sync* instruction rather than by a context synchronizing instruction.

   Section 4.12, "Table Update Synchronization Requirements," on page 446 gives examples of the synchronization required when using *slbie* or *tlbie* in a sequence that alters a Segment Table Entry or a Page Table Entry.

9. Multiprocessor systems have other requirements to synchronize "TLB shoot down" (i.e., to invalidate one or more TLB entries on all processors in the multiprocessor system and be able to determine that the invalidations have completed and that all side effects of the invalidations have taken effect).

10. The alteration must not cause an implicit branch in effective address space. Thus the *mtmsr* instruction and all subsequent instructions, up to and including the next context synchronizing instruction, must have effective addresses that are less than 2^{32}.

11. The alteration must not cause an implicit branch in real address space. Thus the real address of the context-altering instruction and of each subsequent instruction, up to and including the next context synchronizing instruction, must be independent of whether the alteration has taken effect.

12. The elapsed time between the content of the Decrementer becoming negative and the signaling of the Decrementer exception is not defined.

Optional Facilities and Instructions

A

The facilities (Special Purpose Registers and instructions) described in this appendix are optional. An implementation may choose to provide all, some, or none of them. If a facility is implemented that matches the semantics of a facility described here, the implementation should be as specified here.

A.1 External Control

The External Control facility provides a means for a problem state program to communicate with a special-purpose device. Two instructions are provided:

- *External Control In Word Indexed* (**eciwx**), which does the following:

  — Computes an effective address (EA) as for any X-form instruction

  — Validates the EA as would be done for a load from that address

  — Translates the EA to a real address

  — Transmits the real address to the device

  — Accepts a word of data from the device and places it into a general purpose register

■ *External Control Out Word Indexed* (*ecowx*), which does the following:

— Computes an effective address (EA) as for any X-form instruction

— Validates the EA as would be done for a store to that address

— Translates the EA to a real address

— Transmits the real address and a word of data from a general purpose register to the device

Depending on the setting of a control bit in a Special Purpose Register, the External Access Register (EAR), the processor either performs the external control operation or generates a Data Storage interrupt. The EAR controls access to the External Control facility. Access to the EAR itself is privileged; the operating system can determine which tasks are allowed to issue *External Access* instructions and when they are allowed to do so.

The data access of *eciwx* and *ecowx* is performed as though the storage access mode bits "WIMG" were 0101 (see Section 4.8).

Interpretation of the real address transmitted by *eciwx* and *ecowx* and the 32-bit value transmitted by *ecowx* is up to the target device. Such interpretation is not specified by the PowerPC Architecture. See the System Architecture documentation for a given PowerPC system for details on how the External Control facility can be used with devices on that system.

Example: An example of a device designed to be used with the External Control facility might be a graphics adapter. The *ecowx* instruction might be used to send the device the translated real address of a buffer containing graphics data, and the word transmitted from the general purpose register might be control information that tells the adapter what operation to perform on the data in the buffer. The *eciwx* instruction might be used to load status information from the adapter.

A.1.1 External Access Register

This 32-bit Special Purpose Register controls access to the External Control facility and, for external control operations that are permitted, determines which device is the target.

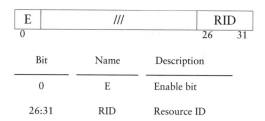

All other fields are reserved.

Figure 84.   **External Access Register**

The high-order bits of the RID field that correspond to bits of the Resource ID beyond the width of the Resource ID supported by a particular implementation are treated as reserved bits.

A.1.2 External Access Instructions

External Control In Word Indexed X-form

eciwx   RT,RA,RB

31	RT	RA	RB	310	/
0	6	11	16	21	31

```
if RA = 0 then b ← 0
else            b ← (RA)
EA ← b + (RB)
if EAR_E = 1 then
    raddr ← address translation of EA
    send load word request for raddr to
        device identified by EAR_RID
    RT ← 32_0 ‖ word from device
else
    DSISR_11 ← 1
    generate Data Storage interrupt
```

Let the effective address (EA) be the sum (RA|0)+(RB).

If $EAR_E=1$, a load word request for the real address corresponding to EA is sent to the device identified by EAR_{RID}, bypassing the cache. $RT_{0:31\{\}}$ is set to 0. The word returned by the device is placed in $RT_{32:63\{0:31\}}$.

If $EAR_E=0$, a Data Storage interrupt is taken, with bit 11 of DSISR set to 1.

EA must be a multiple of 4. If it is not, one of the following occurs:

■ an Alignment interrupt is generated

■ a Data Storage interrupt is generated (possible only if $EAR_E=0$)

■ the results are boundedly undefined

The *eciwx* instruction is supported for effective addresses that reference ordinary segments (T=0) and for EAs mapped by DBAT registers. If the EA refers to a direct-store segment (T=1), either a Data Storage interrupt occurs or the results are boundedly undefined. If this instruction is executed when $MSR_{DR}=0$ (real addressing mode), the results are boundedly undefined.

This instruction is treated as a load from the addressed byte with respect to address translation, storage protection, reference and change recording, and the ordering done by *eieio*.

Special Registers Altered

    None

External Control Out Word Indexed X-form

ecowx   RS,RA,RB

31	RS	RA	RB	438	/
0	6	11	16	21	31

```
if RA = 0 then b ← 0
else            b ← (RA)
EA ← b + (RB)
if EAR_E = 1 then
    raddr ← address translation of EA
    send store word request for raddr to
        device identified by EAR_RID
    send (RS_32:63{0:31}) to device
else
    DSISR_11 ← 1
    generate Data Storage interrupt
```

Let the effective address (EA) be the sum (RA|0)+(RB).

If $EAR_E=1$, a store word request for the real address corresponding to EA and the contents of $RS_{32:63\{0:31\}}$ are sent to the device identified by EAR_{RID}, bypassing the cache.

If $EAR_E=0$, a Data Storage interrupt is taken, with bit 11 of DSISR set to 1.

EA must be a multiple of 4. If it is not, one of the following occurs:

- an Alignment interrupt is generated

- a Data Storage interrupt is generated (possible only if $EAR_E=0$)

- the results are boundedly undefined

The *ecowx* instruction is supported for effective addresses that reference ordinary segments (T=0) and for EAs mapped by DBAT registers. If the EA refers to a direct-store segment (T=1), either a Data Storage interrupt occurs or the results are boundedly undefined. If this instruction is executed when $MSR_{DR}=0$ (real addressing mode), the results are boundedly undefined.

This instruction is treated as a store to the addressed byte with respect to address translation, storage protection, reference and change recording, and the ordering done by *eieio*.

Special Registers Altered

None

Assembler Extended Mnemonics

B

In order to make assembler language programs simpler to write and easier to understand, a set of extended mnemonics and symbols is provided that defines simple shorthand for the most frequently used forms of *Branch Conditional, Compare, Trap, Rotate and Shift,* and certain other instructions.

This appendix defines extended mnemonics related to *mtspr* and *mfspr,* including privileged SPRs.

Assemblers should provide the mnemonics and symbols listed here, and may provide others.

B.1 Move To/From Special Purpose Register Mnemonics

The *mtspr* and *mfspr* instructions specify a Special Purpose Register (SPR) as a numeric operand. Extended mnemonics are provided that represent the SPR in the mnemonic rather than requiring it to be coded as an operand. Also shown here are extended mnemonics for *Move From Time Base* and *Move From Time Base Upper*, which are variants of the *mftb* instruction rather than of *mfspr.*

Note: *mftb* serves as both a basic and an extended mnemonic. The assembler will recognize an *mftb* mnemonic with two operands as the basic form, and an *mftb* mnemonic with one operand as the extended form.

Special Purpose Register	Move To SPR		Move From SPR[1]	
	Extended	*Equivalent to*	*Extended*	*Equivalent to*
Fixed Point Exception Register	mtxer Rx	mtspr 1,Rx	mfxer Rx	mfspr Rx,1
Link Register	mtlr Rx	mtspr 8,Rx	mflr Rx	mfspr Rx,8
Count Register	mtctr Rx	mtspr 9,Rx	mfctr Rx	mfspr Rx,9
Data Storage Interrupt Status Register	mtdsisr Rx	mtspr 18,Rx	mfdsisr Rx	mfspr Rx,18
Data Address Register	mtdar Rx	mtspr 19,Rx	mfdar Rx	mfspr Rx,19
Decrementer	mtdec Rx	mtspr 22,Rx	mfdec Rx	mfspr Rx,22
Storage Description Register 1	mtsdr1 Rx	mtspr 25,Rx	mfsdr1 Rx	mfspr Rx,25
Save/Restore Register 0	mtsrr0 Rx	mtspr 26,Rx	mfsrr0 Rx	mfspr Rx,26
Save/Restore Register 1	mtsrr1 Rx	mtspr 27,Rx	mfsrr1 Rx	mfspr Rx,27
Special Purpose Registers G0 through G3	mtsprg n,Rx	mtspr 272+n,Rx	mfsprg Rx,n	mfspr Rx,272+n
Address Space Register	mtasr Rx	mtspr 280,Rx	mfasr Rx	mfspr Rx,280
External Access Register	mtear Rx	mtspr 282,Rx	mfear Rx	mfspr Rx,282
Time Base [Lower]	mttbl Rx	mtspr 284,Rx	mftb Rx	mftb Rx,268
Time Base Upper	mttbu Rx	mtspr 285,Rx	mftbu Rx	mftb Rx,269
Processor Version Register	–	–	mfpvr Rx	mfspr Rx,287
IBAT Registers, Upper	mtibatu n,Rx	mtspr 528+2×n,Rx	mfibatu Rx,n	mfspr Rx,528+2×n
IBAT Registers, Lower	mtibatl n,Rx	mtspr 529+2×n,Rx	mfibatl Rx,n	mfspr Rx,529+2×n
DBAT Registers, Upper	mtdbatu n,Rx	mtspr 536+2×n,Rx	mfdbatu Rx,n	mfspr Rx,536+2×n
DBAT Registers, Lower	mtdbatl n,Rx	mtspr 537+2×n,Rx	mfdbatl Rx,n	mfspr Rx,537+2×n

[1]Except for *mftb* and *mftbu*.

Table 14.   **Extended mnemonics for moving to/from an SPR**

Cross-Reference for Changed POWER Mnemonics

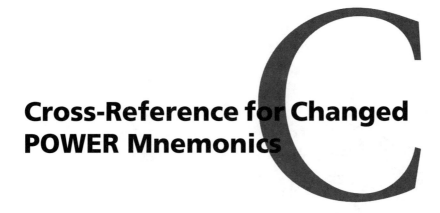

The following table lists the POWER instruction mnemonics that have been changed in the PowerPC Operating Environment Architecture, sorted by POWER mnemonic.

To determine the PowerPC mnemonic for one of these POWER mnemonics, find the POWER mnemonic in the second column of the table: the remainder of the line gives the PowerPC mnemonic and the page on which the instruction is described, as well as the instruction names.

POWER mnemonics that have not changed are not listed. POWER instruction names that are the same in PowerPC are not repeated: i.e., for these, the last column of the table is blank.

Page	POWER		PowerPC	
	Mnemonic	Instruction	Mnemonic	Instruction
441	mtsri	Move To Segment Register Indirect	mtsrin	
378	svca	Supervisor Call	sc	System Call
444	tlbi	TLB Invalidate Entry	tlbie	

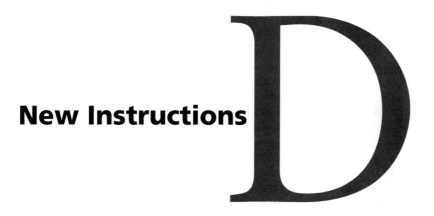

New Instructions

The following instructions in the PowerPC Operating Environment Architecture are new: they are not in the POWER Architecture. *dcbi* exists in all PowerPC implementations, *mfsrin* exists only in 32-bit implementations, and the SLB instructions exist only in 64-bit implementations. The SLB and TLB instructions are optional.

dcbi Data Cache Block Invalidate

eciwx External Control In Word Indexed

ecowx External Control Out Word Indexed

mfsrin Move From Segment Register Indirect

slbia SLB Invalidate All

slbie SLB Invalidate Entry

tlbia TLB Invalidate All

tlbsync TLB Synchronize

Implementation-Specific SPRs

This appendix lists Special Purpose Register (SPR) numbers assigned by the PowerPC Architecture Review Process for implementation-specific uses. If a register shown here is present in a particular implementation, a detailed description will be found in Book IV, *PowerPC Implementation Features*.

The intent of this list is to ensure that if an SPR is needed for a particular function on more than one implementation, the same SPR number will be used.

Note that ordering of the bits shown in the table below matches the descriptions of the *Move To/From Special Purpose Register* instructions on pages 384 and 387. The two 5-bit halves of the SPR number are reversed from the order in which they appear in an assembled instruction.

decimal	SPR $\text{spr}_{5:9}$ $\text{spr}_{0:4}$	Register name	Privileged
1022	11111 11110	FPECR	yes
1023	11111 11111	PIR	yes

Floating-Point Exception Cause Register (FPECR)
This register identifies the reason a Floating-Point Exception occurred.

Processor ID Register (PIR)
This register holds a value that distinguishes this processor from others in a multiprocessor.

Interpretation of the DSISR as Set by an Alignment Interrupt

F

For most causes of Alignment interrupt, the interrupt handler will emulate the interrupting instruction. To do this, it needs the following characteristics of the interrupting instruction:

Load or store
Length (halfword, word, or doubleword)
String, multiple, or elementary
Fixed or float
Update or non-update
Byte reverse or not
Is it *dcbz*?

The PowerPC Architecture provides this information implicitly, by setting bits in the DSISR that identify the interrupting instruction type. It is not necessary for the interrupt handler to load the interrupting instruction from storage. The mapping is unique except for a few exceptions that are discussed below. The near-uniqueness depends on the fact that many instructions, such as the fixed- and floating-point arithmetic instructions and the one-byte loads and stores, cannot cause an Alignment interrupt.

See Section 5.5.6, "Alignment Interrupt," on page 464 for a description of how the opcode and extended opcode are mapped to a DSISR value for an X-, D-, or DS-form instruction that causes an Alignment interrupt.

The table that follows shows the inverse mapping: how the DSISR bits identify the interrupting instruction. The following notes are cited in the table.

1. The instructions *lwz* and *lwarx* give the same DSISR bits (all zero). But if *lwarx* causes an Alignment interrupt, it should not be emulated in any precise way. It is adequate for the Alignment interrupt handler simply to emulate the instruction as if it were an *lwz*. The emulator must use the address in the DAR, rather than computing it from RA/RB/D, because *lwz* and *lwarx* have different instruction formats.

If opcode 0 ("Illegal or Reserved") can cause an Alignment interrupt, it will be indistinguishable to the interrupt handler from *lwarx* and *lwz*.

2. These are distinguished by DSISR bits 12:13, which are not shown in the table.

The Alignment interrupt handler will not be able to distinguish between a floating-point load or store interrupting because it is mis-aligned and one interrupting because it addresses direct-store. But this does not matter; in either case the access will be emulated using fixed-point instructions.

The interrupt handler has no need to distinguish between an X-form instruction and the corresponding D- or DS-form instruction if one exists, and vice-versa. Therefore, two such instructions may yield the same DSISR value (all 32 bits). For example, *stw* and *stwx* may both yield either the DSISR value shown in the following table for *stw*, or that shown for *stwx*.

If DSISR 15:21 is:	then it is either X-form opcode:	or D/DS- form opcode:	so the instruction is:
00 0 0000	00000xxx00	x00000	lwarx, lwz, reserved[1]
00 0 0001	00010xxx00	x00010	ldarx
00 0 0010	00100xxx00	x00100	stw
00 0 0011	00110xxx00	x00110	–
00 0 0100	01000xxx00	x01000	lhz
00 0 0101	01010xxx00	x01010	lha
00 0 0110	01100xxx00	x01100	sth

If DSISR 15:21 is:	then it is either X-form opcode:	or D/DS- form opcode:	so the instruction is:
00 0 0111	01110xxx00	x01110	lmw
00 0 1000	10000xxx00	x10000	lfs
00 0 1001	10010xxx00	x10010	lfd
00 0 1010	10100xxx00	x10100	stfs
00 0 1011	10110xxx00	x10110	stfd
00 0 1100	11000xxx00	x11000	–
00 0 1101	11010xxx00	x11010	ld, ldu, lwa[2]
00 0 1110	11100xxx00	x11100	–
00 0 1111	11110xxx00	x11110	std, stdu[2]
00 1 0000	00001xxx00	x00001	lwzu
00 1 0001	00011xxx00	x00011	–
00 1 0010	00101xxx00	x00101	stwu
00 1 0011	00111xxx00	x00111	–
00 1 0100	01001xxx00	x01001	lhzu
00 1 0101	01011xxx00	x01011	lhau
00 1 0110	01101xxx00	x01101	sthu
00 1 0111	01111xxx00	x01111	stmw
00 1 1000	10001xxx00	x10001	lfsu
00 1 1001	10011xxx00	x10011	lfdu
00 1 1010	10101xxx00	x10101	stfsu
00 1 1011	10111xxx00	x10111	stfdu
00 1 1100	11001xxx00	x11001	–
00 1 1101	11011xxx00	x11011	–
00 1 1110	11101xxx00	x11101	–
00 1 1111	11111xxx00	x11111	–

If DSISR 15:21 is:	then it is either X-form opcode:	or D/DS- form opcode:	so the instruction is:
01 0 0000	00000xxx01		ldx
01 0 0001	00010xxx01		–
01 0 0010	00100xxx01		stdx
01 0 0011	00110xxx01		–
01 0 0100	01000xxx01		–
01 0 0101	01010xxx01		lwax
01 0 0110	01100xxx01		–
01 0 0111	01110xxx01		–
01 0 1000	10000xxx01		lswx
01 0 1001	10010xxx01		lswi
01 0 1010	10100xxx01		stswx
01 0 1011	10110xxx01		stswi
01 0 1100	11000xxx01		–
01 0 1101	11010xxx01		–
01 0 1110	11100xxx01		–
01 0 1111	11110xxx01		–
01 1 0000	00001xxx01		ldux
01 1 0001	00011xxx01		–
01 1 0010	00101xxx01		stdux
01 1 0011	00111xxx01		–
01 1 0100	01001xxx01		–
01 1 0101	01011xxx01		lwaux
01 1 0110	01101xxx01		–
01 1 0111	01111xxx01		–
01 1 1000	10001xxx01		–

If DSISR 15:21 is:	then it is either X-form opcode:	or D/DS- form opcode:	so the instruction is:
01 1 1001	10011xxx01		–
01 1 1010	10101xxx01		–
01 1 1011	10111xxx01		–
01 1 1100	11001xxx01		–
01 1 1101	11011xxx01		–
01 1 1110	11101xxx01		–
01 1 1111	11111xxx01		–
10 0 0000	00000xxx10		–
10 0 0001	00010xxx10		–
10 0 0010	00100xxx10		stwcx.
10 0 0011	00110xxx10		stdcx.
10 0 0100	01000xxx10		–
10 0 0101	01010xxx10		–
10 0 0110	01100xxx10		–
10 0 0111	01110xxx10		–
10 0 1000	10000xxx10		lwbrx
10 0 1001	10010xxx10		–
10 0 1010	10100xxx10		stwbrx
10 0 1011	10110xxx10		–
10 0 1100	11000xxx10		lhbrx
10 0 1101	11010xxx10		–
10 0 1110	11100xxx10		sthbrx
10 0 1111	11110xxx10		–
10 1 0000	00001xxx10		–
10 1 0001	00011xxx10		–

If DSISR 15:21 is:	then it is either X-form opcode:	or D/DS- form opcode:	so the instruction is:
10 1 0010	00101xxx10		–
10 1 0011	00111xxx10		–
10 1 0100	01001xxx10		eciwx
10 1 0101	01011xxx10		–
10 1 0110	01101xxx10		ecowx
10 1 0111	01111xxx10		–
10 1 1000	10001xxx10		–
10 1 1001	10011xxx10		–
10 1 1010	10101xxx10		–
10 1 1011	10111xxx10		–
10 1 1100	11001xxx10		–
10 1 1101	11011xxx10		–
10 1 1110	11101xxx10		–
10 1 1111	11111xxx10		dcbz
11 0 0000	00000xxx11		lwzx
11 0 0001	00010xxx11		–
11 0 0010	00100xxx11		stwx
11 0 0011	00110xxx11		–
11 0 0100	01000xxx11		lhzx
11 0 0101	01010xxx11		lhax
11 0 0110	01100xxx11		sthx
11 0 0111	01110xxx11		–
11 0 1000	10000xxx11		lfsx
11 0 1001	10010xxx11		lfdx
11 0 1010	10100xxx11		stfsx

If DSISR 15:21 is:	then it is either X-form opcode:	or D/DS- form opcode:	so the instruction is:
11 0 1011	10110xxx11		stfdx
11 0 1100	11000xxx11		–
11 0 1101	11010xxx11		–
11 0 1110	11100xxx11		–
11 0 1111	11110xxx11		stfiwx
11 1 0000	00001xxx11		lwzux
11 1 0001	00011xxx11		–
11 1 0010	00101xxx11		stwux
11 1 0011	00111xxx11		–
11 1 0100	01001xxx11		lhzux
11 1 0101	01011xxx11		lhaux
11 1 0110	01101xxx11		sthux
11 1 0111	01111xxx11		–
11 1 1000	10001xxx11		lfsux
11 1 1001	10011xxx11		lfdux
11 1 1010	10101xxx11		stfsux
11 1 1011	10111xxx11		stfdux
11 1 1100	11001xxx11		–
11 1 1101	11011xxx11		–
11 1 1110	11101xxx11		–
11 1 1111	11111xxx11		–

PowerPC Operating Environment Instruction Set

G

Form	Opcode		Mode Dep.[1]	Priv.[2]	Page	Mnemonic	Instruction
	Primary	Extended					
X	31	470		P	439	dcbi	Data Cache Block Invalidate
X	31	310			491	eciwx	External Control In Word Indexed
X	31	438			492	ecowx	External Control Out Word Indexed
X	31	83		P	389	mfmsr	Move From Machine State Register
XFX	31	339		O	387	mfspr	Move From Special Purpose Register
X	31	595	{}	P	441	mfsr	Move From Segment Register
X	31	659	{}	P	442	mfsrin	Move From Segment Register Indirect
X	31	146		P	389	mtmsr	Move To Machine State Register
XFX	31	467		O	384	mtspr	Move To Special Purpose Register
X	31	210	{}	P	440	mtsr	Move To Segment Register
X	31	242	{}	P	441	mtsrin	Move To Segment Register Indirect
XL	19	50		P	379	rfi	Return From Interrupt
SC	17				378	sc	System Call

Form	Opcode Primary	Opcode Extended	Mode Dep.[1]	Priv.[2]	Page	Mnemonic	Instruction
X	31	498	()	P	444	slbia	SLB Invalidate All
X	31	434	()	P	443	slbie	SLB Invalidate Entry
X	31	370		P	445	tlbia	TLB Invalidate All
X	31	306		P	444	tlbie	TLB Invalidate Entry
X	31	566		P	445	tlbsync	TLB Synchronize

[1]Key to Mode Dependency Column

Parentheses () are shown if the instruction is defined only for 64-bit implementations.

Braces {} are shown if the instruction is defined only for 32-bit implementations.

All instructions in the PowerPC Operating Environment Architecture are mode-independent, except that if the instruction refers to storage when in 32-bit mode, only the low-order 32 bits of the 64-bit effective address are used to address storage.

[2]Key to Privilege Column

P   denotes a privileged instruction.

O   denotes an instruction that may be treated as privileged or non-privileged, depending on the SPR number.

Index